D1412754

© 2001 Algrove Publishing Limited
ALL RIGHTS RESERVED.
No part of this book may be reproduced in any form, including photocopying without permission
in writing from the publishers, except by a reviewer who may quote brief passages in a magazine
or newspaper or on radio or television.

Algrove Publishing Limited
1090 Morrison Drive
Ottawa, Ontario
Canada   K2H 1C2

Canadian Cataloguing in Publication Data

Main entry under title:

    Popular mechanics shop notes for ...

(Classic reprint series)
Includes indexes.
Originally published: Chicago : Popular Mechanics Co., 1905-
"Compiled from the "Shop notes" department of Popular mechanics
    magazine, and "Written so you can understand it;" tells easy
    ways to do hard things" --Added t.p., v. 1.
Cover title.
Contents: v. 21. 1925.
ISBN 1-894572-27-0 (v. 21)

    1. Do-it-yourself work. 2. Industrial arts. 3. Bricolage. 4. Métiers. I. Title: Shop notes
for ... . II. Series: Classic reprint series (Ottawa, Ont.)

TJ1160.P66 1999   600   C99-900763-7

Printed in Canada
#10301

Publisher's Note

Virtually every woodworking magazine in the English-speaking world has a shop notes section and has published an accumulation of them in book form. This was all started in 1905 with the first annual issue of *Popular Mechanics Shop Notes*, a compilation of advice on jigs, fixtures, methods of work, processes and projects. The earlier issues focussed primarily on metalworking, but with tips for a variety of other trades liberally sprinkled throughout. As years went by, the contents shifted more and more to woodworking and handyman projects. Each book is profusely illustrated. The line drawings of the earlier issues were supplanted by superb engravings until photographs started to creep in during the 1920s. Each year has its charm but all issues share the attribute of being clear, concise and widely informative.

Leonard G. Lee, Publisher
Ottawa
September, 1999

WARNING

This is a reprint of a book compiled in the early 1900s. The book describes what was recommended to be done in accordance with the knowledge of the day.

It would be advisable to treat all corrosive, explosive and toxic materials with much greater caution than is indicated here, particularly any materials that come in contact with the body.

Similarly, some of the recommended projects were dangerous then and remain so now. All of this material should be regarded with a judicious eye and necessary precautions taken.

POPULAR MECHANICS

SHOP NOTES

FOR 1925

VOLUME XXI

WITH 596 ILLUSTRATIONS

———

POPULAR MECHANICS PRESS

CHICAGO

THE Wide Interest in this 1925 issue of Shop Notes is indicated by the following list of subjects treated. Most readers will probably be interested in from five to ten of these subjects, and many will derive benefit from all the 519 articles.

Complete Index, Page 243

Shop Notes

Driving the Farm Pump Electrically

By J. R. KOONTZ

IN these days of private electric-light plants on the farm, and with the extension of city light and power lines far out into the country, the thoughts of the farm dweller naturally turn to the utilization of the current in as many practical ways as possible.

One of the best uses to which it can be trying to do the job by electricity. The fact that a ¼-hp. motor is plugging merrily away every day on my farm, pumping water from a 180-ft. well for nearly 150 head of horses, cattle, and hogs proves that a large, expensive motor is not by any means necessary.

An ordinary pump jack such as used

12"
SHAFT

BEARING

FRAME FOR
BEARINGS

Adapting the Farm Pump to Electric-Motor Drive Is a Simple Job, but One that Will More than Pay, in Comfort and Convenience, for the Time Spent on It

adapted is that of pumping the daily supply of water. The price of a good motor is considerably less than that of a gas engine, and the motor is much easier to handle. It is generally thought that a motor of at least 1 hp. is necessary to drive the pump, and this deters many farmers from with a gas engine, is used; if there is one already on the pump, so much the better. To reduce the speed of the motor to the correct speed for the pump, it is necessary to provide a secondary jack, or countershaft, and this can readily be made from material found around the farm, or at any

1

junk dealer's. Two pulleys will be needed, one 12 in., the other 4 in. in diameter, by 3 in. face; also a piece of 1-in. shafting, 12 in. long, and two bearings or pillow blocks to fit the shaft.

Two pieces of 2 by 8-in. plank, one 10 in. long, the other 12 in., are spiked together to form an inverted vee, as shown in the details, and the V-frame bolted to another piece of 2 by 8-in. plank, long enough to carry the motor also. Bolt the bearings in place as shown, taking care to shim them so that the shaft will run freely, then attach the pulleys.

Bolt the motor to the end of the plank, with its 1½-in. pulley alined with the 12-in. pulley on the V-frame, then fasten the plank so that the 4-in pulley will aline with the 12-in. pulley on the regular jack. It is best to cut slots in the plank for the motor and V-frame bolts, so that the belts can be tightened easily. Cut and splice the belts in place, and connect the motor to the switch, and the job is complete. The pulley sizes given here are correct for a motor speed of 1,750 r.p.m., with a 1½-in. pulley on the motor, and a 12-in. pulley on the pump jack.

The running expenses for this outfit have been only 27 cents per month during the hottest months of the year, when the most water is consumed.

A Work-Chute Distributor

The drawing illustrates a very simple distributing device, used in connection with a chute that delivers the work from

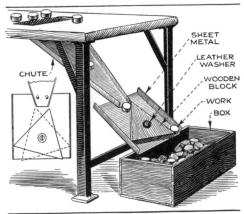

Distributing Work from Machine So that Box Is Evenly Filled

an automatic cutting machine into a box beneath. Before this attachment was used, considerable trouble was experienced, as the pieces always dropped in the same place and formed a pile, which "overflowed" before the box was actually full. The attachment consists of a square piece of sheet iron, with the outside edges turned up, riveted to the chute. Loosely attached to this by means of a nut and screw and two leather washers is a triangular piece of wood. The device works as follows: As one piece drops down the chute it slides down one side of the triangular block, and, in passing between this and the turned-up edge of the metal to which it is attached, forces the block over so that the next piece drops down the opposite side. The process is thus repeated until the box is filled, which is done evenly without any attention from the operator.—Harry Moore, Montreal, Can.

Transferring Hole Centers

The usual practice, when transferring the centers of large holes, is to scribe around the diameter and afterwards mark off the center of the scribed circle. The work is simplified considerably with the use of the tool shown in the drawing, which is made especially for this kind of work. A piece of good, straight tubing is drilled through for a scriber or pointer, and a short piece of round bar is also drilled the same size. This part is also drilled and tapped at one end, to take a knurled tightening screw, which extends up to the hole drilled through it.

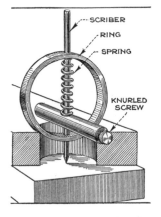

When finished, the parts are assembled as shown, with a light coil spring over the scriber. To transfer the center of a hole already drilled to another piece to be drilled the same size, the body of the tool is placed on top of the hole, and the scriber pushed down to touch the face of the second piece. Then with the knurled screw tightened, the tube is pressed down snugly and rocked back and forth once or twice, the same procedure being carried out after the tool has been turned to a position at about right angles to the first. The result is a cross marked in the exact center of the hole. No accuracy is required when setting the scriber to depth; it must, of course, touch the face of the second piece, but if set a little heavy it will lift on the high spot as the tool is rocked.

Unscrewing Separable Plugs

The usual method of unscrewing separable plugs for cleaning, putting in new gaskets, or replacing porcelains, is to hold the body of the plug in one hand by means of a wrench, while the packing nut is unscrewed with another wrench, or a pair of pliers. A much handier method is shown in the drawing. A hole is bored in the edge of the bench, large enough to receive the porcelain head, and over this hole is screwed a metal plate, shaped like the head of a wrench, and with an opening that fits the packing nut. It is but the work of a moment to slip the plug between the jaws, and to loosen the body with a wrench.

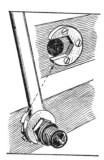

Holder for Inside Micrometer

When using an inside micrometer, it must be moved vertically and horizontally, and considerable adjustment is necessary to obtain an accurate measurement. The work can be greatly facilitated by using the attachment shown in the illustration, which makes it possible to set the tool across the center of the bore at once. The attachment is a circular disk of brass, or steel, with a boss which is drilled to a good sliding fit on the thimble of the micrometer, so that it can be slipped on and off easily. The diameter of the disk is about 2½ in. when used for bores having a diameter of 5 in. or more. For smaller bores, the diameter should be about 2½ inches.

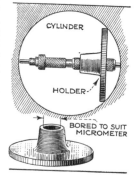

Lowering Storage Tanks

While various methods are employed for installing underground storage tanks, the method shown in the drawing has been

A Simple and Convenient Method of Lowering Large Metal Storage Tanks into Pits Dug for Them

found highly satisfactory, as it is only necessary to dig a pit that is just large enough to receive the tank, and because the tank can easily be turned around so as to bring the openings to their proper positions. Planks are placed over the pit and the tank is rolled on these until it is directly over the pit and in position to be lowered. The chain or rope slings are then put in place and the tank is raised a little with the block and tackle, which is lashed to the simple wooden frame shown in the illustration. The boards are then removed from under the tank and it is lowered into place. This method makes it unnecessary to dig an incline on one side of the pit to slide the tank down on skids.

Improvised Polishing Wheel

A simple and effective polishing wheel can be made by mounting a wooden disk on the shaft of a small motor, or on the screw chuck of a lathe, and covering the circumference of the disk with ordinary friction tape, which is then sprinkled with carborundum powder of suitable fineness. The disk must be turned down to a true edge and the tape must be wound in the direction that the wheel revolves, otherwise it will unwind in use. The carborundum powder should be well rubbed and patted into the tape, and, as it is quite easily torn from the tape by polishing, it must be renewed frequently. For the finest grades of powder it is well to rub the surface of the tape with tallow, before applying the powder.

Casters Facilitate Tinsmith's Work

Ordinary furniture casters, set in holes in the workbench, as shown, have been found to facilitate the handling of milk

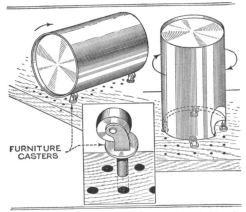

Furniture Casters, Set in Holes on the Workbench, Facilitate the Handling of Cylindrical Containers

cans and other cylindrical work, while soldering or repairing. A number of holes, large enough to receive the shanks of the casters, are drilled in the benchtop, and four casters inserted at points most convenient for the work, whether in horizontal or in vertical position. The time-saving features of this idea will be understood instantly by anyone who has done much repairing on such work.

Lubricating Lathe Centers

While running work at high speed in the lathe, the centers are apt to run dry, and if this is not detected in time, to burn out. With the device illustrated, there is always a small supply of oil at the center, and when necessary, the oil can be forced out quickly.

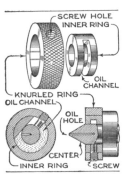

First, a small hole is drilled down along the axis of the center, and another is drilled through the side to break into this. A ring of cold-rolled steel is made, the hole being a snug fit on the straight part of the center. This piece is then slotted in the center, leaving a solid segment on one side, as shown. Another and larger ring is made,

the hole of which is a nice working fit on the outside diameter of the inner ring. The outside ring is knurled, and tapped for a special screw; the latter has a plain part extending into the slot in the inner ring, in which it is a good sliding fit.

The device fits on the center in the position shown. To fill with oil, remove the screw, and pour the lubricant through the hole. The oil is held in the slot in the inner ring, which forms a reservoir. Replace the screw and tighten until it touches the center. It will be seen that the screw holds the two rings together, and that, when the outer ring is turned to the right, the oil in the slot or reservoir will be forced out by the plain part of the screw through the small holes to the center of the work.

Wedge Jack for Planer

The small wedge jack shown in the drawing is for use on the planer, under castings where there is not enough space

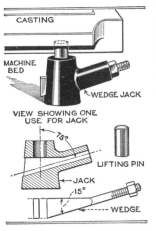

to use a screw jack. The jack consists of four pieces; the jack body, a lifting pin, and a wedge, with a nut on the threaded end. The jack is a steel casting of the shape shown; the holes are drilled at a 75° angle, and the upper surface of the wedge hole is slotted as shown, so that the two sides are at an angle of 15°, the surface of the wedge being machined to suit. In use, the wedge is inserted in the jack, the nut screwed on the threaded end, and the lifting pin put in place. By turning the nut, the horizontal surface of the wedge is lowered or raised, and this, of course, lowers or raises the lifting pin. The shanks of the jack and wedge can be made as long as necessary so that they will clear the work.

¶Do not use paint containing compounds of lead about stables or outbuildings where the fumes of decaying organic matter arise, as these gases are likely to darken the color of lead paints.

Cocoa Mats for Workers

There are numerous places where it is not desirable to use wooden gratings or slat flooring for protecting the workers' feet from hard concrete floors. Under such conditions it will be found that ordinary cocoa matting will afford a cheap and durable protection.

Wheelbarrow for Soft Soil

An ordinary wheelbarrow has little value on soft or sandy soil, as the wheel sinks into the ground, and it becomes almost impossible to push the barrow ahead. However, a wheelbarrow of the kind shown in the photo, will easily carry a heavy load over soft ground. It does not resemble an ordinary wheelbarrow, but has a drum about 1 ft. long and the same in diameter, substituted for the

A Wheelbarrow Equipped with a Drum Instead of a Wheel Is Convenient to Handle on Soft Ground

wheel. The drum is made by cutting two circular pieces of wood about 10 in. in diameter, from 1-in. boards, to form the ends. These ends are reinforced with cleats of 1 by 4-in. material, nailed or screwed across the grain of the disks. Strips of wood, 1 ft. long and 1 in. square, are nailed to the edges all around the disks, to form the drum. A 1¼-in. hole is drilled through the ends in the exact center, and a 1¼-in. pipe pushed through, to serve as an axle or shaft. It is securely fastened to the ends of the drum by drilling a small hole through the pipe, on each side of the drum, driving a small rod through each hole, and then fastening the rod to the drum with staples. The load is carried on a frame made of any material convenient, mounted above the drum, and pivoted on the axle shaft, as shown in the photo.—W. W. Fairbanks, Fort Bragg, Calif.

Power Hacksaw Made from Auto Engine

The photo shows an efficient power hacksaw made from an old automobile engine. The cylinder block of the engine,

An Efficient Power Hacksaw, Made from an Old Automobile Engine Mounted on a Steel Frame

with the crankshaft in place, was turned upside down, and set at one end of a channel-steel frame. The block was then cut so that the connecting rods of the first and last cylinders could be swung outward on one side. To the ends of these connecting rods is attached a frame that holds the sawblade frame, which is made from a steel bar, bent to the shape shown. The regular flywheel and clutch are left in place and a pulley is fitted on the end of the crankshaft so that a belt can be used to run the saw.

Making a Leather Pulley

A homemade leather pulley that was used on an electric motor is shown in the illustration. It was made from a number of leather disks, two steel collars, and a steel bushing. The leather disks were cut from old belting, to a diameter larger than the finished size of the pulley, and were glued together. A hole was drilled through the center so that they would fit snugly

on the bushing, which was cut from steel tubing and threaded on both ends; the collars were drilled and tapped to fit the bushing. When the collars had been drawn up so as to clamp the leather disks as tightly as possible, the pulley was put in the lathe and crowned.—R. M. Thomas, Denver, Colorado.

Built-Up Pipe Vise

The drawing shows a built-up steel pipe vise that is much stronger than the usual cast or malleable-iron pipe vise. The jaws used are taken from an ordi-

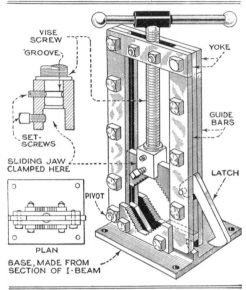

A Homemade Pipe Vise, Made from a Section of I-Beam and a Number of Short Steel Bars

nary vise, or they can be sawed and filed from tool steel, and then hardened and tempered. Owing to the various sizes and shapes of these jaws, and the different methods of holding them, no dimensions have been given, but with a set on hand the vise can be built up around them, changing the design to suit.

All parts of the vise are made of stock sizes of structural and machine steel. The base is part of a short section of I-beam, the fixed jaws being bolted to each side of the central web as shown, using shims if necessary, to set them out far enough. The frame consists of two central bars, joined at the top by a yoke, riveted or bolted on. The central bars must be of the same thickness as the web on the base. Two sets of guide bars, which may be of thinner stock than the yoke, are bolted to the sides of the center bars to guide the movable jaw. One center bar is cut and filed to take a latch, which pivots on a pin driven through the side of the bars. The opposite set of guide bars is drilled for a pivot bolt and the end of the web is rounded off to permit the frame to swing open when inserting the pipe.

It is best to fill up the center of the yoke with a steel filler, riveted in place securely. The yoke is then drilled and tapped for the vise screw, which is made of a machine bolt ¾ in. in diameter, and threaded up to the head. A hole is drilled through the square head to accommodate a steel tightening bar or handle. A rectangular groove is drilled and filed in the end of a piece of square or round machine steel to take the sliding jaw, which is held securely by a setscrew. If the jaw has bolt holes in it, a long yoke of different pattern will have to be made. The easiest method of attaching the vise screw to the movable-jaw yoke is to turn down the end to fit into a hole drilled in the yoke. A hole is drilled through the side of the yoke and partly into the end of the vise screw, then the screw is removed and a groove turned in it where it is spotted by the drill. The hole is tapped and a setscrew fitted; this will prevent the vise screw from coming out as the jaw is raised. When turning the end of the vise screw a flange is formed, which must take the pressure when the movable jaw is turned down, and for this reason it should be as wide as possible. The stationary jaws are bolted in place and the center part of the web is cut down to conform to them in shape. A notch is also cut in the edge of the web to take the latch.

Corn-Shock Tightener

The illustration shows a quick-acting corn-shock tightener that has been found very convenient. It is made from a length of rope, long enough to go around the shocks, and a piece of wood 1 by 2 by 10 in. in dimensions. A hole is drilled near one end, and notches are cut at the points indicated, all being large enough to admit the rope. Small nails are then driven into the wood, to

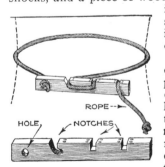

prevent it from splitting between the notches, and the rope is knotted at one end and passed through the hole. The method of bringing the rope around the shock and tightening it in the grooves is clearly shown in the upper illustration.—A. L. Gillis, Mount Pleasant, Ia.

Repairing Auto Clutch Shaft

A certain type of automobile has two ⅝-in. fine-thread screws fastening the yoke end of the clutch shaft to the clutch, as shown in the illustration, at the upper left. These screws often become loose, and are then likely to strip, making it impossible to release the clutch.

This happened on my own car, and to make a quick, but permanent repair, the job was done in the following manner: The clutch and its shaft were taken out of the car, and after the two screws were removed, the screw holes were reamed out to exactly ⅝ in. in diameter. This removed all the threads and left the surfaces of the holes perfectly smooth. Long capscrews were then obtained, and the threaded ends were cut off, leaving plain studs, about 1½ in. long. With the yoke and studs in place, holes were drilled, as indicated, for 9/32-in. tool-steel pins; these were a tight fit, and kept in place with a piece of soft wire, passed through small holes in the ends and then brought around the clutch hub and twisted, as shown.

This repair was found to be just as strong as the screw arrangement, and there was much less danger of its com-

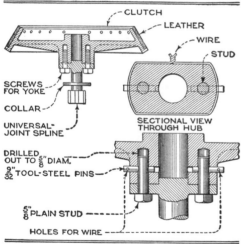

Quick Repair on an Auto Clutch: The Screws Are Removed and Plain Studs Substituted for Them

ing loose than before. Furthermore, it was easy to dismantle the clutch when necessary.—J. V. Romig, Allentown, Pa.

¶A test-tube brush, obtainable at any wholesale druggist's or laboratory-supply house, has been found to be very satisfactory for cleaning chips and dirt from the hollow spindle of a small lathe.

Circle-Marking Tool

The tool shown in the drawing and photograph was made for the purpose of scribing true lines around light rods, the

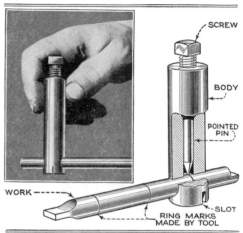

An Easily Made Tool for Scribing Circles on Light Rods Accurately and Quickly

lines being afterward used to locate the position of holes drilled partly through the rods. The body of the tool is round cold-rolled steel. A hole is drilled lengthwise in the center to take a pointed pin and the hole is tapped at the end for a screw. Another hole, the approximate size of the rods, is drilled at right angles to the first at one end, and a slot is cut in the end at right angles to the hole for the rods. In using the tool the position of the circle on the work is first determined and after marking this with a fine punch the tool is slipped on and located in line with this mark by bringing the mark in the center of the slot. The screw is then turned in until the hardened point of the pin touches the rod, when, by revolving the tool, a true line is marked around the rod.

A Simple Spirit Lamp

A new oil can with a wick of cotton string makes an excellent spirit lamp. For applying intense heat at a small joint it is only necessary to press the bottom of the can; the pressure will then force out a hot flame, making the lamp act as a blowtorch. On small work the lamp may be used sideways or at an angle, which is not possible with the ordinary kind of spirit lamp. For soldering small wires in radio work, or for light brazing, this lamp has few equals.

A VERTICAL - SPINDLE
BENCH SANDER
by
J · V · Romig

A VERY handy and profitable type of bench machine for the small woodworking shop is the vertical-spindle sander. This type of sander is particularly useful in the finishing of internal surfaces, and irregular shapes on patterns, either wood or metal, coreboxes, circular work, etc., being worked in far less time than they can be finished by hand.

On pattern work, the necessary draught is obtained by tilting the table to the required angle, and this eliminates the trouble due to "back draught," so often found on hand-finished patterns.

The sander described in this article is easily built, and will give years of efficient service. It is practically fool and accident proof, as the driving belt runs in the hollow sub-base which guards the operator in case of belt breakage.

The base of the machine is an extra-heavy 2-in. pipe flange, which is used just as purchased, without any further machining. The standard is a 6-in. length of

Finishing Irregular Work on the Homemade Vertical-Spindle Sanding Machine

2-in. extra-heavy pipe, machined for the bearings and threaded as shown in the detail drawing The lower thread is cut standard length, and screwed into the flange; the upper thread is 1¾ in. long, and is screwed into the tapped hole in the table support. The inside of the pipe is bored 2 in. deep at each end, for the oilless spindle bushings. These bushings are made of wood, impregnated with oil; they take on a high internal polish with wear, and provide enough oil for the spindle so that lubrication after installation is un-

necessary. They should be a good press fit in the standard.

The table support may be a casting, machined out of a block of machine steel, or built up, by welding, out of steel plate. The top is drilled and tapped to fit the standard, and the sides drilled and tapped for the ⅜-in. studs that clamp the table.

The table may also be a casting, or built up from plate; the semicircular slots in the sides should have as their center the point shown in the drawing, on the table top, so that the table may swing on the four studs accurately, with the spindle as a center. The top of the table is ground and polished to a perfectly flat surface, the smoother the better. Two lines should be deeply scribed on the surface of the table, one parallel to the axis, the other at right angles to it, to assist in placing and moving the work.

The spindle of the machine is made of a good grade of steel, to the dimensions shown in the drawing. The top is threaded to take the roll-tightening nut, and the bottom is faced perfectly square, and polished. A collar is made to be pressed down over the ¾-in. diameter of the spindle, and to the bottom of this collar is screwed a sheet-metal dust cap, shaped like an inverted dish, which keeps the dust out of the bearing. The collar and cap seat on the shoulder of the spindle.

The spindle is supported by a thrust

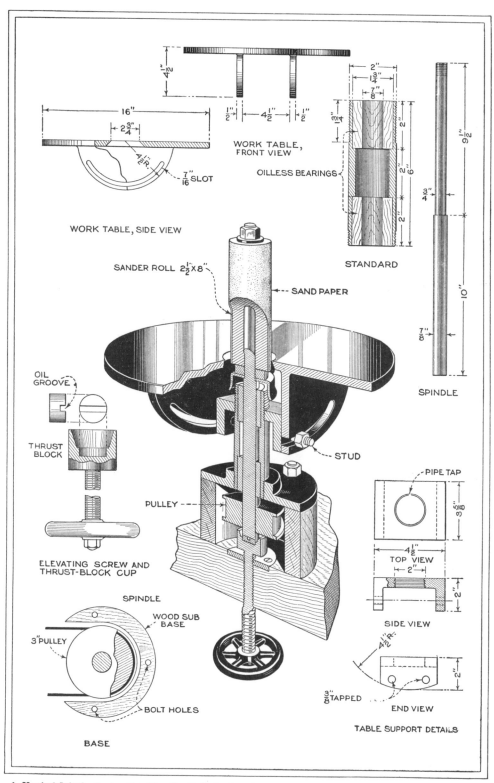

4½"

16"

2¾"

4½"R

7/16" SLOT

WORK TABLE, SIDE VIEW

½" | 4½" | ½"

WORK TABLE,
FRONT VIEW

2"
1¾"
7/8"

3¾"

2"

2"
6"

2"

OILLESS BEARINGS

STANDARD

9½"

¾"

10"

7/8"

SPINDLE

SANDER ROLL 2½"X8"

SAND PAPER

OIL
GROOVE

THRUST
BLOCK

STUD

ELEVATING SCREW AND
THRUST-BLOCK CUP

PULLEY

PIPE TAP

3⅝"

4½"

TOP VIEW

2"

2"

SIDE VIEW

SPINDLE

WOOD SUB
BASE

3" PULLEY

BOLT HOLES

BASE

4½"R

3/8" TAPPED

2"

END VIEW

TABLE SUPPORT DETAILS

A Vertical-Spindle Sander that May Be Built in Any Small Shop, and that Will Prove of Great Value to Woodworkers and Patternmakers

bearing consisting of a bronze disk, slotted as shown, to insure that a constant supply of oil will reach the bottom of the spindle. The disk is carried by a thrust-block cup, which is machined so as to form an oil reservoir. The cup is machined on the top of a ¾-in. elevating screw, working through a plate-steel nut screwed to the top of the bench, directly under the center of the spindle. A large square nut, sunk into the bench, can be used here, if desired. The bottom of the screw is fitted with a hand wheel, which may be taken from an old valve.

The driving pulley is made of steel or cast iron, turned with flanges to prevent the belt from running off; it may be fastened to the spindle either by a key or by two headless setscrews. The face should be made to carry a 1-in. belt.

The sub-base is cut out of hardwood, on the band saw, and mounted on the bench with the belt opening to the rear of the machine.

The sander rolls may be made either of steel or cast iron, and should be per-

fectly smooth and straight. The bore must also be true with the outer surface. The roll is raised by means of the elevating screw when being covered with abrasive paper or cloth, and lowered for working until the lower edge is below the level of the table top.

The abrasive paper can be purchased in rolls or sheets, and in many grades of fineness. A piece is cut that will fit neatly around the roll, the ends meeting closely, without any lap, and it is cemented to the roll with a special adhesive sold for the purpose. After applying, the roll is tightly wrapped with heavy string and allowed to remain until the cement is dry.

Garnet paper is generally used for wood finishing, and emery paper for metal-pattern work.

The machine is driven, by means of a quarter-turn belt, from a small motor; the speed of the roll should be from 1,600 to 1,800 r.p.m.

A snap switch should be located on the front edge of the bench, for convenience in controlling the motor.

Flattening the Ends of Coil Springs

The illustration shows a handy tool for flattening the ends of coil springs, and one that can be made in a few moments to suit

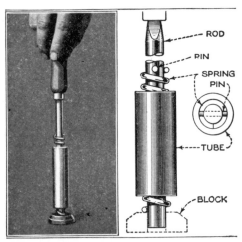

ROD
PIN
SPRING
PIN
TUBE
BLOCK

An Effective Tool for Flattening the Ends of Coil Springs Can Be Made from Scrap Stock

any size spring. It consists of two parts; a length of round-steel rod to fit the inside diameter of the spring, and a piece of pipe or tube to fit the outside diameter. The rod is driven into a wooden handle and drilled for a pin, as shown. The tube, which is only half the length of the rod, is

used to cover the spring except the last coil, which is to be held over a gas flame, the tube protecting the rest of the spring from the heat. The spring is held in the flame long enough to anneal the exposed part, and then, while this end is hot, the end of the rod is slipped into a hole drilled in any convenient metal block, and the handle pressed down quickly. The coils, will, of course, close for a certain distance before the end is pressed back and the tube will slide back over the pin as the tool advances into the hole. This method of flattening the end is particularly effective in case of brass springs.

Avoiding Waste of Envelopes

Frequently, in my office, I found that envelopes had become practically useless due to the gummed flaps sticking to the back, which was caused by the dampness of the storeroom. Having a supply of these envelopes on hand one day, I instructed the porter to attempt to pry the flaps open, my own attempts having resulted in tearing them. The porter spread them out on a long table until he had finished the work he was doing. Upon returning, he found that the air circulated by the ceiling fan, which was located directly above the table, had dried the gummed flaps so thoroughly that no trouble was experienced in opening them. —L. H. Unglesby, Baton Rouge, La.

Raising Sunken Floor Boards

The flooring defect shown in Fig. 1 of the drawing is a common one. The primary cause is, of course, careless workmanship, or defects in the sub-floor, which allow the edge of one piece of flooring to drop down from ¼ to ⅜ in. below the level of the remainder of the floor. A simple method of remedying this is shown in the drawing. A screw is driven in near the edge of the sunken piece, and using a wrecking bar with a block of wood as a fulcrum, the edge is pulled back into place, as indicated in Fig. 1. Then holes are drilled and 8-penny finishing nails driven along the edge as far as necessary, as shown in Fig. 2. When the nail and screw holes have been puttied and stained, the repair is unnoticeable.

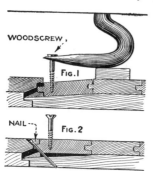

Adjustable Spanner Wrench

Every shop has some machines or tools fitted with slotted nuts, and it usually happens that one of the hardest things to find is a spanner wrench to fit a particular nut. An adjustable spanner that will accommodate itself to nuts of different sizes can be easily made, and when it is remembered that these nuts are quite generally abused with a hammer and chisel when no wrench is at hand, such a tool is well worth making. The body,

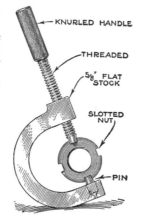

it will be seen, is similar in appearance to the frame of a micrometer caliper. One end is drilled and tapped to take a screw, which is turned from a piece of ⅝-in. cold-rolled steel. A pin, driven in the opposite end of the tool, is turned to the form illustrated. The tapered points of the plug and screw are casehardened.

Vat for Scalding Hogs

The most arduous job in the task of butchering hogs on the farm is the handling of the carcass, which usually weighs

A Large Vat for Scalding Hogs Is Set over a Trench and a Fire Is Built under It

more than 200 pounds. To facilitate the work of scalding the carcass, and to make carrying of hot water unnecessary, an Oklahoma farmer built the movable scalding vat shown in the drawing. It measures 6 ft. long and about 30 in. wide, and is made of 2 by 14-in. material, the bottom and sides being covered with sheet zinc. In use, it is placed over a small trench dug for the purpose, and a fire is built under the vat to heat the water. Three 8-ft. lengths of chains are attached to two handles as shown, and with their help the hog is lifted in and out of the boiling water, two men being required to do the work. A length of stovepipe is set at one end of the fire trench, to serve as a chimney.—J. M. Collins, Kansas City, Mo.

Packing Piston Head on Pump

The piston head on a pump was packed with square 1-in. packing, which upon being worn out could not be replaced by any local supply house, and this made it necessary to devise an emergency packing. Having plenty of ¾-in. packing on hand, we fitted a ⅛-in. iron band on the head and put the packing over this, which resulted in a good fit. Although this packing was intended for temporary use, it has proved as satisfactory as 1-in. packing.—L. W. Brown, Braemar, Tenn.

Auxiliary Handle for Shovel

When a shovel is used on work requiring little high lifting, as is the case when clearing away snow, usually more of a

An Auxiliary Handle on a Shovel Used for Clearing Away Snow, Is of Considerable Assistance

pushing operation than a lifting one, an extra handle attached to the shank of the shovel handle as shown will prove to be of considerable assistance. The auxiliary handle is cut from an old discarded shovel, and is fastened on the shank by means of sheet-metal straps.—Harold E. Benson, Boulder, Colo.

A Homemade Sprayer

The photo shows an efficient sprayer for combating potato bugs. It is made from an old milk can, a length of rubber hose, some lengths of ¼-in. pipe, and fit-

tings that can usually be found in every farm workshop. The cover of the can is soldered tight and a short length of pipe put through a hole in the top and soldered in place, the lower end being about ½ in. from the bottom, so that the entire contents of the can will be used. The upper end of this pipe is fitted with a valve and nipple,

and a length of rubber hose is attached to the latter. A tire valve is also soldered in the top of the can, so that the liquid can be put under pressure by means of a tire pump. The sprayer is carried by two men and has been found to be just as satisfactory as any portable sprayer on the market.—Elmer Raihala, Floodwood, Minnesota.

Machining Two Cone Pulleys on One Mandrel

By forging or grinding a double-pointed lathe tool, two cone pulleys, or similar castings may be machined while in place on a single mandrel. A roughing tool is first used, making both longitudinal and end cuts. Its cutting edge is the same as the ordinary lathe tool but a double point is provided, as shown in the drawing, for cutting in opposite directions, the shank of the tool being clamped parallel to the cross slide. The pulleys can be set closely enough together so that both ends can be faced at one cut; the tool is then withdrawn, and the

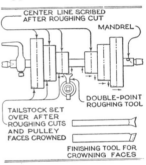

small step of one pulley faced, then fed over without changing the cross feed, and the second casting faced. The second step of this pulley is then faced, and the tool fed along up to the end of the largest step, when, reversing the carriage, it is moved over to the second step of the other pulley. The third step is then end-turned and surface-turned, and the tool is fed over to the third-step surface of the opposite casting. This will rough-turn both pulleys to identical diameters, the face widths being turned to measurement. Next the center line of each step is determined and scribed off, and the tailstock set over enough to turn down the pulley faces to the requisite crown. All steps are beveled until the cuts touch the scribed center lines; the tailstock is then set over in the other direction, or the mandrel reversed, for finishing the opposite tapers, which also meet the scribed lines, thus crowning the steps and completing the job. The finishing tool used for the crowning is similar to the roughing tool except that the noses are ground sharper.

Shaft-Centering and Calipering Tool

The drawing shows a serviceable and convenient tool for centering shafts and measuring their diameters directly without using calipers. It consists of a steel plate $\frac{3}{16}$ in. thick, 4 in. long, and 2¼ in. wide, having a V-shaped cut at one end as shown, the included angle of the vee being 38°-56'. A groove for the scale to slide in is cut in one side of the plate, with one edge bisecting the apex of the cut. Index marks for reading the scale are made on the surface of the plate at the point of the vee, and at right angles to the slot. A small spring, made of $\frac{3}{32}$-in. spring steel, of the shape shown, is riveted on the plate, to hold the scale when adjusted.

The method of reading the diameters of shafts and cylinders is illustrated in the upper detail. The vee is pressed against the shaft as shown, and the scale is then pushed down until it touches the shaft. The distance from the index line to the point where the scale touches the shaft is equal to the diameter of the shaft and is read directly on the scale. When used for centering shafts, the scale is slid over the vee, as shown in the lower detail, and a line is marked with the scriber across the

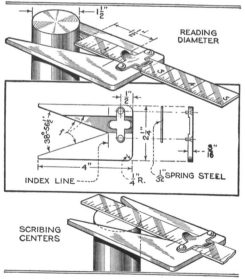

A Serviceable and Convenient Tool for Centering and Measuring Shafts

end of the shaft. Another mark is scribed at right angles to this, the point of intersection being the center of the shaft.

¶For a first coat on wood, wood turpentine should be used as a thinner.

A Hand-Operated Riveter

The work of riveting small parts can be greatly facilitated by providing a small riveter of the kind shown in the drawing, and

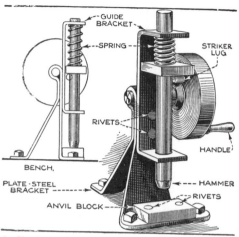

A Simple Hand-Operated Machine which Facilitates Riveting Operations Considerably

much more work can be done with it than is usually done by hand.

The riveter is simple to make; it consists of a steel-plate bracket on which is mounted an anvil block, a hammer, a wheel, and a coil spring. The main bracket is screwed to the benchtop and is bent to the shape shown, with an eye bearing at the top to receive the spindle on which the wheel revolves. A guide bracket, also made of steel plate, is riveted to the main bracket at the point indicated; the ends are drilled and bent over so that both holes will be in line to receive the hammer, which is a short round rod of tool steel. A hole is drilled through the hammer and a square collar is pinned on at this point. A strong coil spring is placed between the flange and the upper guide, so that the hammer is held down on the anvil block with considerable pressure. The anvil block is riveted to the base of the bracket, as indicated, and a heavy steel or iron wheel is mounted on the spindle. The wheel is fitted with a striker lug or roller to lift the hammer, and a handle is provided on the other side so that the wheel can be turned by hand. Almost any type of pulley or heavy-rimmed flywheel can be used for this purpose. The ease with which the tool can be operated depends on the weight of the wheel and, therefore, the heavier the latter is, the more smooth and satisfactory will be the operation of the riveter.

A Septic Tank for the Farm

By A. J. R. CURTIS

THE farmer and small-town dweller can easily obtain all the advantages of running water and bath, with perfect protection against contamination of water supply and filth diseases, by means of a septic tank. This method is the most satisfactory for the disposal of household and other wastes, where a regular sewer system is not available, and the ordinary septic-tank installation is not at all difficult to make.

Household wastes are carried from the house sewer or plumbing outlet directly to the tank, where the solid portions are converted into liquids and gases. The bacteria that cause this change are vigorous only in the absence of oxygen, so the tank chamber should be sealed to exclude air. The sewage should remain in the tank at least 24 hours. After leaving the tank, the liquid, in a semi-purified state, flows into a tile line, where an entirely different kind of bacteria, known as aerobies, which require air in order to live, attack the liquids and complete the process of purification.

The simplest form of septic tank, and one that gives successful results for small-residence use, is a plain, watertight, concrete tank set below ground. Its size will vary with the amount of sewage to be treated. The tank should be made so that a depth of not less than 4 ft. of liquid may be maintained, and any increase in capacity may be obtained by extending the length rather than the width. In this way the sewage has a longer path to travel before being discharged from the tank and the septic action is more thorough. The wastes should enter the tank at the lowest possible velocity, and for this reason the tank end of the house sewer should have very little pitch. A baffle board must be erected immediately in front of the sewer outlet to reduce the velocity of the flow still further. Likewise, the discharge of the treated sewage should be made with a minimum of disturbance to the contents of the tank. To allow this, the outlet must be provided with an air vent.

The concrete for the tank should be made of a mixture of 1 part of cement, 2 parts of sand, and 3 parts of pebbles or clean broken stone. The walls and floor should be 6 in. thick and reinforced with ¼-in. steel rods spaced 12 in. apart in both directions, or with heavy woven wire. The reinforcement should extend down the walls and across the bottom, forming a sort of basket. The cover should be not less than 4 in. in thickness and reinforced with ¼-in. rods spaced 4 in. apart. It should be made in slabs to make it easily removable for cleaning. In case the tank must be set at a considerable depth, with the weight of several feet of soil upon its top, the cover must be made thicker and stronger than this. A hollow extension to the surface of the ground, large enough to admit of cleaning when necessary, may also be found advisable.

The smallest size tank that is practical is one for a family of five persons, which upon the assumption that the daily sewage production is 50 gal. per person, should have a capacity of 250 gal., if the general practice of sewage retention for at least 24 hours is to be followed. In most cases septic action will begin practically as soon as sewage enters the tank but in rare cases it may be necessary to introduce a quantity of septicized sewage from some other tank. Once started, the action rarely ceases.

The forms for the tank are very simple; the inner form consists of a box, with holes bored in the ends to receive the sewer-pipe "ells" that form the inlet and outlet of the tank. Strips of wood are nailed to the sides at the points indicated, to form grooves in the inner walls for the reception of the baffle boards. Where the soil is self-supporting, an outer form may be dispensed with, and the earth itself used to support the concrete. Where the soil is loose, however, an outer form, consisting of a bottomless box, must be used. The lumber used for the forms should be clean, preferably surfaced, and the joints must be made tight to prevent leakage of the

DIMENSIONS OF SEPTIC TANKS				
NO. OF PERSONS	CAPACITY IN GAL.	WIDTH	LENGTH	LENGTH OF TILE IN FT.
5	250	2'- 0"	4'- 0"	150 TO 250
10	500	3'- 0"	5'- 4"	300 " 500
15	750	3'- 6"	6'-10"	450 " 750
20	1000	4'- 0"	8'- 0"	600 " 1000
25	1250	4'- 6"	9'- 0"	750 " 1250
ALL TANKS 5 FEET IN DEPTH				

Table Showing Dimensions of Septic Tanks for Various Sizes of Residences

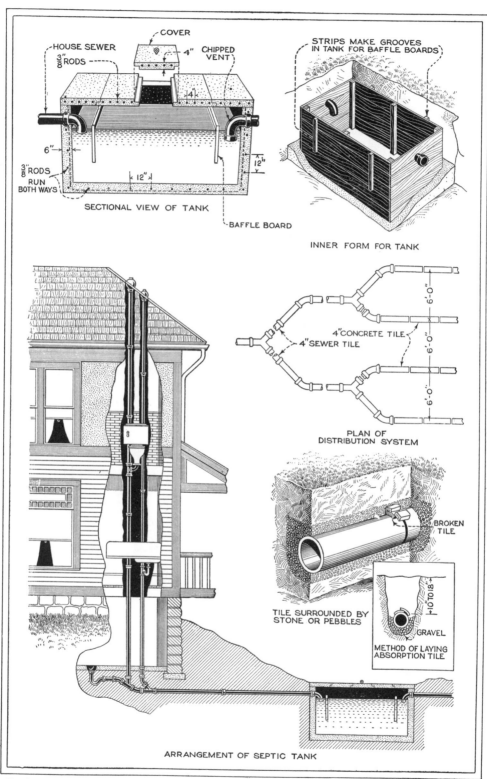

COVER

HOUSE SEWER

3/8" RODS

4" CHIPPED VENT

4"

6"

3/8" RODS
RUN BOTH WAYS

12"

12"

SECTIONAL VIEW OF TANK

BAFFLE BOARD

STRIPS MAKE GROOVES
IN TANK FOR BAFFLE BOARDS

INNER FORM FOR TANK

6'-0"

6'-0"

6'-0"

4" CONCRETE TILE

4" SEWER TILE

PLAN OF
DISTRIBUTION SYSTEM

BROKEN TILE

TILE SURROUNDED BY
STONE OR PEBBLES

10 TO 18"

GRAVEL

METHOD OF LAYING
ABSORPTION TILE

ARRANGEMENT OF SEPTIC TANK

Details of the Making and Installation of a Simple Concrete Septic Tank: This Allows the Farmer to Install
a Modern Plumbing System Where Sewers Are Not Available

15

concrete. A thorough wetting of the form before placing the cement will swell the wood and assist in making the joints tight. The forms should be greased or oiled before placing the concrete and the mixture must be well spaded in the forms to insure filling all corners.

Since the purifying action is only partly completed in the septic tank, the tile distribution system, in which the aerobic bacteria complete the process, is of almost equal importance to the tank. The liquids should never be allowed to pass directly from the tank into a pond or stream, neither should they be discharged directly into a sump or on the surface of the ground.

The disposal or distribution system should consist of a line or lines of 4-in. drain tile, preferably laid as indicated in the drawing, in order to get a maximum length of tile in a small area. If the septic tank is located near the residence, as is usually the case, the tile leading from this point to the disposal or absorption field should be laid as closely together as possible and sealed with cement mortar in the same manner as a sewer. In the absorption field, however, the tile are laid with open joints near the surface, where the soil carries an abundance of oxygen.

In mild climates 10 in. is sufficient depth for the distributing tile, this being increased to a maximum of 18 in. in colder regions. The open joints are protected by pieces of broken tile to prevent dirt from falling into them and clogging the line. Uniform absorption by the soil along the entire length of the distributing tile will be facilitated by laying the tile to an accurate grade with a fall of about 2 in. per 100 ft. Some authorities prefer a steeper grade at the beginning, changing gradually to a level grade at the end.

The length of the lines of tile will depend upon the amount of sewage discharged and upon the character of the soil. In sandy soils of an open texture which admit of an even absorption, good practice indicates that 3 ft. of tile should be laid for each 5 gal. of daily discharge. In tight, clayey soil this should be increased to 1 ft. or more for each gallon. In certain cases where thorough absorption seems difficult, it is well to surround the distributing tile with gravel, cinders, broken stone, or some other similar porous material.

Moisture-Resisting Coats for Wood

Shrinking and swelling, and internal stresses that cause wood to warp and check, are caused by changes in the moisture content. Such changes are occurring continually when wood is exposed to changing atmospheric conditions, and the only way to prevent or retard them is to protect the wood from the air with some moisture-resisting finish or coating.

In order to determine the protection against moisture afforded by various coatings, a series of tests is being conducted by the U. S. Forest Service, at the Forest Products Laboratory, Madison, Wis. No coating or finish which is entirely moisture proof has yet been discovered, but several have been found that are very effective.

Linseed oil, although it is probably recommended more frequently than most of the other materials for moisture proofing wood, was found in the absorption tests to be quite ineffective. Five coats of hot oil followed by two coats of floor wax failed to give any great protection.

Oil paints form a film over wood which is very durable even in exterior locations. Laboratory tests show, however, that such a film, although it may be continuous, does not prevent moisture changes in wood. Graphite paints and spar varnish are about as effective as the ordinary oil paints with the heavier pigments.

The cellulose lacquers rank somewhat higher than the foregoing in moisture resistance, and considerable improvement can probably be effected in them by the addition of solids. They have the advantages of being fast drying and forming a film over the wood that is very elastic.

Rubbing varnishes afford much more protection against moisture than do spar or long oil varnishes. The larger amounts of gum solids present in rubbing varnish probably account for their greater moisture resistance.

Enamel coatings made by the addition of pigments, such as barytes, to ordinary varnish are about as effective as rubbing varnish. A "bronze" coating, composed of a cheap gloss oil and aluminum powder proved in test to be superior in moisture resistance to any of the coatings mentioned above. This mixture is very fast drying; three coats can be applied in the course of half an hour.

The aluminum-leaf coating developed at the Forest Products Laboratory particularly for the protection of airplane propellers is highly efficient in preventing moisture changes in wood. Such a coating can best be applied to large, unbroken surfaces. The laying of the leaf on small intricate parts or assemblies is less practical.

Some asphalt and pitch paints are highly moisture resistant. They are rather cheap and may be applied almost any place where their color is not objectionable. Attempts to discover a means of covering asphalt and pitch paints with lighter-colored materials have met with little success.

For temporary protection against moisture changes, vaseline smeared over varnish is one of the most moisture-resisting coatings yet tested. Another good temporary protection is a heavy coat of paraffin. Neither of these coatings, however, can be used on surfaces subjected to wear.

Straightening Sheet Metal

From various causes light sheet metal often becomes bruised or dented along the edges, and before the material can be used, it must be straightened. Wooden or soft-metal hammers are generally used for this purpose, but it is difficult to make the metal perfectly flat with these. For this reason one shop uses the "follow-up" tool shown in the drawing. It consists of two rollers, each fitted with a set-screw to tighten it on a

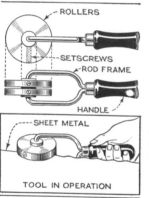

sleeve, which, in turn, is drilled to turn on a frame made from a round steel rod, bent to the shape shown. The shank of the frame is driven into a wooden handle. To operate the tool, it is first set so that the metal fits snugly between the rollers, and after these are tightened on the sleeve, the tool is rolled along the edge of the sheet, with the result that the edge of the metal is made as flat as it was originally.

Handy Fixture for Woodworker's Bench

Many irregularly shaped pieces of wood cannot be held in an ordinary clamp vise when shaving, scraping, or sandpapering them, and for this reason the fixture shown in the drawing has been found very useful. It consists of a 2 by 4-in. frame about 5 ft.

long, with a fixed clamp at one end and an adjustable clamp at the other. The frame is held by vertical pieces, also of 2 by 4-in. stock, nailed to the edge of the bench. The adjustable clamp is made from a length of

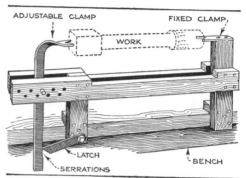

A Simple Clamp for the Woodworker's Bench Holds Work for Scraping, Shaving, or Sanding

flat steel, bent to shape, and drilled to receive a steel pin, which fits in a number of holes drilled through the end of the frame, and staggered as shown. Serrations are filed in the edge of the adjustable clamp near the lower end, as shown, for a latch, which is also made of flat steel. The method of using the fixture is obvious.

Adjustable Cable Hook for Hoist Tackle

The hooks generally used in connection with slings or hoist tackle are clamped with screws or bolts and, when they must be adjusted, it is usually necessary to search for tools, causing much loss of time. A hook adapted for general hoisting work, which can be adjusted without delay, is shown in the illustration The hook proper is a simple flat-steel forging, drilled for a loose rivet and for the cable or sling A U shaped catch is made

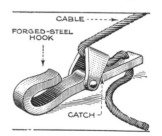

as shown, and riveted over the hook, the edges being first rounded off to prevent cutting the cable.

The cable or rope is passed under the catch and through the hole in the hook as indicated. When necessary, the end of the cable can be hitched around the hook, for additional security. It will be seen that the greater the strain on the cable the tighter the catch will hold.

Soldering Thin Pieces

One source of annoyance when soldering thin pieces end to end is the liability of the work moving during the operation; often a slight touch of the soldering iron

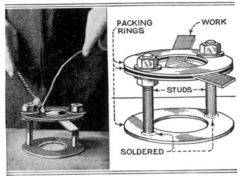

A Useful Clamp Made from Rings and Studs, Used for Holding Thin Pieces While Soldering

is sufficient to disturb their position. A clamp that holds pieces of this character together securely is shown in the photo and drawing; it can be made in a short time from three old packing rings, or something similar, two studs and four nuts, and washers to fit.

One ring forms the base of the tool, and into it are driven the studs, directly opposite each other as shown, a touch of solder holding them permanently in position. The other rings are a loose fit, adjustment being effected by the nuts. The work is held between the top rings, the nuts being tightened by hand. When using this holder, one will also find that the soldering iron will hold its heat much longer than if the pieces are laid on a metal surface as usual.

Glucose for Antifreezing Solution

A substitute for denatured alcohol, in antifreezing solutions for automobile radiators, has been discovered by the chemist of the Bureau of Foods of the Pennsylvania Department of Agriculture. Tests conducted over a period of four years have demonstrated that the substitute is, within certain limits, as efficient as an alcohol or other antifreeze solution, and much more economical.

The substitute is ordinary glucose, a simple sugar made from starch, and extensively used by confectioners and bakers. Glucose is about one-half as sweet as ordinary sugar and costs only 5 or 10 cents per pound. It comes in the form of a colorless liquid.

The investigations conducted prove that a solution consisting of 1½ pt. (1 lb.) of glucose, dissolved in 1 gal. of water, will not freeze until the temperature drops to 5° F. The mixture becomes "slushy" at 10°, but does not freeze, and this does not interfere in any way with the circulation.

The glucose will not evaporate, and is in this respect entirely different from alcohol, which evaporates rapidly upon exposure to air. One filling of water and glucose will last for months, provided there are no leaks in the circulating system. Another point in favor of glucose is the fact that it has no harmful effects on the radiator, engine, or on the rubber connections. For the ordinary small car, 3 lb. of glucose are sufficient; larger cars require more.

To farmers and others not having heated garages, the above-mentioned solution is invaluable. When the temperature drops below 5° F., however, the system should be flushed out, drained, and an alcohol solution used.

Drawing an Ellipse by Projection

Every machinist has occasion to do some sketching and drawing at one time or other, but is handicapped considerably by not having the proper instruments, and is therefore "stumped" when confronted with the problem of drawing a figure such as an ellipse. Two tacks and a length of string are sometimes resorted to, but this method is not always satisfactory. A better method is shown in the drawing. A wire ring is fitted to a surface gauge instead of the usual scriber, the long spindle of the gauge being used. The drawing board is then placed directly under a strong electric lamp of the gas-filled type, and the ring placed under it so that a distinct shadow is thrown on the paper. The gauge is placed on the board so that the axis of the wire ring is parallel to the major axis of the ellipse to be drawn. By moving the ring up or down on the spindle of the gauge, the size of the shadow can be varied. When the correct size is obtained for the major

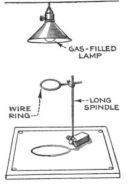

dimension, the ring is turned until the minor dimension measures correctly. The shadow is then traced and a fairly accurate ellipse will be drawn. Of course, no method of this kind can be precise, as it is intended only for sketching and rough layout work.—Edwin J. Bachman, Fullerton, Pa.

Mixing Paint

An eggbeater, such as every housekeeper uses in the kitchen, is far superior to a wooden stick or paddle for mixing paints. When different colored paints are used, it will be found convenient to use a separate beater for each color They cost only a few cents apiece and can easily be cleaned by working them in kerosene after using.—Walter Chas. Michel, Jersey City, New Jersey.

Quick-Action Can Opener

The can opener illustrated has been found to be of considerable assistance in hotel kitchens and restaurants where a great number of cans are opened every day. The opener consists of a 1-in. board

about 6 in. wide and 10 in. long and a 2 by 2-in. upright, which is slotted to receive the end of a handle. A number of holes are drilled through the upright, as shown, so that the handle can be quickly adjusted to any desired

height by means of a pin, which also serves as the fulcrum for the handle. The cutter is made from a strip of sheet steel, cut to the shape shown in the lower detail, and sharpened on one edge. It is bent to a circular form, the ends being held together with a bolt and wingnut. The ends should be slotted so that the diameter can be varied to suit cans of different sizes. The cutter is held in place by a strip of spring steel passed over the notched handle and having the ends passed through slots made in the sides of the cutter.—G. A. Luers, Washington, D. C.

Preventing Scouring of Bridge Abutments

In repairing a stone bridge having a 16-ft. span, it was necessary to devise a method of preventing scouring at the

A Concrete-Covered Stone Floor on a Stream Bed to Prevent Scouring of Bridge Abutments

bridge abutments, as the stream had a swift current and a sandy-loam bottom. A stone floor, made of heavy "riprap" stones, and about 18 in. thick, was built on the bed of the stream, the smaller stones being wedged and tamped between the larger ones, and a wet mixture of concrete poured over the floor, making it a solid mass. A wall 30 in. deep was built on the upstream side at the end of the floor, to prevent the water from undermining it.—R. F. Mundorff, Kansas City, Missouri.

Acid Clears Clogged Pipe

The 1-in. drain pipe carrying away the warm cooling water of a small gasoline engine became clogged with cotton waste at an elbow located under the concrete floor. Clearing the pipe was found to be a problem, as the elbow could not be unscrewed, and a wire stiff enough to push the obstruction away could not be used, as there was another elbow in the way. However, the pipe was cleared in an hour's time by treating the cotton waste with acid. The water above the obstruction was pumped out by means of a small hand pump and a length of rubber tubing, which was only $\frac{3}{8}$ in. in diameter and could easily be dropped into the pipe. About 10 oz. of concentrated sulphuric acid was then poured into the latter, and this removed the waste completely.—C. A. Oldroyd, Barrow-in-Furness, England.

Removing Roller or Ball-Bearing Races

If a special puller or driver is not available for removing the ball or roller-bearing cup of an automobile steering

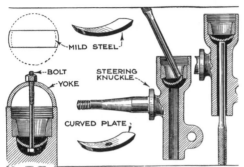

Method of Extracting Roller-Bearing Race without Distorting the Shell

knuckle, the cup must be broken before it can be removed, and this should not be done if possible to avoid it, because the hammer blows necessary to break the cup will distort the shell, and the new bearing will not fit properly.

A good method of removing the cup is shown in the illustration. A piece of steel, ³⁄₁₆ by 1 in., and ¼ in. longer than the smallest inside diameter of the cup, is bent to form a curved plate, which can easily be forced under the cup. The ends of the plate are rounded to conform to the curvature of the shell. By applying a long punch under the plate the cup can easily be driven out. Where this cannot be done, the cup can be pulled out by drilling a hole in the center of the curved plate, and attaching a long bolt with yoke and nut.

Breaking Off Lathe Cuttings

Accidents are often caused by long, curled lathe cuttings wrapping around the work, or becoming entangled with the chuck or faceplate, and striking the operator as they fly around. This danger can

be avoided by cutting or breaking the cuttings off before they become very long. A simple tool for this task is shown in the illustration. It consists of a short strip of flat iron with a hole drilled near one end, and a V-shaped piece cut out as shown. The size of the tool can

be varied to suit heavy or light work. To use the tool, the V-end is pushed over the cutting, which enters the hole. Then the tool is twisted and given a quick jerk to break off the cutting. The best results are obtained if the tool is ground on both sides and hardened, and the hole reamed.

A Simple Acid Pump

Pouring acids and other corrosive liquids from carboys or large bottles is in most cases a highly dangerous operation, and therefore special pumps are often used to transfer the liquids. These pumps are usually quite expensive and for this reason, the homemade pump shown in the illustration was made in one laboratory and found entirely satisfactory. It can be made from odds and ends of broken apparatus found in every laboratory, which makes the cost negligible.

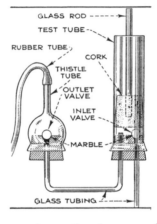

The pump cylinder consists of a test tube with a broken bottom, the rough edges of the break being filed or ground off smoothly. A glass rod, fitted with a rubber stopper, forms the plunger and piston. A rubber stopper with two holes drilled through it, fitted in the lower end of the test tube and lengths of glass tubing are pushed through the holes as shown. A conical depression is cut over one of the holes for a marble to fit in snugly, forming the inlet valve. The outlet valve is made from a thistle tube with the stem broken off; it is fitted with a rubber stopper, having a hole drilled through it for the glass tube from the cylinder, and a seat cut in for a marble. A length of rubber tubing is then attached to the end of the thistle tube.

The joints must be airtight and the piston should be well greased. When the piston is drawn up, a vacuum is created and the inlet valve is opened, which allows the acid to flow in. On the downstroke of the piston the inlet valve is closed and the outlet valve opened, allowing the acid to flow through the thistle tube and into the receiving vessel.

Shop Notes

Mounting the Grindstone

By J. V. ROMIG

GRINDSTONES of various diameters and widths may be purchased complete with the necessary bearings and spindle, ready to mount in a suitable frame, at a price much less than that of a mounted stone, and, as "store" mountings are not always satisfactory, many prefer to purchase only the stone and build a frame to suit it. For the farm or home workshop, a substantial wooden frame which provides a seat for the operator, is recommended.

A post or a wall upright in a convenient location is chosen upon which to mount the frame. Two long pieces of 3 by 4-in. stock are bolted to the upright, as shown in the illustration, using filler blocks as necessary,

to space the sills the proper distance apart for the grindstone bearings. A 2 by 10-in. upright is then fastened to the floor, between the ends of the sills, and jointed to the latter.

The treadles are made of flat iron, bent and drilled as shown in the detail drawing, and pivoted on a ⅝-in. rod run through the post. The end of each treadle is bent at right angles to serve as a foot rest, and the treadles are connected to the cranks by ⅜-in. iron rods with eyes at each end. The treadles, when down, should clear the floor by at least 1 inch.

The seat is made from a flat board, and may be padded and covered with burlap, if desired. A wooden tool rest is also made as shown; this

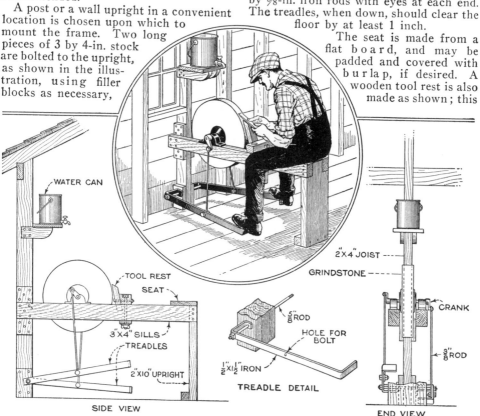

WATER CAN

TOOL REST

SEAT

3"X4" SILLS

TREADLES

2"X10" UPRIGHT

SIDE VIEW

⅝"ROD

HOLE FOR BOLT

½"X1½" IRON

TREADLE DETAIL

2"X4" JOIST

GRINDSTONE

CRANK

⅜"ROD

END VIEW

A Very Substantial and Satisfactory Frame for the Farm and Small-Workshop Grindstone, and One that **Will** Appeal to the Man Who Likes to Make His Own Equipment is adjustable, to allow moving it in as the stone wears down.

Six inches above the center of the wheel a drip can is mounted on a small shelf. Just enough water should be allowed to drip to keep the wheel face wet. The wheel should be used over its whole face, so that it will wear evenly.

The stone, if worn unevenly, can be trued by means of a piece of pipe, resting one end of the pipe on the tool rest, and pressing against the wheel firmly. The pipe should be turned constantly, while moving it across the face of the stone, so as to present new cutting edges continually as it rolls along the rest.

Wrench for Welding Torches

Users of acetylene torches know how easily the torches can be damaged by rough usage. One of the most frequent

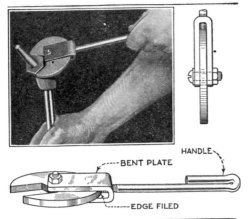

Insert, Loosening Torch-Tip Nut; Below, Details of Wrench Construction

causes of trouble is the nut used to hold the various tips. When tightening or loosening this nut, the wrench should be held at right angles to the torch tubes, otherwise it is difficult to hold the torch at all, as the effect is to push it to one side or the other. The torch should never be placed between heavy objects or in the vise to loosen the nut. A much better method is to use a tool specially made for the purpose. Such a tool is shown in the photo; it consists of a circular piece of steel plate, cut out to fit the nut. A strip of the same material is doubled and attached to the circular piece with a screw and nut, and a handle made of steel rod and threaded into the bent piece as shown. In use the wrench is placed on the nut with the handle loose so that no matter what position the flats of the nut happen to be in, the handle of the wrench can be brought to the right position and tightened. The screw hole is slightly off center, so that the harder the handle is pulled, the harder it presses against the cross-filed edge of the disk.

Hot-Weather Comfort for Autos

An automobile top, exposed to the sun's rays, absorbs an amount of heat that renders it rather uncomfortable for the occupants, especially during the summer time. Experience has shown that the application of a coat of aluminum paint to the under side reduces the absorption of heat to a great extent, and painting the outside with the same kind of paint helps still more. Practically one-half of the heat absorption can be prevented by applying aluminum paint to either inside or outside.

A Combined Drill and Reamer

When all the holes of a lathe turret are occupied by tools and still another tool is needed on the job, some combination is necessary, and the drawing shows how, in one instance, a drill and reamer were combined.

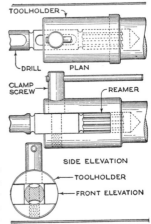

A toolholder was turned to fit the turret hole, and drilled at the front to take the combination drill and reamer, then slotted the width of the tool. The drill-reamer was made from square stock, left square at the center and slotted to take a clamping screw, which threads into the bottom part of the holder.

In using this combination tool the work was first drilled, the clamp loosened, and the tool pulled out a little way to allow the reamer to clear the locating hole in the holder. The reamer is swung around and the drill end pushed back into the holder, when the clamp screw is tightened and the next operation performed.

Tightening Barrel Spigots

Wooden spigots of the kind used on cider and vinegar barrels are apt to leak after being used for some time, due to the cork lining becoming compressed. It can be expanded to make the spigot tight again, by taking out the plug, and holding a burning match under the spigot body, so that the flame will char the cork slightly.

Roofing-Cement Holder

It is very inconvenient to be obliged to hold a cement can while working on a roof, and for this reason the holder shown

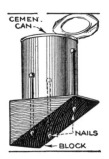

in the illustration should appeal to all who must do such work. It consists of a wooden block, with one side cut to correspond to the angle of the roof and three nails driven through it as shown, the pointed ends projecting just far enough to catch the roofing paper and prevent the block from sliding. The upper ends of the nails keep the can from sliding off the block.—John A. Blaker, West Auburn, Mass.

Moving Tank on Runway

When moving a heavy iron tank up a wooden runway by means of a block and tackle, using lengths of iron pipe for rollers, it was found that the rollers were forced slightly into the wood, due to the weight on them, and this caused them to stop turning. Increasing the pull on the tackle did not help, but merely caused

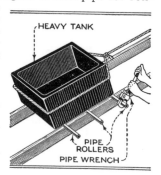

the tank to slip over the rollers. One of the men obtained two pipe wrenches and applied them to the front and rear rollers in the same manner shown in the drawing. Turning the wrenches caused the rollers to turn while the load was being pulled up and also exerted an additional force in moving the load.

Motor-Driven Sieve for Foundry

In foundries and elsewhere a considerable saving of labor and time can be effected by using a motor-driven sieve of the

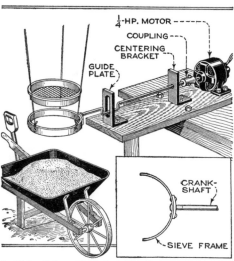

A Motor-Driven Sieve that Has Been Found a Time and Labor Saver

kind shown in the drawing. The sieve is held by a ring suspended from the ceiling on three cables, to prevent it from upsetting and to permit some lateral motion. The shaft that actuates the sieve fits loosely in the side of the ring, the hole being reinforced by a small piece of sheet metal, riveted on and drilled for the shaft to fit loosely. The other end of the shaft is coupled to the motor, as shown. Two brackets made of steel plate are used to support the shaft and to serve as bearings; the one nearest the sieve has a vertical slot a trifle wider than the diameter of the shaft cut through it so that the shaft, which is bent to form a crank at this point, will oscillate at this end when rotated. The other support is simply drilled to a neat fit for the shaft. The size of the motor to use for this purpose, of course, depends on the size of the sieve; for small sieves a $\frac{1}{4}$-hp. motor has been found large enough. In use, the operator places a wheelbarrow or other container under the sieve and then shovels the sand into it. Besides being useful for sand, it can be used for sifting grain, ashes, and other materials.

¶To keep milling cutters from slipping on the arbor, put writing-paper washers between the steel washers and the cutters. Very thin copper or brass washers can also be used.

A Substantial Lumber Rack

The lumber rack shown in the illustration has some excellent features, and

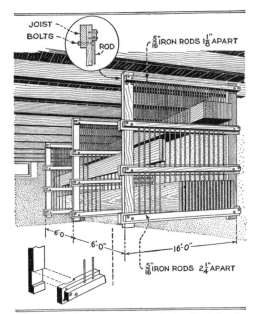

JOIST
BOLTS
ROD
5/16" IRON RODS 1⅛" APART

6'-0" 6'-0" 16'-0"
5/16" IRON RODS 2¼" APART

A Novel and Substantial Lumber-Drying Rack for the
Woodworking Shop

should prove a valuable addition to any woodworking shop.

There are three frames, ends and center. Each frame consists of two upright pieces bolted to the floor joists, and four crosspieces, half-checked and screwed to the uprights. The novel feature lies in the separators used in the frame. In building a lumber rack, it is common practice to use stock about ⅞ in. thick by 1 or 1¼ in. wide; these not only waste valuable space, but are easily broken. In this rack, ⁵⁄₁₆ in. iron rods are used, held in strips screwed to the crosspieces of the frame. In the two center strips, ⅜-in. holes are bored right through, spaced 2¼ in. between the rods. In the bottom strip these holes are spaced the same, but are ¾ in. deep only. In the second strip from the top, ¾-in. deep holes are bored between the through holes, and in the top strip the holes are spaced 1⅛ in. apart, and bored through.

Thin stock, ½, ⅜, ¾ in. thick, etc., is stored in the upper rack, and the heavier stock in the lower ones. If it is necessary to remove one or more rods, to store very thick stock, or to replace bent rods, it is only necessary to raise the rod out of the bottom hole, draw it out enough to clear the strip, and pull it out. Putting in

new rods only means reversing the operations. The rods, of course, are cut to such a length that they can be raised enough to clear the bottom strips.—M. E. Duggan, Kenosha, Wis.

Replacing Wire-Wheel Rims

Repairmen who occasionally have to replace a bicycle rim, know how puzzling it is to put the spokes into the new rim correctly. This difficulty can easily be overcome by securely tying every pair of spokes together at the point where they cross, which will hold them in position until they have been attached to the new rim. A good method of doing this is to twist a short length of iron wire around them with a pair of pliers. If it is necessary to replace any of the spokes, this should be done after they are in place on the new rim, in order to avoid making mistakes.

Centering Round Work on Milling Machine

It is a slow and tedious task to find the center of a shaft when cutting a keyway or other groove in it. To eliminate this difficulty we made a center-finding tool of the kind shown in the drawing. It consists of an iron base, a vertical guide rod, with a keyway cut lengthwise as shown, and a centering block, which is drilled to fit the guide rod, and has a V-groove on each side. This block is provided with a pin, the end of which slides in the groove of the

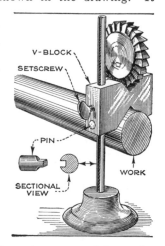

V-BLOCK
SETSCREW
PIN
WORK
SECTIONAL
VIEW

guide rod, and a setscrew to tighten the block on the rod at any point desired.

In use the block is raised and dropped onto the shaft, which automatically centers it, then the setscrew is tightened. The milling-machine table is then raised and moved until the cutter is in the center of the upper V-groove.—L. H. Moore, Toronto, Can.

Building a Blower for the Forge

By RAY F. KUNS
Principal, Automobile Trade School, Cincinnati, O.

PRACTICALLY all machine shops and garages are equipped with some style of forge, often "knocked up" hastily from scrap material, but, while the making of the forge is quite simple, many mechanics are "stumped" when it comes to designing a blower.

The blower shown in the accompanying illustration was designed to supply a forge having four tuyere irons, and, when driven at a speed of 2,000 r.p.m., it provides

drums was chucked in the lathe, and the edge faced off until it was ½ in. wide. The points at which the lugs were to be attached were then marked on both drums, and the lugs turned, drilled, and welded in place, leaving generous fillets of filler material on each lug, as indicated in the side elevation. The separate parts of the hous-

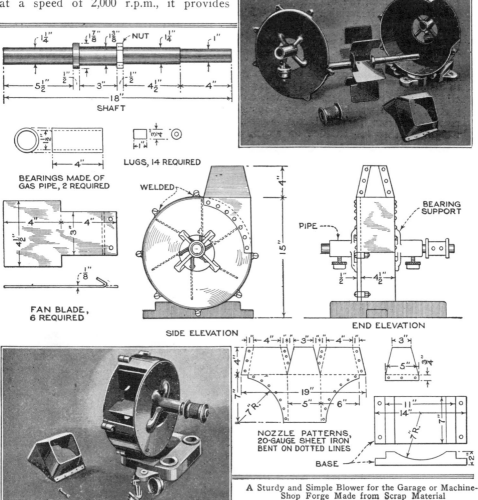

A Sturdy and Simple Blower for the Garage or Machine-Shop Forge Made from Scrap Material

enough pressure to operate all at the same time, when driven by a 1-hp. motor. The materials for its construction were found in the scrap heap.

Two 12 to 14-in. brake drums are required for the body or housing of the blower. In this case the drums were 14 in. in diameter by 4½ in. wide. One of the

ing were then chucked and faced true in the lathe, after which the half-lap joint was turned.

The boxes for the bearings were made of 1½-in. pipe, 4 in. long. Short lengths of ½-in. iron rod were shaped to fit against housing and boxes, for supports, and the supports welded to the boxes as shown. The base was made from an old cast-iron jig base; to provide a good seat for the housing the base was set up on the lathe carriage, and a fly cutter used to cut an arc of 7-in. radius in it. The housing was then hot-riveted to the base. A piece of hardwood may be used as a base if cast-iron is not available.

The shaft was made from an old automobile axle shaft, but, of course, machinery steel is quite as good. As may be noted, a collar was turned for the fan assembly to butt against, and threads chased for a nut to lock the fan assembly. The fan blades, six in number, were cut from ⅛-in. sheet steel, and welded to a built-up spider sleeve bored to fit the shaft. After mounting and locking the fan assembly on the shaft, the latter was placed between centers on the lathe, and the blades turned to insure that the lengths and widths were all equal. After all machine work was completed, the fan was balanced by placing a rivet or rivets in the blades rquiring weight, testing for balance on a pair of straightedges. The fan was made ¾ in. smaller in diameter than the housing.

The fan was then assembled with the bearings, and the latter placed so that the blade edges would just clear the point on the housing to which the upper edge of the nozzle is attached, the opening for the latter having previously been cut; the bearings were then welded to the housing, and babbitted, after all machine work was completed and the parts assembled. This insures the bearing being in alinement. The shaft should be heated and smoked before the babbitt is poured. Wick oilers, from attached oil cups, are used to lubricate the shaft.

The nozzle was made from 20-gauge sheet iron, cut to the pattern shown, in two sections, the sections riveted together, and the nozzle riveted to the housing. While the design shown was perfectly satisfactory, it may, of course, be changed to suit individual requirements, or if different materials are used.

Making and Using Cross Valves

A much neater and stronger pipe job can be done by using a cross valve than by using an ordinary angle valve, because

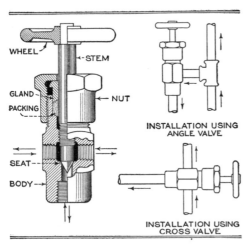

Left: An All-Steel Angle Valve for Use as a Cross Valve. Right: Comparative Installations

the tee and nipple, which must be used with the latter, are eliminated. A cross valve can readily be made by drilling and tapping the side of an all-steel needle-point angle valve, as indicated in the sectional view to the left in the illustration. The run of the valve is used in the main feed line, and when the valve is closed, the liquid flows in only one direction.—J. V. Romig, Allentown, Pa.

Clamping a Grooved Pulley

The novel pulley clamps shown in the illustration were successfully adopted when it became necessary to place a grooved pulley on a shaft already in place. To enable the pulley to be placed without disturbing the shaft the following work was done: First, four small holes were drilled as shown and pins slightly tapered at both ends were driven in place; two holes for bolts were then drilled, and four clamping pieces drilled in the center to clear the bolts used for tightening, and at either side to suit the pins, the distance between the holes being a little

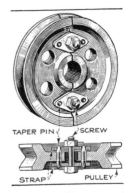

less than the center-to-center distance of the pins. The pulley was then sawed in two, on the line of the bolt holes. When assembled on the shaft the bolts were tightened, which drew the clamps together; the center distance of the holes being less than that of the pins, both sides of the pulley were drawn together, binding it securely on the shaft.

¶Oil the rocker arms on overhead-valve motors at least every two days. This takes only a moment and prevents wear.

Compressing Auto Springs

When installing snubbers on an automobile it is necessary to pull the strap as tight as possible, and this makes it necessary to compress the spring, which is impossible to do by hand or with a "C" clamp. The springs can be compressed without any difficulty by running the car in the garage doorway so that the middle of the spring is located directly under the doorframe header. The wheels are then blocked to make them stay in place and a length of 2 by 4-in. timber forced between the car frame and the header, directly over the axle, a piece of cloth being placed below the wood to prevent damage to the enamel. The wheel is then jacked up as far as necessary to attach the snubber snugly, making a nice tight job when the spring is released.—Rev. Philip Jonker, Peekskill, N.Y.

Locking Drill Chuck

The drawing shows an effective method of locking a drill chuck of the threaded-sleeve type. This chuck finds favor in many shops, as it is easily opened and closed by hand, but this very feature is a disadvantage if the chuck is run in the reverse direction. Small shops, which are compelled to utilize tools to the fullest capacity, often find it necessary to use a drill chuck in the milling machine for holding small shank end mills, etc., and

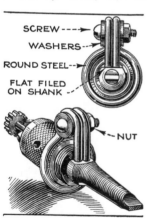

SCREW
WASHERS
ROUND STEEL
FLAT FILED ON SHANK
NUT

in such cases the lock shown is very useful. It can be made in a few moments to suit any size chuck by bending a piece of round steel around the chuck sleeve and forming the ends so as to bear on a flat spot filed on the shank. In use, the chuck is first tightened on the cutter in the usual way, and the ends of the lock are then squeezed together by a nut and screw, locking the chuck sleeve securely. Left-hand cutters can be held firmly in this manner, whereas if the sleeve is not locked the action of the teeth in cutting will loosen the chuck by unscrewing the sleeve, and perhaps spoil the job or break the cutter.

Preparing Castings for Welding

Welding on some work is very difficult, because the piece to be welded is of such a form or the break is at such a point that

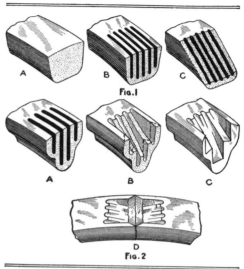

Fig. 1

Fig. 2

Improved Method of Doing a Good Job of Welding on Small, Irregularly Shaped Pieces

it is almost impossible to clamp it tightly in a vise for beveling, to provide a scarf for the weld, without danger of further breakage by pressure.

A good method of handling such a job, if the piece is of the general form shown at A in Fig. 1, is to clamp the work lightly in a vise and then make a series of parallel cuts with a hacksaw, as shown in B. The cuts are made almost to the bottom edge and at an angle which will make sufficient clearance for the welding operations to follow. The end is then beveled as shown in C, breaking off the sections by the wedging action of a thin-bladed cold chisel. In case the piece to be welded is of a more irregular contour, as shown in Fig. 2, the saw cuts are made of a depth proportional to the thickness of the material, as shown in A, and cut out as in B. The end is then beveled, as shown in C, by means of a file or emery wheel. When both sides of the break are prepared in this way, they are set together as indicated in D, and a good weld can easily be made.—C. R. Van Druff, McLouth, Kan.

¶Grease or vaseline, rubbed on the hands before starting on a dirty job, will keep the dirt out of the pores, and enable the hands to be cleaned much more easily afterward.

Resurfacing Worn Street Pavements

Worn-out pavements with large "potholes" may be transformed into first-class boulevards by resurfacing with sheet asphalt. Recent developments in paving practice have shown that this can be done whenever the original base is in good condition, no matter how irregular the surface may be, or from what material it is constructed. The work of resurfacing can be accomplished in a few days without seriously inconveniencing traffic, as only half of the street need be surfaced at a time, leaving the other half open to traffic, whereas, when making a new pavement, traffic must be stopped until the concrete base has had time to set properly.

The area to be resurfaced is first thoroughly cleaned of all foreign matter by sweeping with rotary sweepers or hand brooms. The larger "potholes" are filled with concrete, defective gutters are rebuilt, and loose bricks are either relaid or replaced with concrete. The surface is then sprinkled with pure asphalt, heated to a temperature of about 300° F. This seems to produce a more effective bond between

Above, Dumping the Heated Sheet Asphalt; Below, Spreading Pure Asphalt over the Old Pavement

the sheet asphalt and the original surface than can be obtained if the sheet is laid directly on the old pavement. The sheet asphalt is then brought from the plant, at a temperature a little higher than 300° F., dumped just ahead of the part already laid, shoveled into place with heated shovels, and raked to a uniform surface with heated iron rakes. It is then tamped, sprinkled with limestone dust, and thoroughly compressed by rolling with a 15-ton roller. After rolling, squares are cut out around valve boxes, manhole covers, etc., the castings raised to the new grade and reset in concrete, and asphalt laid around them. The asphalt layer is allowed to thin out to a feather edge at the gutter, so as to avoid building a new gutter.

In Dayton, Ohio, some streets resurfaced in this way with layers averaging about ½ in. in thickness, have given satisfactory service for two years, with no indication of the asphalt pulling loose from the surface. The resurfacing cost 49 cents per square yard.—Ivan E. Houk, City Engineer, Dayton, Ohio.

Wood Preservatives

During the last 10 years it has been proved by tests performed by the U. S. Bureau of Agriculture that coal-tar creosotes are more effective in protecting wood against boring insects such as "white ants," and Lyctus-powder post beetles, than any other wood preservative known. Wood, impregnated with the creosote under considerable pressure, has been found to last for at least 25 years. The open-tank method of creosoting

wood, if carefully done so that good penetration is obtained, will render the wood resistant for at least 15 years. On farms where it is impossible to use this method on the wood of buildings already erected, or on fence posts, the best method is to apply several coats of creosote with an ordinary paint brush or spray; this will add from 2 to 5 years to the life of the wood, providing it is not too old when the creosote is applied. By adding pigments to the oil a very neat and presentable appearance will be given to the wood.

Interior woodwork should be treated with zinc chloride, bichloride of mercury, sodium fluoride, or chlorinated naptha-lene. Mercuric chloride is very poisonous, and, as it has a tendency to come off in small quantities, should not be used. Lumber, implement handles, wagons, etc., that cannot be treated with coal-tar cre-osote, for various reasons, should be stored in creosoted sheds.

Grinding Screw Ends

Sometimes screws of standard sizes are just a few threads too long for some particular job, and this makes it necessary to grind down the ends. If any number of screws of the same size must be ground down in this way, a simple holder of the type shown in the illustration will be found of considerable assistance, as, with it, the grinding can be accomplished without the necessity of frequent dipping in water to keep the screw cool.

The shank or body of the tool is a short length of $\frac{5}{8}$-in. machine-steel rod, pointed at one end so that it can be driven into a wooden handle, and a piece of $\frac{3}{32}$-in. flat steel about $\frac{5}{8}$ in. wide, bent as shown and drilled through the center to receive a

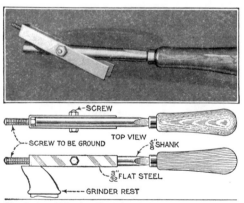

Simple but Effective Tool for Grinding Small Screws Rapidly

small screw, with which it is attached to the shank. The end of the flat piece is drilled to suit the diameter of the screw to be held, just enough space being allowed between the end of the shank and the screw heads to hold the screws securely. With this holder the operator need not touch the hot screws at all as they drop out themselves when the tool is opened. In use, both parts of the tool are held together and steadied on the toolrest, as shown in the lower detail.—Harry Moore, Montreal, Can.

Divider Attachment Marks Gears

The divider attachment is well worth including in a repairman's kit for its use-fulness when "pegging" gears.

When several teeth of a gear have been

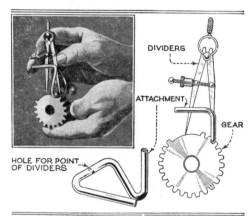

Simple Attachment that Enables the Repairman to Space Pegs Correctly When Repairing Gears

sheared off it is, of course, important to place the inserted pegs in the same position as the broken teeth, and it is for the purpose of marking the correct position that the attachment shown in the photo is used. It is made from a length of drill rod, bent to the shape indicated and drilled for the point of the dividers. The attachment and dividers are then assembled, the cross leg of the attachment set between two of the gear teeth, and the free point adjusted to the center of any convenient tooth. It is not necessary to open the dividers enough to span the complete gap in the gear teeth; about half the distance will do, as the dividers are used from each side of the gap. After filing or grinding off the remnants of the broken teeth, the surface is blued and the attachment moved across the tooth with the free point of the dividers touching the blued surface. The same process is repeated in the next tooth space and so on until the position of each missing tooth has been marked.

It will be seen that the dividers are held securely at right angles to the axis of the gear, so that the lines marked will run straight across, besides preserving the correct pitch. If the lines are followed closely in drilling, it will be found that no trouble will develop from "off-pitch" pegs.

¶Celluloid triangles may be written upon with anhydrous acetic acid. This may be colored to contrast with the celluloid.

Homemade Pipe Bender

In a Kansas shop, where it was necessary to turn out a number of short lengths of 1-in. pipe, bent at one end to a half cir-

A Homemade Pipe Bender that Is Attached on the Lathe, Has Been Found Very Efficient

cle, having a radius of 6 in., all attempts to do this by heating the pipe, packing it with sand and then bending, and by numerous other methods, were entirely unsatisfactory.

One of the mechanics then decided to make a bender that would do the work. In looking for material to make it, he was fortunate to find a cylindrical casting of about the right diameter. This he chucked on the lathe, reduced it to the proper diameter and grooved it to fit the 1-in. pipe as shown in the drawing. It was then drilled out so that the side extension of an old discarded socket wrench would fit into it when the hexagon was turned as shown by the dotted lines. A small roller, also grooved to fit the pipe, was attached to the handle of the wrench extension with a shouldered bolt, and a stop was bolted to the chuck face. A length of pipe was run between the roller and the casting and between the stop and the casting, the stop being behind the roller when the handle rested on the ways of the lathe. The lathe was then revolved slightly more than a half revolution, so that the pipe would spring back to a half circle when the tension was removed. This bender made almost perfect bends without denting or flattening the pipe in the least.— Earl Pagett, Independence, Kan.

❡ The arc of contact of a grinding wheel on the work has a very important bearing on the grade of wheel required. The smaller the arc, the harder the wheel should be, and vice versa.

Removable Grip for Babbitt Ladle

When babbitt is melted in an ordinary gas furnace the ladle handle is almost sure to get too hot to be comfortable, and it is the customary practice to cover the handle with a bunch of waste to protect the hands. This is not satisfactory, because thick waste makes the handling of the ladle difficult and the waste often begins to smolder and burn. In one shop, a removable grip for the handle was made that proved very satisfactory in use, and eliminated all trouble. A hole was drilled through the handle near the pot and a pin driven through, as shown in the drawing. The handle was then heated at the end and upset enough

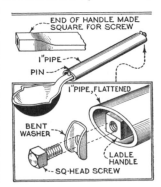

to enable it to be drilled and tapped for a capscrew. A length of iron pipe, slightly flattened, served as the grip, and was held on the handle by means of a screw and a round washer, both sides of the latter being turned up so that it would slip inside the pipe. The ladle is placed in the furnace with the grip off, and, when the metal is ready to pour, the grip is slipped on up to the pin, and the screw and washer in the end given a quarter turn.

Straightening Auto Rims

Dents in clincher rims can be removed very easily by means of the simple tool illustrated. It is merely half of a leaf spring

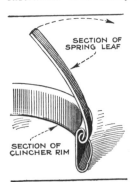

with the shackle eye at the end. A tapered punch is used to spread out the eye to ½ in. in diameter, and the end is then cut off with a hacksaw to form a hook that can be placed under the bent edges of the rim. The dent is readily straightened by pulling the tool in the direction indicated by the arrow.—Fred Bargiband, Pittsburgh, Pa.

A Novel Ground-Feed Sifter

By DALE R. VAN HORN

A NEBRASKA poultry raiser has designed and built a novel ground-feed sifter and grader, with which he is able to separate any ground feed into four groups, graded according to the size of the particles, in one operation. Since all of the parts are such as may be picked up around the farm, making the cost negligible, a sifter of this kind will prove of value to every poultry raiser.

The frame of the sifter may be built of any available lumber, providing it is well j o i n t e d and braced; it is built to suit the size of the agitator, which may be made from any heavily built b o x. This particular agitator is 18 in. square by 14 in. deep. The bottom a n d top are knocked out, and f o u r screens tacked in place as indicated by the dotted lines in the side view, the screen wire or cloth being first stretched on light frames as shown in the detail. The coarsest screen is arranged at the top, the next size just underneath, a n d so on, the finest being at the b o t t o m. W h a t falls through the lowest screen is practically flour, a n d falls into the bin at the bottom.

The agitator is hung in the frame at an angle, as shown, by means of four heavy sheet-metal supports, which are pivoted rather loosely on heavy screws at both ends. Hinged to the bottom edge of the back side of the agitator is a wooden connecting rod or pitman, which shakes the agitator back and forth. The connecting rod is split at the outer end to take a split bushing that rides on the crank. The

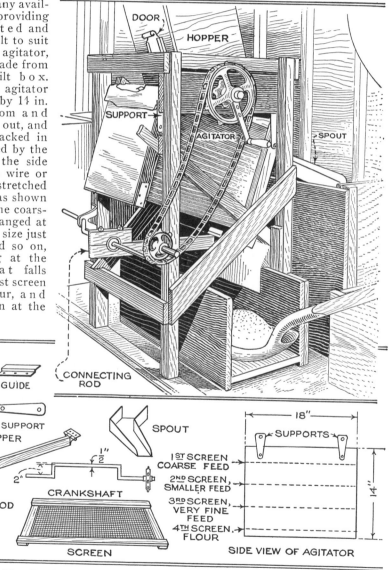

Above, Front View of Sifter, Showing Operating Mechanism; Below, Details of Construction of the Various Parts

crankshaft is made of ½-in. iron rod, as shown in the detail; it has a 3-in. sprocket keyed to one end, and runs in flat-iron bearings bolted to the frame. The crankshaft is driven by means of a chain, from a 7-in. hand-crank operated sprocket mounted on a stud attached to one of the upper frame members. The crank has a

2-in. offset, giving the agitator a motion of 4 inches.

A hopper, tilted in the opposite direction to the agitator, is firmly fastened to the top of the frame, to contain the unsifted feed. The flow to the agitator is controlled by a sheet-iron door, sliding in guides nailed at the sides of the opening.

Tightening Concrete Forms

Concrete forms for walls are usually tightened by means of lengths of wire, which are doubled, run through the sides of the forms at regular intervals, and twisted in the center by means of a stick. This method of tightening the wire necessitates working within the forms, which is very often difficult. A better method, which allows the wire to be tightened outside of the form, is shown in the illustration. The chuck end of an old brace is flattened at one end, and two holes, slightly larger than an ordinary fence staple, are drilled as shown. The end is then slotted with a hacksaw as indicated and closed slightly to create a slight spring.

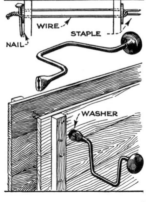

As the forms are erected the wires are passed through the holes drilled for them, a staple with a washer under it being hooked under the doubled end. The two free ends are twisted together and a nail inserted under them, a washer being provided under the nail to prevent the nail from being sunk into the form. To tighten the wires, the brace is slipped onto the staple and is then turned to twist the wire to the desired tension. The forms can later be removed by simply slipping the staple out of the wire and the washers will not be damaged. The holes in the staple side of the forms, of course, are large enough to take the doubled wire.

❧Frequently a solid tire run out of line will develop lumps or an uneven tread. To remedy this, take the tire to any pneumatic-tire store and have the rubber buffed.

Turning Gasoline Car on Track

Turning a gasoline-propelled car around on railroad tracks can be accomplished easily and quickly by means of the device shown in the drawing. It consists of a 12-in. jack and a piece of 1 by 4-in. iron bar, bent to the shape shown and fastened to the frame of the car, in the center, with U-bolts. A hole is drilled in the bottom of the attachment to fit the top of the jack. Screw-

ing up the jack lifts the car, and as soon as it clears the tracks sufficiently it can be swung around. This can be done by one man in two or three minutes. The bar, of course, is permanently attached to the car frame and the jack is always carried on the car.—L. W. Brown, Braeman, Tenn.

Facing Bosses to Gauge

In machining a large number of castings, the bosses of which had to be faced to an accurate dimension A, a simple gauge

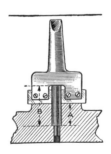

was made that greatly facilitated the operation, and prevented spoiled work. The facing tool used was of special form, as shown in the illustration, and a hardened-steel pin was used with it to serve as a gauge. The pin was of such a length that, with the tool seated on its top, the cutters had faced the boss to the correct height. Knowing that he could not spoil any work as long as the pin was in place, the operator made much better time than was possible by any other method.— J. H. Moore, Toronto, Can.

Curing Blowing Out of Gaskets

Some gasoline engines of the type having a detachable head are constantly blowing out gaskets. This usually occurs at the narrow points, as between the cylinder bores, or in the valve-chamber area, and is usually due to a slightly warped cylinder casting. A permanent remedy for this trouble is to cut two pieces of sheet copper, .005 in. thick, large enough to cover the place where the gasket blows out. One piece is placed below the gasket and the other above, and the head is then clamped down tightly. A new gasket must, of course, be used in making this repair.—G. C. Douglas, Raleigh, N. C.

Pan Catches Automatic Screw-Machine Work

Most automatic screw machines are so tooled that one operator can attend to several, but allowance must be made for a certain amount of spoiled work, as the operator's time must be divided between the machines. In a factory where small wire goods are made, the pan shown in the illustration is used to prevent spoiled pieces from entering the box containing work passed as correct. The pan is made of

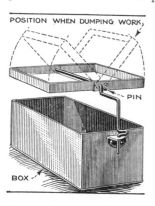

sheet metal and consists of two pieces, made in the shape of half trays. One piece fits over the other as shown and has its sides extending beyond the bottom of the other a short distance so that there will be space for the work to pass through when both sides of the pan are lifted to the position indicated by the dotted lines. Both sides pivot on a length of steel rod, bent to the shape shown, and passed through the hole in the box handle. A pin is riveted to the outside of the larger pan, and rests against the rod holding the pans, so that the weight of the work, which drops on this side, will not cause the pan to tip over. The operator inspects the work in the pan, and, if it contains no spoiled pieces, the sides are lifted and the work slides into the box below. If it contains spoiled pieces the work is emptied into another box.

Cutting Wire Safely

Above a certain diameter, steel wire cannot be cut conveniently with ordinary pliers, and therefore a chisel is often used

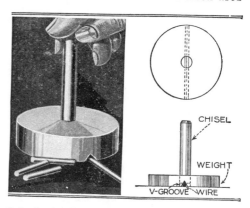

Left, Cutting Heavy Wire; Right, Details of Cutting Fixture

for the purpose. This method is rather dangerous, however, as the small pieces are likely to fly into the worker's face, and it is also somewhat inconvenient, as the pieces are apt to be lost. A better method of cutting the wire is to use a flat block of steel as shown, with a V-groove cut across the bottom, and a hole drilled through the center for a round-shank chisel. The wire is pushed along the groove and is cut off with the chisel.

To cut the wire in equal lengths, it is either nicked with a file at the points to be cut and the wire then pushed along until the nick comes directly in the center of the hole, or a weight is placed on the block and a stop is provided on one side so that the wire can be pushed up against this and then cut off. Spring wire can be cut safely in this way without any danger.

Adding to Usefulness of Micrometer

It is often necessary to take micrometer readings on work of the kind shown in the illustration. This is made possible by grinding down the head and part of the anvil about $\frac{3}{32}$ in. as shown, leaving a $\frac{3}{32}$-in. lip projecting. This will not affect the accuracy of the micrometer and will add considerably to its usefulness.—F. J. Haas, Milwaukee, Wis.

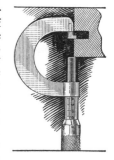

Bench Vise with Universal Base

Due to the limitations of the ordinary stationary vise, a workman must often stand in an uncomfortable posture in order to apply the file or other tool to the work properly. To overcome this difficulty, the vise illustrated has been devised and found very successful; it has a spherical base that can be adjusted to any position within an arc of 90°; this makes the vise especially adapable for use in assembling small parts where individual fitting is necessary.

The constructional details and dimensions are clearly indicated in the drawing, but may be varied somewhat to suit individual tastes and requirements. The vise jaws slide in a T-guide that forms part of the body of the vise. A screw with right and left-hand threads, turned with a small socket wrench, moves the jaws. The jaws are, of course, made of steel, and are hardened and tempered.

The body, as well as the flange base and the plate underneath, is made of cast iron, although steel or brass will serve equally well. Machine bolts hold the flange base and the plate securely to the bench. A screw, provided with a ball-shaped head that seats in the body of the vise, and with a wingnut that can be loosened or tightened to permit adjustment, clamps the body when set. A setscrew in the side of the guide may be used to lock one jaw of the vise in position.

Bench Vise that Will Be Found Very Useful by Toolmakers and Machinists, as the Base Can Be Adjusted to Many Positions

---

Simple Lock for Hand Crank

On certain types of machinery, such as printing presses, some sort of hand crank is required to complete a certain cycle of operations or to bring a certain part of the machine to a position for adjustment or repairs. In case a gear-driven manual movement is used, the gears can be prevented from accidentally meshing by means of a simple catch of the type shown in the illustration. A semicircular groove is milled in the shaft to receive a flat-steel dog, which is fastened to some convenient point on the machine frame. The groove should be cut in the top of the shaft as the weight of the crank handle will cause this side to remain up at all times. When it is desired to engage the crank with the machine gear, it is only necessary to turn the crank to disengage the dog, and the gears can then be meshed.

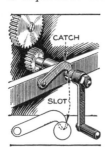

Tearing Off Stamps

Generally the hardest and most disagreeable part of getting out a large lot of mail is the stamping of it, as the stamps soon become sticky if handled very much, and any attempt to tear up a number of sheets at once while flat, results in mutilating some of them. An easy method of tearing off a large number of stamps into strips is to roll several sheets into a tight roll about 1 in. in diameter. The successive rolls can then be broken off at the perforations without any danger of tearing the stamps. As many as ten sheets can be torn at one time in this way.—James Ellis, Memphis, Tenn.

Carpenters' Improved Tool Box

By EDWIN M. LOVE

THE ideal carpenters' tool box should be light and strong, simply built, with space enough for all tools used on the ordinary job, and have a special place for each tool, so that the owner can see at a glance what tools, if any, are missing.

The tool box shown in the accompanying illustration fulfills these requirements almost perfectly, being but 31¼ in. long, 8¼ in. wide, and 13⅜ in. high when closed, yet it opens into a vertical rack displaying all tools to the sight, with the most frequently used tools removable instantly and independently of the rest.

Three-ply birch panel veneer, ⅜ in. thick, is the material used, the main grain of the wood running lengthwise of the box on top, bottom and sides and vertically on the ends.

Make glued butt joints, nailing with three-penny common nails every 2 inches. Lay out the lid, bore the hinge holes in the top of the box, and then rip the lid loose; this insures a perfect fit without further work. Attach the hinges with machine screws and nuts. The handles, made of hardwood in two pieces, as shown in the drawing, enable both lid and box to serve in the carrying strain.

Make a bit rack, as shown, of two tapered blocks, A and B, and place in the lid, block A being bored and B slotted. This rack is for seven sizes, from ⅛ to 1⅛ in., and the bits are placed shank to lip, to save space. This rack is covered by the small-bit rack shown in the lower right-hand detail. Make this, on a ⅜ by 6⅝ by 9½-in. veneer back, with ⅜ by ⅝-in. strips, and attach turnbuttons to hold the bits. This rack is held firmly by the large-bit rack end stop, two small stops glued to the bottom and side of the compartment, and a small hook and eye attached to the end stop. By means of light turnbuttons, a butt chisel, spokeshave, bevel square, and gouge are held on the back of the smaller bit rack.

Nest the planes in the bottom, on their sides, as shown in the drawing, with the level behind; slip the take-down square behind the level and fill the spaces with butt gauge, greaser, oilcan, etc. The boxlike shelf at the right

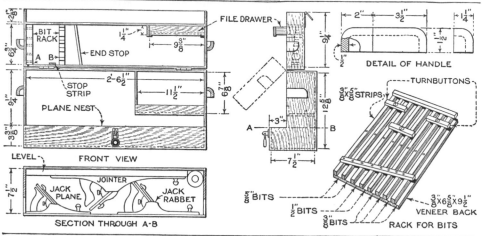

Above, Tool Box Open Ready for Work, with Saws on Shelf; Below, Full Details of Construction, and Method of Nesting Planes

contains a No. 45 universal plane, suspended upside down, with the boxes of cutters below in a vertical position, and the iron rabbet plane in front. The push drill lies behind the edging of the shelf, the block plane stands on end at the left side, and the hand drill is tucked in as well. The arrangement of the other small tools must be governed by the number and style, but turnbuttons seem to be the most practical means of keeping them in position. It is a good idea to silhouette all tools in black on the inside of the box, in position, so that any missing may be noticed immediately, when the box is packed.

Rip a hardwood strip 7 in. long to slip over the saws and keep them well nested as they lie in the bottom of the box, on top of the planes. With this strip they can be lifted out bodily and set up on the upper shelf of the lid, as shown in the photo. Note that this shelf is exactly 2⅛ in. below the edge, so that it will slip over the saws when the lid is down.

Make and attach the small file drawer shown in the upper right-hand corner of the lid. Reinforce the edges of the box with ¾ by 1-in. galvanized-iron window flashing, nailing with ⅝-in. brass escutcheon pins, well clinched. Put on a hasp and catch, and paint the box, and the job is done. If the box must stand out in the rain, carry a small strip of oilcloth to lay over the top.

Right-Angle Attachment for Straightedge

In building construction every part must be made plumb or square and the tools used to do this are a large steel square, a plumb line, a chalk line, and a spirit level.

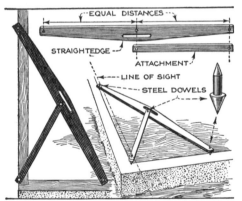

Accurate Method of Laying Off Right Angles by Means of a Simple Attachment for the Straightedge

An easily improvised tool that will serve the purpose of these tools in many cases, with results that are just as accurate, is an ordinary 8-ft. straightedge fitted with the attachment shown in the illustration. Two pointed steel dowels are driven into the ends of the straightedge, and a similar dowel exactly halfway between. Pivoted loosely on the center dowel is a length of 1 by 3-in. piece of wood, also fitted with a dowel at the end. The distance between the center dowel and each of the other three dowels must be exactly equal, as the accuracy of the device depends on this.

In using this device for laying off the corners and other right angles of walls, the dowel on the attachment is carefully set on the corner as shown in the drawing, and, with one end dowel on the straightedge in line with it on the edge of the wall, the other dowel will lie on a line that is exactly at angles to the first. The correct position of a mark at the other end of the wall, or any other point in line with either side of the right angle, can be sighted over two dowels as indicated by the dotted lines. The three end dowels will always be located at the point of a right angle and its sides, regardless of the position of the attachment.—G. A. Luers, Washington, D. C.

Gravity Feed for Drill Press

Sensitive drill presses may be made self-feeding by means of the simple arrangement shown in the drawing. This works well for small holes through material of medium thickness. The regular feed handle is removed and a piece of round stock of the same diameter, doubled over at one end as shown, is substituted for it. On this piece a weight made of heavy round stock drilled near one end is placed. The outer end of the bent handle is upset a little to prevent the weight from sliding off. In operation the weight is slid out to the long end of the handle, as indicated, to feed the drill through the work while the operator is engaged with other work. The drill head is raised automatically by slipping the weight to the back.

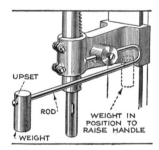

Jack Aids in Assembling Clutch

Considerable difficulty is usually experienced in removing and replacing the clutch spring while dismantling or assembling an automobile disk clutch. However, the special jack shown has been found to overcome the difficulty.

The illustration shows plainly how the jack is assembled and used. The base, which is made of cast iron, is drilled and tapped at the top for a ⅞-in. screw and at the bottom for a 1¼-in. plug, which is counterbored to fit the drive shaft.

The head that holds the clutch spring is made of a suitable piece of steel or wrought-iron pipe. It is counterbored at one end, 1⁄32 in. larger than the diameter of the spring washer, and has large slots cut in the sides to admit the thrust bearing and nut, when the spring is compressed. It is fitted with a standard pipe cap on the other end, the cap being drilled to fit over the small pivot turned on the end of the screw. The screw is made of a good grade of steel, and has a hexagon head.

In use, the clutch is first assembled;

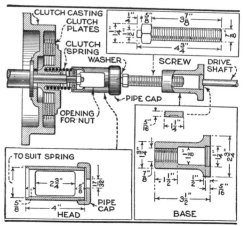

A Jack for Compressing an Automobile Multiple-Disk Clutch Spring that Has Been Found to Save Time

the head of the jack is then placed over the spring washer, and the base against the drive shaft; after the spring is compressed, the thrust bearing can be put in place on the clutch spindle. The jack can then be released.

Boring and Turning Attachment for Small Lathes

An attachment that will bore and turn short lengths with speed and accuracy, is very useful on small lathes, especially those that are not equipped with a tool-rest or carriage.

The tool consists of a forged center

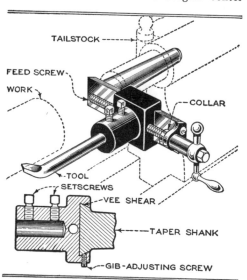

A Useful Attachment on Small Lathes for Boring and Turning Short Lengths Accurately

shank, which fits the taper in the tailstock spindle. On the front end a V-slide extends at right angles to the axis of the shank. On this V-slide is mounted a tool saddle, made from a steel block of suitable proportions, which can be made to slide in or out by the action of a feed screw. The tools are made of drill rod, the largest ones of ½-in. stock. When using smaller tools, bushings are used to take up the play in the tool slide, the bushings being split so as to allow the setscrews to hold the tools. To work to the best advantage and accuracy, the tail spindle should be clamped just snugly enough to prevent vibration under a cut. In making the shank of the tool it is advisable to turn up the taper shank and face the front of the slide between centers. Then the faced slide can be mounted on parallels on the shaper and the angular sides of the vee can be shaped. This method of making it will insure the squareness of the fixture. In order to have the tool-receiving hole in alinement with the headstock center, this hole should be drilled, after assembling, with a drill chucked in the head and with the attachment fitted in the tailstock. The operations possible with this attachment are drilling, boring, turning, facing, and cutting off. When used for cutting off, a support, such as a tee rest, should be placed below the tool.

An Acetylene-Torch Rest

Many jobbing welders have felt the need of a simple rest for holding the torch during the short time required to move the work to a new position, or to place a new

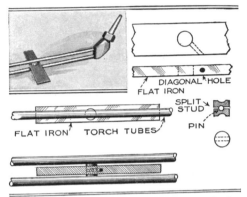

A Rest for the Acetylene Torch, of Utility when Laying
Aside the Tool to Change Work

piece. A very convenient attachment for this purpose is shown in the illustration.

A short length of flat bar is drilled in the center for a pin, or stud, which fits between the torch tubes. The method of making this stud and assembling it is as follows: It is first drilled through the center crosswise and then sawed in two through the center of the hole. Both ends are then filed concave so that when a pin is inserted in the two halves of the hole, the split stud is a snug fit between the tubes. The last operation consists in drilling a diagonal hole the same size as the pin through the side of the bar as shown. In assembling, the stud is placed in the hole in the bar, and, the pin being out, it slips easily between the tubes. Then the bar is turned to the angular position neces-

sary to line up the diagonal hole with the hole in the stud and the pin driven in the latter, clear of the bar. This arrangement is necessary to prevent the pin from working out, for, as the bar is always held lengthwise except when the torch is to be set down, the two holes are never in line. With the bar attached to the torch in this manner the latter is supported so that the flame is directed upward and away from the operator.

A Solid Adjustable Wrench

On production work it is highly desirable to use special wrenches with as little adjustment as possible, to suit the nature of the work for which they are used. A wrench of this kind, which was designed to fit three sizes of nuts, is shown in the drawing. The body of the wrench is made of flat stock and two small jaw pieces are bent and slotted as indicated to fit the jaws, and attached by means of small screws and nuts. When using the wrench on the largest size nuts, both jaw pieces are swung to the outside position as

indicated by the dotted lines in the lower detail. When used for the next size, one jaw is swung to the inside, as at the left, and when used for the smallest size, both jaws are swung to the inside. This wrench was used on a milling fixture, where it was found much more convenient to have one wrench for this purpose than three separate wrenches.

Substitute for Trailer

The demountable attachment shown in the photograph was made by a paperhanger, and has proved to be an excellent substitute for a trailer. It is very

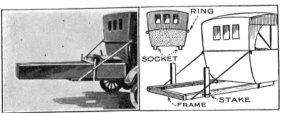

Attachment for Light Touring Car Permits Bulky Objects
to Be Carried Easily

sturdy, and can be attached or detached in a few minutes.

The framework is made of 2 by 4-in. lumber, constructed as shown in the drawing. To the underside of the frame ¾-in. boards are nailed to form the floor. A 2 by 4-in. stake is fastened on each side and the load is kept in place by lashings, tied around the stakes. The inner ends of the frame extend beyond the flooring, and fit into two U-shaped metal sockets, bolted to the chassis. Iron rods, attached to eyes or rings on the back of the body, as shown, support the rear of the carrier.

Replacing the Charging Indicator

Many older-model cars are fitted with a charging indicator, which merely indicates "charge," "off," and "discharge." It will be found a great convenience to replace this indicator with an ammeter, as this will not only show the rate at which the charging or discharging is taking place, but, by abnormal readings, will warn of any grounds in the circuits. The ammeter will also show when the generator is not charging at the correct rate. When connecting, care should be taken that the starting-motor current is not taken through the ammeter, as this will ruin it immediately; only the lighting, ignition, horn, and charging current should pass through either ammeter or indicator.

Handling Shock Covers

When curing alfalfa, it often occurs that wet weather sets in and much of the hay in the shocks is damaged. This damage can be prevented by using heavy canvas covers, which will save the fodder from being saturated by rain. A weight is, of course, tied at each corner to prevent the wind blowing the covers off.

An Illinois farmer found it practical to make a large number of small concrete

Weighted Canvas Shock Covers that Protect Alfalfa Crop from Rain, and Skid Used to Carry Them

weights for this purpose, and a simple skid for carrying the weighted covers around. The covers are neatly hung on the top rail of the inverted V-shaped skid, so that they can be instantly lifted off and placed over the shocks, one by one.

❡ Painters, carpenters, and others, using ladders frequently, will find that if the center of the ladder, where it balances, is marked with a strip of bright-colored paint, the workman can grasp the ladder at this point immediately when preparing to carry it, thus saving energy and time.

Balancing Tool Divides Strips

In a factory where a quantity of brass-strip binding is used, a novel tool for

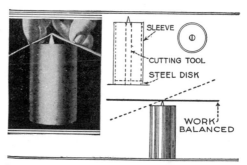

Tool for Dividing Brass Strips Equally: Insert, Bending Balanced Strip Before Cutting

cutting the material has recently been adopted.

Two strips of regular length are often cut in two to suit the smaller sizes, and because so many different lengths have thus to be divided equally, the balancing tool shown in the illustration has been found more efficient than the old method of marking the strips for center and then cutting them.

The tool consists of a piece of round steel, flattened at one end and shaped to a chisel point, and a sleeve, a trifle shorter, cut from iron pipe; both of these pieces are a drive fit on a steel disk. In use the brass strip is laid on the cutting tool and moved until it balances. It is then bent down on both sides, as shown in the photo, tapped with a hammer and broken in two.

Square for Filing Templates

When filing templates having several straight edges in the vise, considerable time can be saved and eye strain prevented by using a vise square of the type shown in the drawing. It should be made of tool steel, hardened and ground, and should be just as long as the width of the vise jaw. After the template has been roughly cut down to the desired size, about $\frac{1}{32}$ in. outside of the lines, it is ready for filing and is clamped in the vise as shown, matching the line with the edge of the square. The latter prevents the workman from filing the template down too far.
—Chas. Homewood, Ontario, Calif.

Level Clamps for Carpenters' Straightedge

Plumbing and straightening door jambs by the usual method necessitates holding a straightedge against the jamb, and pressing the spirit level against the straightedge. A California carpenter clamps his level to the straightedge and uses the two as a single unit, thus simplifying the handling and leaving one hand free to shift the jamb into position. The draw-

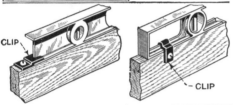

Above, Plumbing a Door Jamb; Below, Clips for Solid or Open-Frame Levels

ing shows two different kinds of clips, which can be made to hold the solid or open-frame type of level.

Quick-Acting Test Valve

The drawing shows how an ordinary valve, used to control the water pressure on a testing bench, was made quick acting. The testing operations made it necessary to open and close the valve every few minutes, and this consumed considerable time; whereas the device shown in the illustration enabled the operator to spin the valve wheel, opening and closing the valve in a fraction of the time otherwise consumed. The device consists of a short length of tube,

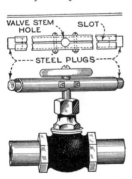

two round steel plugs, and a couple of nuts and screws. The tube is drilled in the center to fit the valve stem and at right

angles to this on each side to take the screws, and afterward slotted along its length as shown. The end plugs are a snug fit in the tube, and before the final tightening of the tube on the stem, the weights are moved in or out to attain correct balance. When correctly set, a slight spin of the wheel opens or closes the valve.

Brazing and Soldering Flux

Steel or copper brazing, and tin or copper soldering, can be greatly facilitated by using a flux of the following ingredients: Muriatic acid 4 oz., zinc, 1 oz., sal ammoniac 1 oz., English resin, 1 oz. Add the zinc to the acid, a little at a time, and then add the other ingredients. If one wishes to economize, 2 oz. of water may be added. The surface of the steel to be brazed is first swabbed with the flux and then wiped dry with a clean cloth; for soldering, however, it is not necessary to wipe the metal dry. Ordinary resin can be used if English resin is not obtainable.

Self-Closing Cover for Box

In shops doing a great deal of valve and plug grinding it is necessary to keep a cover on the box containing the grinding compound, as the smallest piece of foreign matter may cause a scratch that will take considerable extra grinding to remove. The box shown in the drawing is made of tin, and is fitted with a special cover, extending well beyond the front edge and bent to fit down over the sides as

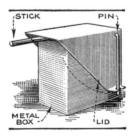

shown. Holes are punched in the top of the can and in the cover, and a wire pin is passed through the holes and bent down over the sides. The ends of the cover sides are bent out at right angles, as shown, and slotted to fit over the lower ends of the pin. After taking some compound out of the can, which is done with a stick, the cover will close itself as soon as it is released. The stick used for applying the compound should be thin enough to pass between the cover and the front end of the box, so that it can be placed in the position indicated when not used, to protect it from foreign matter also.

A Cheap Grain Conveyor

By R. A. FRANKLIN

UNLOADING heavy grain sacks into the granary by hand is by no means an easy task and a conveyor for this purpose is of considerable usefulness. But, taking into consideration the price of a conveyor and the fact that it is used only a few days in each year, most farmers prefer the old method of filling their granaries by hand.

A conveyor that does the work just as well as a purchased one, and costs much less, can readily be made at home from materials available on every farm. The frame is made of two side boards and a bed board of 1 by 12-in. material, the bed board being nailed between the side boards in the manner shown in the lower left-hand detail of the illustration. The side boards must extend about 15 in. beyond the bed board at each end, so that there will be plenty of room for the rollers on which the conveyor chain runs. The rollers are cut from a 6-in. fence post and are drilled lengthwise in the center for a ⅜-in. iron rod, which is driven through and serves as a journal.

Holes of the same size are drilled through the side boards and steel or brass sleeves used as bearings. The journal of the lower roller is extended on one side and a drive pulley is attached. A 2 or 3-hp. gasoline engine, belted to this pulley, provides sufficient power to run the conveyor. Sprockets of equal size are securely screwed to the ends of the rollers, and two chains, taken

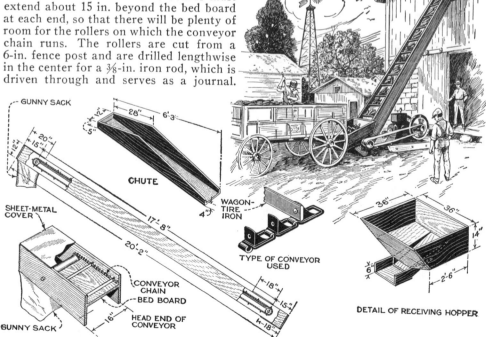

A Homemade Grain Conveyor that Can Be Made from Materials Available on Every Farm, and Costs Approximately $18: It Is Run by a Two or Three-Horsepower Gasoline Engine

from an old silage-cutter conveyor, are run over the sprockets, and both ends of the chains connected to make them endless. Lengths of wagon-tire iron are straightened and used as crossbars of the chains; they are spaced about 1 ft. apart, and are bolted or riveted to the links of the chain as shown. The top surfaces of the rollers are flush with the surface of the bed board on the top side so that the chain will run snugly over the board and onto the rollers.

At its upper or head end, the conveyor is provided with a sheet-metal cover to prevent the grain from being scattered. A canvas gunny sack is attached under the head to receive the grain and direct it into a wooden chute, which in turn distributes the grain into the bins. This chute is made

of 1-in. material and measures about 6 ft. in length; its shape and dimensions are clearly indicated in the detail. A receiving hopper, into which the grain can be shoveled from the wagon, is provided at the lower end of the conveyor; it is made of 1-in. boards and built as shown in the lower right-hand detail. Cleats are nailed to the side boards to hold the hopper in place. The grain shoveled into the receiving hopper is automatically taken up by the conveyor and discharged into the granary.

In building a conveyor of this kind, the cost was approximately $18, which is much less than the cost of a manufactured one. It was used during the threshing season for 8 years by the builder and his neighbors with whom he "changes work," and can still be used for many years.

Novel Drift-Pin Punch Set

Mechanics, especially those employed in the automotive industry, will appreciate a drift-pin punch set of the kind shown in the illustration. A set of this kind has been

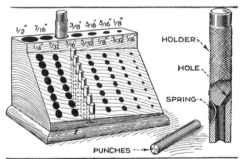

Drift-Pin Punches That Replace the Common Type, Which Are Easily Broken

used for 7 years and has been found to save considerable time and trouble, as cases are met hourly where cotter pins, straight pins, taper pins, etc., have to be removed as carefully as possible. After ordinary straight-drift punches were broken or bent, these punches were used and the work done without any trouble.

The punches are made of drill rod, hardened and drawn to a brownish-purple; they range in size from $\frac{1}{16}$ to $\frac{1}{2}$ in. in diameter, and are of varying lengths to be used progressively as the pin is driven out. Holders are provided for each size, of the same material as the punches, and hardened and drawn to a dark-blue color. The end of each holder is drilled as shown, a small hole being drilled through the side to permit the punches to be driven out in case of breakage. On the other side a slot

is cut to take a spring that keeps the punches securely in place in the holder. A wooden block is drilled as shown to hold the punches and holders in an orderly way so that any size can be located without trouble.—S. H. Candy, Montreal, Can.

Riveting Sheet-Metal Pipe

Anyone who has riveted together sections of sheet-metal pipe knows the difficulties involved in placing and holding the small rivets, and will appreciate the following method, which has been found very practical. A sheet-metal band is made to fit fairly closely on the steel bar or stake on which the pipe is riveted, and a slot is cut in it as shown to hold the rivet. The two sections of pipe to be riveted are slipped over the bar, the ends brought together over the rivet and a hammer and rivet setter used in the usual way to force the rivet through the metal. It is surprising how much time can be saved by this method and how easily and neatly the work can be done.—L. H. Georger, Buffalo, N. Y.

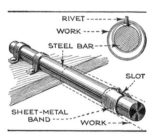

❡ To make a paint of dry white lead of the proper consistency requires about half its weight of linseed oil; dry zinc white will take nearly its own weight in oil.

Lubricant for Brass-Cutting Tools

Anyone familiar with copper and its alloys and other soft metals, knows that when chipping them, the chips tend to adhere to the surface of the tool and interfere with the cutting edges. The same is true when filing, drilling, and sawing. An excellent method of preventing this trouble is to use water as a lubricant. A can or tray of water is located near by so that the tool can be constantly dipped in it. The water avoids the gumming or clogging of the chips between the teeth of the saw, in the flutes of the drill, and on the surface of the file.

Simple Spring Seat for Wagon

Common farm wagons without springs do not provide much comfort for the drivers and therefore the simple wooden spring seat shown, which is constructed similarly to a spring board for diving purposes, will be greatly appreciated by teamsters and farmers. A seat of this kind can be made from two 1-in. boards about 10 or 12 in. wide and just as long as the regular wagon

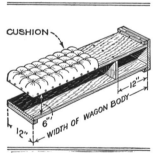

seat, and two 6-in. pieces of the same material. The long lengths are nailed to the short pieces, the short ones being spaced about 12 in. apart at one end. A pad or cushion on the seat provides additional comfort.—L. H. Unglesby, Baton Rouge, Louisiana.

A Kink for the Auto Mechanic

Working underneath automobiles is usually a very annoying task as particles of dirt and grease constantly fall into the worker's eyes. This trouble can easily be prevented by using a pair of goggles, which can readily be made from a piece of celluloid, cut to the shape shown in the illustration. A piece of rubber or string is tied on, as shown, to serve as a headband.—William Calvert, Vickery, Tex.

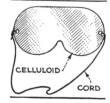

Alarm for Pneumatic-Tube System

Persons familiar with pneumatic-tube systems in large stores realize the inconvenience caused customers by delay of the

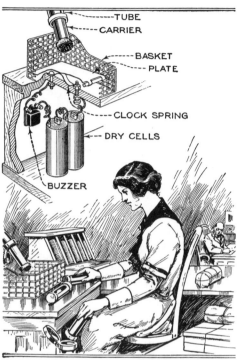

A Buzzer Connection to the Receiving Basket of a Pneumatic Tube Announces Arrival of Carrier

cashiers to open the carriers immediately when received, as it often occurs that they are allowed to lie in the baskets for several minutes before they are even noticed. This trouble was eliminated in a large department store by providing a buzzer which was sounded automatically by the weight of the tubes in the receiving basket. The arrangement is clearly shown in the illustration.

A sheet of brass is cut to fit inside of the basket over the bottom, allowing about ¼-in. space on each side, and three "fingers" are left on one end to hinge on a rod as shown. Two ⅛-in. holes are drilled through the shelf on which the basket rests, for stove bolts, and a short length of clock spring, attached to one of the bolts, is bent as indicated so that a slight pressure on the brass plate will cause it to touch the other bolt and thus close a circuit that sounds the buzzer. A carrier dropping into the basket immediately starts the buzzer, which continues to sound until the carrier is taken out.— Marshall W. Gelette, New Bedford, Mass.

Street-Cleaner's Dustpan

Municipal street-cleaning departments will find the dustpan shown in the illustration of considerable usefulness. It is simply a piece of heavy sheet metal, bent

DUST PAN

Convenient Dustpan for Street Cleaners. It Can Be Swung Over and Emptied by Raising the Handle

to the shape indicated and hinged to the frame of the dust carrier so that it can be dropped when sweeping dirt onto it, then swung over and the contents emptied into the can. The can swings freely on the axle so that it is always in a vertical position. A flat-iron bar, which is attached to the handles and constitutes part of the frame, extends below the handles to support them when the cart is left standing.

Repairing Leaking Suction Pipes

Leaking suction pipes, whether large or small, can easily be repaired. In a government power house a 4-in. underground suction pipe, attached to a steam pump, began to leak at the ends of a coupling where the threads had become corroded. The earth was removed around the coupling and a wooden form built of 1-in. material. The form was 18 in. square, open on the top, and the ends were each made of two pieces and had a 4½-in. hole for the pipe to pass through. A mixture of cement and plaster of paris was then packed into the box around the leaky coupling and allowed to set for an hour, which was sufficient, due to the proportion of plaster of paris. Then the pump was started again

and the leak was found to be effectively stopped. The cost of doing this was, of course, much less than the installation of a new coupling. Many mechanics forget that on a suction pipe there is no internal pressure, and that the only thing to guard against is leakage from the outside to the inside of the pipe. A knowledge of this fact will often save expensive repair jobs. —James E. Noble, Toronto, Can.

Tack Rag for Auto Finishers

A tack rag for automobile finishers can be made very easily by thoroughly saturating a piece of cheesecloth with rubbing varnish. Spread the rag out until almost dry, then fold and it is ready for use. By wiping off the car body or parts to be varnished with the rag all dust and lint will be removed, leaving a very clean surface.

As the tack rag is usually folded the danger of fire due to spontaneous combustion is always present, therefore it is a good idea to destroy all tack rags and scraps around the finishing room every evening and make new ones the following day. This can be done in a few minutes.— Vernon F. Clayton, Detroit, Mich.

Wire Tightener Acts as Gate

Although it is handy to have many gates on the farm, wooden gates are easily broken by cattle running against them, and steel gates are expensive. However, a simple homemade gate, which cannot be

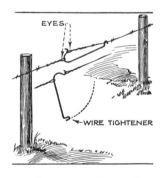

EYES

WIRE TIGHTENER

broken easily and is not expensive, is shown in the illustration. It consists of lengths of ½-in. iron rod, with one end bent to an S-shape, and the other end bent to form a hook. Each fence wire is cut in two, midway between two posts, and the ends are turned back and twisted around to provide eyes, which are hooked on the S-shaped ends of the rods. Then by bringing the other ends of the rods over the wire, they will be stretched just as tightly as before and will be held in this position securely, while the hooks are easily dropped to afford a passage.— Alphonse F. Wolters, Albany, Minn.

A "Pick-Up Stick" for Varnish Work

Automobile finishers find it very annoying to discover a nicely finished panel covered with lint, brush hairs, or dirt. If there is not too much of this, however, it can readily be removed by means of the "pick-up stick" described in this article.

Take equal parts of rubbing varnish and turpentine, mix thoroughly and place in a warm place near a steam pipe or stove. After a few weeks the mixture will be very gummy and may be rolled between the fingers like putty. Prepare a small ball of this and place it on the ends of a short stick, about 15 in. long. Before the varnish has set, or become too tacky, look it over carefully for dirt. Any particles can readily be removed by touching them lightly with the ball on the stick. If the varnish is too dirty it is the best policy to remove it and do the job over.—Vernon F. Clayton, Detroit, Mich.

Hand Groover for Casement Sash

Grooving the bottom edges of a casement sash to form water drips is, at best, a slow and tedious job, but it can be greatly expedited by using the simple homemade tool shown in the illustration. It consists of a hardwood block about ¾ by 1¼ by 7 in. in dimensions, with a saw kerf 1 in. deep cut in the ¾-in. edge, ¼ in. from one side. Make another block ¼ in. by 1¾ in. by 7 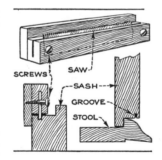 in. to act as a "fence," slip a 5-in. length of old compass-saw blade into the saw kerf, allowing the teeth to project about ₁₆ in., and drive a wood screw into each end of block and fence to keep the whole assembly together firmly. In use the fence is pressed against the outside of the sash and the tool slid back and forth, applying pressure to force the saw teeth into the wood.

¶Never put an inside patch in a slit tube, where the slit is over 1 in. long, because this will weaken the tube. However, when the slit is small, about ¼ in. long, an inside patch can be used. A slit tube should always be cut on the bias before repairing.

A Kink for the Cleaner

Intended for use in cleaning and dyeing establishments, the device shown in the drawing provides a quick and easy method of slipping bags over finished

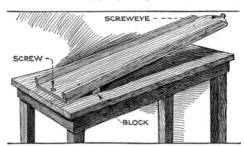

Fixture that Aids in Covering Freshly Cleaned Clothing with Bags

work. In general appearance it greatly resembles a springboard; one end is fastened to the table by a screw or bolt, and a strip of wood is nailed under the board near the end, so that the other end is elevated a few inches above the table. The board is about 6 ft. long and just wide enough for the bags to be slipped over easily. Strips 1 in. deep are nailed to the sides, as indicated, and a large screweye in the end of the board completes the device. In use the clothes are laid on the board and the hanger hooked in the screweye, leaving everything ready for the bag to be slipped over the end of the board. When the bag is in place the hanger is unhooked from the eye, the hook pulled through the end of the bag, and the bag, with the work inclosed, is removed from the board.—A. C. Cole, Chicago, Ill.

Better Whitewash

When the main generating tank of an acetylene farm-lighting plant is cleaned, a milky, white liquid is drained out and thrown away as it is considered useless. This liquid makes excellent whitewash, however, which will not peel off like ordinary whitewash. It is applied in the same way if it is thick enough; if not thick enough it is allowed to stand in an open vessel until enough of the superfluous water has evaporated to give the mixture the right consistency. After application there may be a faint odor of acetylene left in it, but this will soon disappear. If two coats are applied the first should be thoroughly dry before the second is put on. The white material in this kind of whitewash is calcium hydroxide, which is practically the same as water-slaked lime, but more adhesive.

BUILDING AN EIGHT-INCH JOINTER

By J. V. ROMIG

 SMALL bench jointer makes a fine addition to the small workshop woodworking department, and the building of one that can be operated by a fractional-horsepower motor from a light socket presents no very great difficulties.

Where accurate work is necessary, a jointer is essential, and work done on the machine is finished in much less time than if done by hand, and with considerably less effort.

The jointer described in this article can be made easily and cheaply by anyone familiar with machine work. Happily, no castings are necessary, as all parts are of standard structural shapes, pipe, and flat and round bars, easily obtained and worked up.

The work table is made of 8-in. channel iron, of standard weight. The table is divided in two, the rear half being fixed, while the front section is mounted so as to enable the operator to adjust the depth of cut. The pedestal is of pipe, fitted with flanges top and bottom, as shown in the illustrations.

The table is first worked up, in one piece, if the channel selected is true and straight. A light cut is taken over the top and sides, to make them all square with each other. The channel is now cut in two, and the center edges curved to form the clearance for the cutter head, as shown in the side elevation. In order to lock the two halves in their proper relative position, ½-inch side plates, 2½ in. wide, are used, and these are screwed to the rear half of the channel as shown in the plan and section A-A. The plates are cold-rolled bars.

The mechanism used to elevate the front half is a differential screw, the table rising

Simple and Easily Built Jointer for the Small Woodworking or Pattern Shop

and falling on two guide rods passing through angular slots cut in the channel sides.

The rods are ½ in. in diameter, threaded on both ends. One end of each is screwed tightly into a hole tapped in the right-hand side plate, and fastened by means of a locknut. The other ends pass through clear holes drilled in the left plate, and carry knurled-head clamp nuts or knobs, which fasten the table tightly between the plates when the machine is being used.

The holes are first drilled in the side plates, then the front half of the table is clamped in position with its top exactly in the plane of the rear half, and the position of the holes scribed through. This marks the exact location of the center of each slot. It is well to drill a few small holes on a line at right angles to each end of the slot, to provide room for handling the file when making the slots straight and true to size. It will be seen, by reference to the side elevation, that a movement of the front half toward the center will cause it to rise, and vice versa.

This motion is secured by means of the differential screw, riding in two nuts, as shown. One nut is screwed to the channel section, the other is slipped over the front rod. To compensate for the vertical travel of the table, the latter nut is slotted a little vertically. The first nut is tapped ⅜ in.—24 threads per in., the second ½ in.—13 threads per in. The screw is turned and threaded accordingly, and terminates in a long, knurled handle. The action of the differential screw is ideal for fine adjustments, as each turn advances or withdraws the table an amount equal to the difference between the pitches of the two threads.

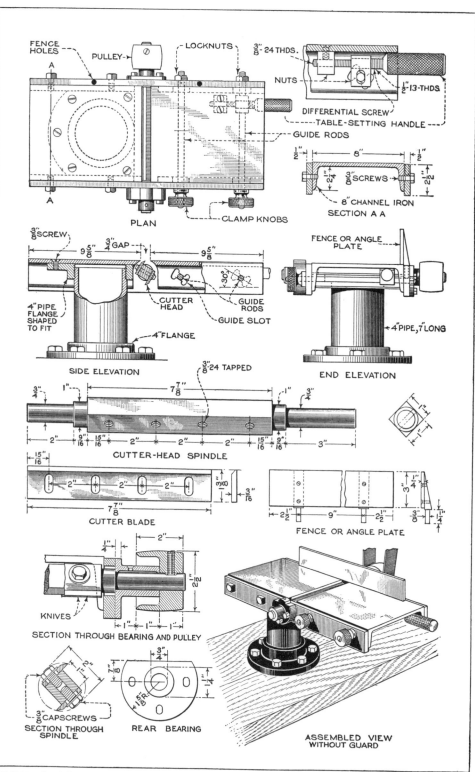

Full Details of Construction of the Homemade Bench Jointer. No Castings are Necessary, and All Material is Standard, and Easily Obtainable

The cutter head is turned from a piece of 1-in. square cold-rolled steel to the dimensions shown. The center portion is left square, and to it are fastened the cutter blades, made of ⅜₆-in. cast-steel

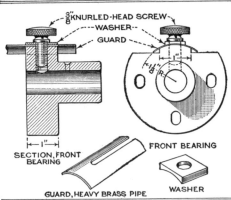

Detail of Adjustable Brass Guard, Attached to Left-Hand Bearing

stock. The journals of the shaft should be exactly round and straight, and be highly polished to run easily in the bronze bearings. Next to the journals, a short portion of each end is turned to 1 in. diameter, providing a thrust surface to keep the head central in the bearings. The head is drilled and tapped for ⅜ in.—24 capscrews, which hold the blades. The holes are drilled and tapped through.

To permit the blades to be adjusted, the holes in them are slotted as shown, and the screws made with very short heads, to provide clearance. Thin washers are used below the heads.

The bearings are made of bronze-bar stock, and the bearing holes are elongated slightly to permit adjustment of the height of the cutter bar. The left-hand, or front bearing is slightly different from the rear one, to allow a guard to be attached. The details of the guard are shown so clearly that no description is necessary. The cutter head is driven by a 2½ by 2-in. pulley fastened by a ⅜-in. headless setscrew. The pulley may be turned from the solid, from steel or cast-iron bar stock, and should be crowned slightly.

The pedestal is made of 4-in. pipe, screwed into two flanges, as shown. The flanges are screwed on very tight, and a freshly made mixture of litharge and glycerin should be applied to the threads before screwing up, to make the joints as tight as possible. The upper flange is shaped on three sides to fit in the channel, and the latter is fastened to it with five ⅜-in. flat-head screws.

The fence or angle plate is made of ¼ by 3-in. flat-steel stock, and is fitted with two supports or braces with round ends, which are a neat push fit in the right-hand side plate. The surface of the fence must be exactly at right angles to the table top.

When finished and assembled, all non-working surfaces should be painted or enameled, leaving the machined surfaces bright.

Paste for Pipe Joints

A mixture of soap and graphite painted on the threads of the filling plugs of gasoline tanks makes them easy to unscrew. The mixture will last longer than any kind of oil or grease, as these are quickly cut by the gasoline, while the soap and graphite mixture is not so readily affected. This mixture can also be used to make tight joints on gasoline pipes and it is easier to break joints made with it than when made with the mixture of litharge and glycerin generally used for this purpose. A mixture of Portland cement and oil applied to pipe threads also makes a tight-fitting joint on cold-water pipes.

An Improvised Faucet

In an emergency a faucet good enough to control the flow of liquid from a tank where the pressure is not great can be improvised from a tee and a short length of threaded pipe to fit. The side outlet of the tee is screwed onto the pipe leading from the tank, and the short pipe, after threading, is tapered on the end so that it jams against the threads on the bottom of the tee, when tightened up. The faucet is completed by drilling a hole through the pipe near the top and driving in a pin. If no machine is available for tapering the pipe and drilling the hole, the first operation can be done with a file, continuing the work until the pipe shows a bearing mark all around where it touches the threads in the tee, and the second can be done by filing a slot on the top and driving in a flat handle instead of a round one. A faucet of this kind takes little time to make, and will answer for many tanks where ordinary faucets are used.

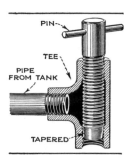

Bar for Unscrewing Gas-Tank Plug

Threaded plugs on tank trucks used for handling gasoline often become so tight that it requires considerable effort to unscrew them, making the use of some kind of a bar necessary. A good bar for this purpose is a length of ½-in. round iron or steel rod, about 16 in. long. The bar is forced into a length of ½-in. rubber hose, a little longer than the bar. This makes the rod less likely to slip, and it is apparent that dangerous sparks cannot be struck with a bar thus protected.—B. E. Dobree, Victoria, Can.

Old Piston Used as Pattern

Occasionally it is necessary to replace pistons on "orphan" cars, and unless the piston happens to be of a standard size that is used by other makes of cars, it must be made specially. However, the expense of patterns and coreboxes can be eliminated by using one of the old pistons for making the molds. The piston is cut in half lengthwise as shown. The two halves are held together with a flat-iron clamp, while ramming up the core. Facing is provided on the outside by means of a layer of flexible packing or other material about ³⁄₁₆ in. thick, tied securely with twine, and the impression is made in the flask after closing the open end with a circular wooden disk. The venting of the mold and provision for risers are details that are carried out in accordance with the regular procedure. It is also possible to core the wristpin hole, although it does not matter much as drilling this hole does not take very long.

Uniformity in weight of the finished piston depends much on the coring inside, and therefore the cores should be made as uniform as possible. The piston heads may vary a little in thickness but this can be remedied by **turning down the top of the piston.**

SECTIONS OF PISTON SPLIT FORMING COREBOX

CLAMP
WIRE
FLEXIBLE PACKING
WOODEN PLUG

Flywheel Prevents Light Fluctuation

When small gasoline engines, especially those of the hit-and-miss governed type, are used for running lighting generators, they will, even if provided with heavy fly-

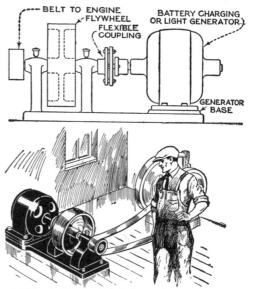

BELT TO ENGINE
FLYWHEEL
FLEXIBLE COUPLING
BATTERY CHARGING OR LIGHT GENERATOR
GENERATOR BASE

Additional Flywheel Added to Generator Prevents Flickering of Lights

wheels, cause more or less flickering of the lights, due to their irregular speed. This trouble can be lessened considerably by providing an additional flywheel, coupled to the generator shaft as shown in the illustration.

A cast-iron base is made for both generator and flywheel, the flywheel being supported separately so that little strain is exerted on the bearings of the generator. The shafts of both flywheel and generator must be in perfect alinement and should be connected by means of a flexible coupling. The flexible coupling can be of stock pattern, or made by bolting heavy leather or fabric disks between two flanges. The flywheel, which should be smaller than the engine flywheel, and run at a greater speed, is very effective in keeping the speed of the generator constant.—H. H. Parker, Oakland, Calif.

❐To prevent a graphite crucible, or any other kind of crucible, from scaling, keep it in a warm, dry place. Never place a new crucible directly in the furnace without first allowing all the moisture to dry out. Before using it, place it upside down in the furnace, and heat until red, then turn over and use for the regular melt.

Platform-Scale Protector

When a car loaded with several tons of castings was pushed across a small platform scale, the capacity of which was far

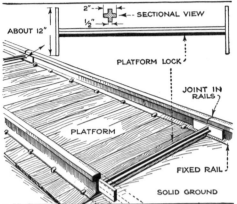

Protecting Platform Scale from Loads Beyond Its Rated Capacity

below the total weight of the castings, the result was a broken set of knife-edges. Still it was necessary to keep this scale on the main line of traffic to weigh certain castings at long intervals.

To keep the platform from deflecting when the heavy loads passed over it, two I-bars were fitted snugly between the head and base of the rails, at the joints between the movable platform rails and the fixed rails. The bars were steel castings, with heads ½ in. thick and 12 in. long, and the connecting bars were cast in the form of a cross, as shown in the sectional view. Whenever it was necessary to use the scale for weighing, the I-bars were slipped past the joint so that the platform was free to move up and down.

Correcting List in Auto Body

Listing of automobile bodies on one side is a natural consequence of the constant weight of the driver on this side. Other contributing causes are the torque of the engine and heavy jars on this side due to dropping into a hole in the road. Some manufacturers take these factors into consideration when making the springs by adding to their thickness and curvature on one side to compensate for this tendency. On closed cars the listing seems to be more pronounced after a short period of use, and this deducts considerably from their value.

A simple method that will effectively cure listing for a long time on transverse

springs, such as used on the Ford, is to turn the spring end for end, and tighten well the center bolts that hold the body on the springs. In the case of semielliptic or cantilever springs, the rear springs are transposed, and if necessary also the front ones. A spirit level is much more dependable than the eye in determining whether the body is level or not.—G. A. Luers, Washington, D. C.

Stopping Dirt in Varnish Jobs

The following kink will be found invaluable to automobile finishers and finishers of fine furniture, as it reduces dirty-varnish jobs to a minimum.

With a ½-in. camel's-hair brush, apply a coating of light-bodied and pale shellac around the door openings, body moldings, windshield stanchions, and in all places where dirt or pumice stone are apt to lurk, before varnishing. In this way the dirt present, which should be as little as possible, will be held in one place rather than be brushed over the large panels where it will be readily noticed.

Oil-Hardening Pan for Small Work

An oil pan for hardening small pieces in oil is shown in the illustration. It was made to overcome the difficulty of cooling such work quickly enough to harden the entire surface. To accomplish this the work cannot be held in tongs or pliers while dipping, and if simply dropped in the oil tank the result is just as bad because the oil immediately surrounding the work becomes hot, which delays the cool-

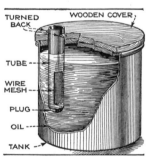

ing and tends to leave the pieces soft. The round oil tank illustrated was fitted with a wooden cover, made up of two thicknesses of wood nailed together and rounded off, the bottom piece fitting inside the tank and the top piece on the edge. The pan in which the work is held consists of a length of 2-in. tube, the bottom end of which is plugged, and the top end slotted with a saw and turned back to form supporting ears. Two rectangular holes are cut in the side as shown, and a piece of wire mesh is inserted to cover them. A hole is drilled in the cover near the edge for the tube, and the small heated pieces are then dropped in the tube. The cover is then revolved quickly so that the oil will circulate freely through the tube and in this way the entire surface of the work is exposed to constantly changing oil, which makes for proper hardness. When removing the pieces the tube is lifted out slowly to allow the oil to drain.

Pencil Sharpener Adapted for Draftsmen

Pencil sharpeners of the ordinary type do not give the lead the chisel-like edge that is required by draftsmen. By a slight modification, however, these sharpeners can readily be adapted to cut down the wood to suit the drafts-man. This alteration consists in enlarging the small hole at the narrow end of the sharpener to a diameter equal to that of the pencil lead, and grinding away the edge of the cutter blade at that end so that it will only cut the wood of the pencil and not touch the lead. The lead end can then be rubbed down to a chisel edge on sandpaper. Pencils sharpened in this way look much neater than if sharpened with a knife, and there is no danger of breaking off the exposed section of the lead.—C. A. Oldroyd, Barrow-in-Furness, England.

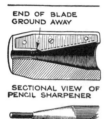

END OF BLADE GROUND AWAY

SECTIONAL VIEW OF PENCIL SHARPENER

LEAD PENCIL

SAND PAPER

Adding to Convenience of Pipe Wrench

It is often impossible to use pipe wrenches in "tight" places because the movable jaw is too large to get behind the pipe. A good method of remedying this trouble was devised and used in the pipe-fitting department of the U. S. Navy Hospital at Portsmouth, N. H. An extra jaw of the same size is obtained and the head ground down as shown in the illustration. It is then substituted for the regular one in tight places and will be found to be of considerable assistance. Of course, this jaw will not be as strong as the other and therefore it must be used with care.—L. E. Fetter, Portsmouth, N. H.

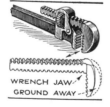

WRENCH JAW GROUND AWAY

Hog-Proof Gates

It is common practice to run hogs in the same field as cattle. To allow the cattle the liberty of passing into adjoining

FIG.1

FIG.2

Two Simple but Effective Gates to Keep Hogs in a Pasture

fields and at the same time prevent the hogs from doing so, a special kind of gate is required. Two types of such gates, that have been found very effective, are shown in the illustration. Fig. 1 shows a gate consisting of two wide planks, one nailed to the gate post and the other arranged parallel to it, with a space of about 2 ft. between. The second plank is nailed to strong stakes that are securely driven into the ground. The hogs can climb over this plank because they can approach it at right angles, but cannot get over the other because the second is so close. A hog (this has been proved many times) will usually climb over the first plank into the chute, and run along it back into the yard, thinking, apparently, that it has accomplished its purpose.

An equally effective gate, w'ich involves the use of an old hot-water tank, is shown in Fig. 2. It is drilled in the center at each end for a heavy gas pipe or iron rod, which is also passed through the gate posts as indicated, allowing the tank to rotate freely. The hog can get on the tank as indicated but the moment the hind legs are clear of the ground the weight on the tank causes it to turn and the hog promptly returns—a rather provoking situation for the hog, but it works.

¶A dull milling cutter wears out faster than a sharp one and does poor work.

Safety Rung for Ladders

Lamp trimmers, painters, and electricians, who are required to use ladders to ascend steel poles, will find the device

A Curved-Iron Rod Ladder Rung Prevents Ladder from Slipping to One Side

illustrated to be very effective in preventing the ladder from slipping over to one side. The device is simply a length of 1-in. iron rod, bent to the curvature of the poles and substituted for the top rung of the ladder. It is allowed to swing freely but is securely held in place by washers and cotter pins as indicated. The bar will immediately adapt itself to the pole and the danger of the ladder slipping sidewise is eliminated. This method was used by the painters of a traction company to paint bands on the poles, designating car stops.

Cutting Nail Heads

Common wire nails with the heads removed often make excellent pins for various purposes. When a sufficient number of such pins are required the operation of cutting off each head with the cutting pliers is much too slow, and a quicker method of doing the work is necessary. A device with which a num-

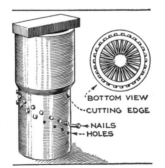

ber of nails can be cut in a few seconds is shown in the illustration. It consists of

two short lengths of steel tubing, one piece a neat sliding fit inside the other. The internal piece is drilled with rows of holes to fit the nails, the holes being laid off in spiral lines as indicated. One end of the external piece is ground to a sharp cutting edge and casehardened. The internal tube is loaded with nails pushed in the holes from the outside and the external tube dropped over it. Then a piece of metal is placed over the top, and the tube pressed down in a drill press, arbor press, or screw press. A press is used in preference to a hammer, as the pressure is applied steadily and evenly. With the holes in the internal tube laid out as shown, only one head will be cut at a time, so that very little pressure is required.

Preventing Back Draft in Ventilating Pipes

Type-setting machines, vulcanizers and other machines employing gasoline burners for heating require some outlet for the fumes in order to keep the atmosphere of the room in a healthful condition. The most effective arrangement is to connect the heating appliance with a chimney, but as this is often impossible many shops employ a small pipe which is allowed to project through the wall or a nearby window. There is, however, a dis-

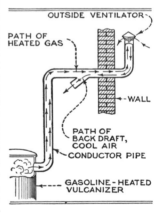

advantage in this arrangement, in that there is often a back draft which causes the fumes and smoke to fill the room and also extinguishes the flame in the burner. This trouble, which was experienced in one shop, was remedied by inserting a Y-joint in the length of pipe so that the lower branch opened into the room as shown in the illustration. This did not materially interfere with the draft of the pipe but the back draft of cold air entering from the outside naturally flowed along the bottom of the pipe and was conducted out into the room as indicated by the arrows. The gases, being warmer than the incoming air, maintained a current along the upper side of the pipe and passed out without interference.

One-Man "Belter" for Concrete Road

The usual method of finishing a cement road is to "belt" it. This is done by drawing a heavy piece of canvas or rubber belting, a few feet longer than the width of the road, back and forth across its surface, the work being done by two men, one at each end of the belt. A simple device which requires only one man for this operation is shown in the illustration.

The device consists of a pipe frame mounted on three wheels, somewhat similar to the hand-power speeder used by signal men on railroads. The belt

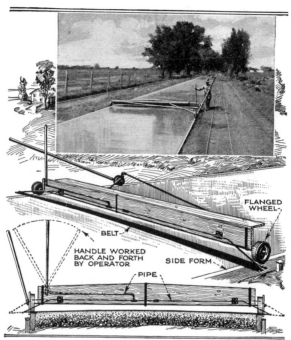

Homemade "Belter" for Concrete Roads, Moved and Operated by One Man

is swung from a length of pipe, which is bent to the proper shape, and mounted in bearings on a wooden cross-piece, and the transverse motion of the belt across the surface of the pavement is obtained by means of a lever at one side of the frame. As the belt is worked back and forth by means of the lever, the whole frame is pushed ahead on the wheels, which ride on the edge of the side forms; the stakes that hold the forms are driven down a trifle deeper than usual to clear the flanges of the wheels. The pipe frame supporting the belt is so pivoted that it can be swung up clear of the surface when moving the entire device backward or forward to a new position. The frame also supports a bridge by means of which the finisher can reach any part of the pavement without stepping on the soft concrete.—T. J. Harris, Chicago, Illinois.

Simple Upholstering Tool

One often wonders how the plaits in automobile upholstery are stuffed so evenly and without the lumps usually found if the work is done by hand. This is accomplished by using cotton wadding inserted under the plaits with the device shown in the illustration. This is merely a hardwood stick slightly narrower than the plaits, with a strip of canvas or similar cloth of the same width tacked to the end. Several thicknesses of cotton

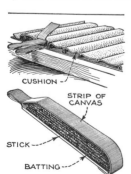

wadding are piled on the stick, the canvas strip is then pulled back tightly over the wadding and the device is inserted into the plait. A second piece of wood of the same width is inserted under the canvas to press the wadding down while the other piece of wood and the canvas strip are removed.

Repairing Large Rubber Stamps

It often occurs that one letter of a large rubber stamp is spoiled and this leaves the whole stamp useless. However, the stamp can easily be repaired and this will save the price of a new one. A piece of smooth leather belting of suitable thickness is obtained and a letter cut out of it, as near a duplicate of the broken one as possible. By trying the stamp out after inking it and making an impression the high spots can be noted. These are then rubbed down by means of a piece of pumice stone.

MECHANICAL POWERS

By CARL W. MITMAN

Curator

DIVISIONS OF MINERAL AND
MECHANICAL TECHNOLOGY
UNITED STATES NATIONAL
MUSEUM

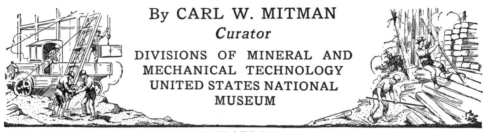

Copyrighted, H. H. Windsor

FOR many months the National Museum in Washington has been designing and building an unusual set of models of remarkable interest. These illustrate most simply and clearly the fundamental principles of the various Mechanical Powers. These models show at a glance, what textbooks have heretofore taken pages to describe. This is the first of a series of articles by Curator Mitman—who is himself an engineer of great ability—which not only explain in simple language what every mechanic and inventor who designs or builds a machine must know, but also tell how any one can exactly duplicate for himself the complete identical set of models in the National Museum. Mr. Mitman tells how to do this with ordinary tools and at practically no expense for materials.

For schools teaching physics or manual training, the opportunity is now presented for the first time of duplicating the set of these models in the National Museum. If one or more classes each year will build a few of the models, which should bear the nameplate of the class, in the course of two or three years the school will possess not only lasting monuments to the classes, but acquire, without cost, the full set for use of all future students, and which can be available to all local mechanics and inventors for all time.

These articles, which will run through many months to come, are being published for the first time and should be preserved for future reference.

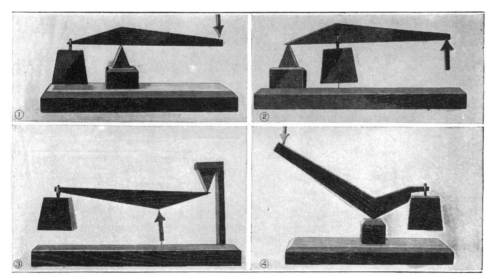

Fig. 1, Completed Model of First-Order Lever; Fig. 2, Model of Second-Order Lever; Fig. 3, Finished Model of Third-Order Lever; Fig. 4, Model Illustrating Angular Lever

Part I—Simple Levers

MECHANICS treats of the action of forces, and their effect. A force is usually defined as any cause tending to produce or change motion. It has only one element, namely, the push or pull exerted. Work, on the other hand, is the result of two elements, force and motion, and work done is the product of force and distance. The mechanical powers, the lever, pulley, screw, etc., depend for their action upon a fundamental principle of mechanics known as the "principle of work." This states that, disregarding friction and other losses, the work done by an

This applies equally to a simple lever and to a complex mechanism, and, incidentally, to the "perpetual motion" machine.

Strictly speaking, the lever is a simple machine and is also the simplest element of a machine. It consists essentially of a rigid bar, straight or bent, which has one point fixed, about which the rest of the lever can turn. The fixed point is called the fulcrum and the perpendicular distances from the fulcrum to the points where the applied force and resisting force act, are called the arms of the lever. When the lever is straight and the applied force

Everyday Examples of the Application of the Principle of Levers of the First Order

applied force always equals the work done against the resisting force. To illustrate this principle consider a lathe in operation. A force, such as the pull of the driving belt, is applied in a given direction at one or more points. The product of this force and the distance through which it moves measures the work that is put into the lathe. The applied force is transmitted to the point where the operation is to be performed (the chuck), but in its transmission the force is changed in direction and amount both by the arrangement of the gearing and by the resisting force of friction, all of which the applied force must overcome. Now, at the chuck the original force, somewhat modified, overcomes a further resistance in any required direction, for example, the resistance of metal, held by the chuck, to a cutting tool. The product of this resistance and the distance through which it is overcome measure the work done by the lathe. Stated simply then: Work put into a machine equals friction losses, etc., plus work done by machine. No machine can be made to do work unless a somewhat greater amount of work (sufficient to cover losses) is applied by some outside agent.

and resisting force act perpendicular to the lever, it is usual to distinguish three classes or orders:

First order. Where the applied force (represented by an arrow) and the resisting force (represented by a weight) act on opposite sides of the fulcrum, as shown in Fig. 1. This order of lever generally gives a mechanical advantage. Its practical use is exemplified by a claw hammer when drawing nails, a pair of simple scales, and the brake of a pump. Double levers of this class are scissors and pliers.

Second order. Where the applied force and resisting force act on the same side of the fulcrum but the former at a greater distance than the latter from the fulcrum, as in Fig. 2. This order always gives a mechanical advantage. Examples of this class are a wheelbarrow, a cork squeezer, a crowbar (with one end in contact with the ground), and an oar (assuming that the blade is in water and at rest); while a double lever of this class is represented by a pair of nut crackers.

Third order. Where the applied force and the resisting force act on the same side of the fulcrum but the former acts at

Illustrations Showing How the Second-Order Lever Is Applied to Common Tasks

a smaller distance than the latter from the fulcrum (Fig. 3). In this order of lever there is a mechanical disadvantage. An

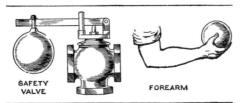

SAFETY VALVE

FOREARM

Common Examples of Third-Order Levers

example is a steam-boiler safety valve, also the human forearm when supporting a weight in the palm of the hand. In this latter instance the elbow joint is the fulcrum and the tension exerted by the muscles is the applied force. An example of a double lever is a pair of sugar tongs.

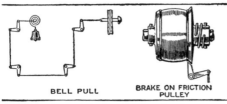

BELL PULL

BRAKE ON FRICTION PULLEY

Everyday Applications of Angular Levers

It is easy to conceive of conditions where the use of a straight lever in a machine could not be made. For such conditions the angular lever is available. Probably its earliest use was in ringing bells, hence its more popular name "bell crank." The angular lever works under exactly the same principles as the straight lever and is similarly divided into three classes or orders. Having treated of the three orders of straight levers, however, only the first order of angular lever is illustrated here (Fig. 4). The bell crank is usually a right-angled lever, but, as will be observed, any angle may be used.

The lever, as well as all the other so-called mechanical powers, is of use to man because: First, they enable him to lift weights or overcome resistances much greater than he could deal with unaided. Second, they may cause a motion imparted to one point to be changed into a more rapid motion at some other point, and third, they enable a force to be applied at a more convenient

point or in a more convenient manner. On the other hand, whatever mechanical advantage is obtained by the use of these powers is gained at a proportionate diminution in speed. No work is ever gained by the use of a machine, though mechanical advantage is generally obtained. All of which may be stated in that old saying, "What is gained in power is lost in speed."

The specifications given below are for the construction of stationary or fixed models, but there is no reason why the same parts cannot be made to operate. Furthermore, it is quite feasible to demonstrate the relative advantages of the various types of levers with these models by simply substituting for the wooden weight, representing resisting force, a series of graduated standard weights and using a spring balance attached to the applied force arm to measure the force required to move the various weights. The question as to the amount of power gained by the use of levers will be discussed in the next chapter.

For the model of a simple lever, first order, the materials required are:

Base, 9" x 3" x 7/8".
Fulcrum block, 7/8" x 1/2", side 1" high.
Fulcrum, base 1½" square x 7/8".
Lever arm, 7½" long, ¼" wide, 7/8" deep at apex.
Weight (resisting force), base 1¾" square, top 1¼" square, side 1½" high.
Arrow (applied force), 1¼" long, ¼" thick, ½" wide across barbs, ¼" shaft.

Square and face the base and block with a finish bevel on top of each. On the center line of the base and 2¾ in. from its end, secure the block by gluing and bradding from beneath. On the center line of the block, and with its longest dimension par-

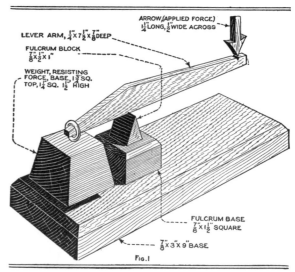

Fig. I

Showing How the Model of the First-Order Lever Is Constructed, with Full Dimensions

allel to the center line, secure the fulcrum by gluing and toenailing. The weight is attached to the lever arm by cutting on

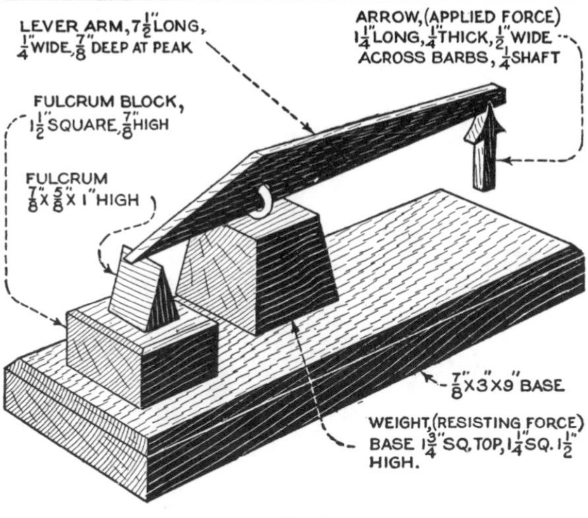
LEVER ARM, 7½" LONG, ¼" WIDE, ⅞" DEEP AT PEAK
ARROW, (APPLIED FORCE) 1¼" LONG, ¼" THICK, ½" WIDE ACROSS BARBS, ¼" SHAFT
FULCRUM BLOCK, 1½" SQUARE, ⅞" HIGH
FULCRUM ⅞" x ⅝" x 1" HIGH
⅞" x 3" x 9" BASE
WEIGHT, (RESISTING FORCE) BASE 1¾" SQ. TOP, 1¼" SQ. 1½" HIGH.

Fig. 2

Details of Model of a Lever of the Second Order, with Sizes of Parts

the shorter end a small notch which will accommodate the screweye used as a handle for the weight. The applied-force arrow is attached closely to the force arm of the lever by inserting it in a small notch. This assembly of lever, force arrow and weight is secured to the fulcrum by the use of an invisible brad as a dowel, inserting the brad into both the peak of the fulcrum and the lower side of the lever arm at a point under the apex, which should be one-third of the distance from the end of the lever. Finish as desired.

For the simple-lever model, second order, the following materials are used:

Base, 9" x 3" x ⅞".
Fulcrum block, 1½" square x ⅞".
Fulcrum, base ⅞" x ⅝", side 1" high.
Lever arm, 7½" long, ¼" wide, ⅞" deep at peak.
Weight (resisting force), base 1¾" square, top 1¼" square, side 1½" high.
Arrow (applied force,) 1¼" long, ¼" thick, ½" wide across barbs, ¼" shaft.

Square and face the base and block with a finish bevel on top of each. On the center line of the base, and ½ in. from the end secure the block by gluing and bradding from beneath. On top of this, glue and toe the fulcrum with its longest dimension running parallel to the center line. The weight is secured to the lever arm by opening a screweye, by which the weight is handled, and running it through a hole bored close to the bottom edge and under the apex of the lever arm. This point of suspension should be one-third of the distance from the fulcrum. The combination of lever arm and weight is secured to the fulcrum and base by invisible brads. The applied-force arrow is inserted in a small notch cut very close to the extremity of the force arm of the lever. Finish as desired.

For the model of the simple lever, third order, use the following material:

Base, 9" x 3" x ⅞".
Fulcrum gallows, consisting of three pieces:
Pillar, 3¾" x ¾" x ¼".
Arm, 1¼" x ¾" x ¼".
Fulcrum, base ⅞" x ½", side 1" high.
Lever arm, 7½" long, ¼" wide, ⅞" deep at apex.
Weight (resisting force), base 1¾" square, top 1¼" square, side 1½" high.
Arrow (applied force), 1¼" long, ¼" thick, ½" wide across barbs, ¼" shaft.

Square and face the base and finish with a bevel. Equally divided on the center line of the base, and ½ in. from the end, cut a mortise ¾ in. x ¼ in. x ⅜ in., in size. Square and dress the pillar and arm of the gallows and secure the arm on top of the pillar by glue and brads. Secure the fulcrum to the under side of the gal-

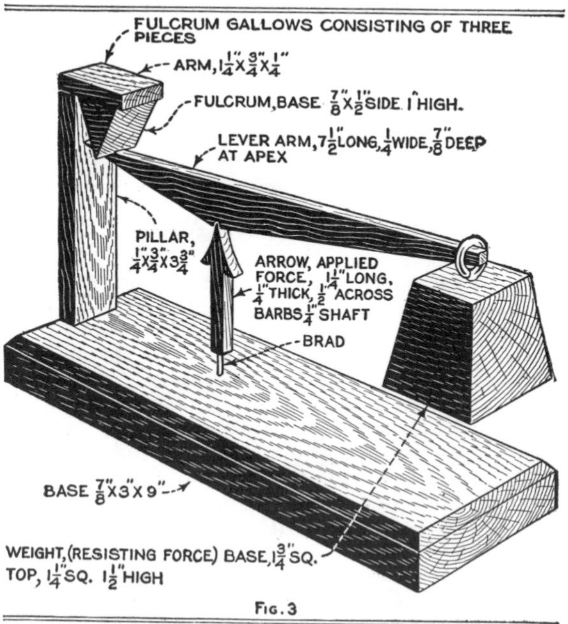
FULCRUM GALLOWS CONSISTING OF THREE PIECES
ARM, 1¼" x ¾" x ¼"
FULCRUM, BASE ⅞" x ½" SIDE 1" HIGH.
LEVER ARM, 7½" LONG, ¼" WIDE, ⅞" DEEP AT APEX
PILLAR, ¼" x ¾" x 3¾"
ARROW, APPLIED FORCE, 1¼" LONG, ¼" THICK, ½" ACROSS BARBS ¼" SHAFT
BRAD
BASE ⅞" x 3" x 9"
WEIGHT, (RESISTING FORCE) BASE, 1¾" SQ. TOP, 1¼" SQ. 1½" HIGH

Fig. 3

Drawing of Model Illustrating Principle of Third-Order Lever

lows arm by glue and brads. Insert this assembly into the mortise and secure by glue. On the long end of the lever arm fasten the weight by accommodating the screweye, used as a handle, in a small notch cut on the flat edge of the lever arm. Secure the applied-force arrow to the apex of the fulcrum by inserting its point in a notch. This assembly is fastened to the remainder of the model by bradding the toe of the lever arm to the peak of the fulcrum, using a brad as a dowel to support the force-indicating arrow in a vertical direction. Stain, finish, and polish in any manner desired.

For the angular lever; first order:

Base, 9" x 3" x 7/8".
Fulcrum block, 1½" square by 7/8".
Angular lever:
    Force arm, 6" by ¼", 1" at apex, ¼" at end.
    Weight arm, 3" x ¼", 1" at apex, ¼" at end.
Weight (resisting force), base 1¾" square, top 1¼" square, side 1½" high.
Arrow (applied force), 1¼" long, ¼" thick, ½" wide across barbs, ¼" shaft.

Square and face the base and block, with finish bevel on top of each. Upon the

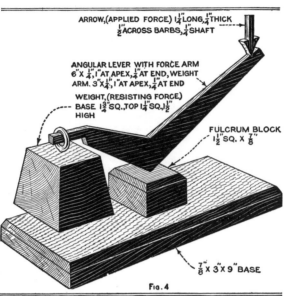

ARROW,(APPLIED FORCE) 1¼"LONG,¼"THICK ½"ACROSS BARBS,¼"SHAFT

ANGULAR LEVER WITH FORCE ARM 6"X ¼",1"AT APEX,¼"AT END, WEIGHT ARM. 3"X¼",1"AT APEX,¼"AT END

WEIGHT, (RESISTING FORCE) BASE 1¾"SQ.,TOP 1¼"SQ.,1½" HIGH

FULCRUM BLOCK 1½"SQ. X 7/8"

7/8"X 3"X 9" BASE

FIG.4

Model of Angular Lever of the First Order, with Dimensions of All Details

center line of the base and 4 in. from the end secure the block by gluing and bradding from beneath. The angular lever may be constructed in either of two ways, the simplest being to lay out the dimensions given upon a one-quarter inch board, placing the arms at an included angle of 130°, and sawing out the arm. Another method, which would be more economical in wood, and would obviate the danger from weak grain, would be to build up the angular lever from two pieces, joining them at the apex with a halved-together lapped joint. The weight is attached to the short arm of the angular lever by inserting the screweye, used as a handle, in a small notch and cutting away a portion of the weight arm to allow the weight to swing vertically. The applied-force arrow is secured to the force arm of the lever by inserting the point in a small notch. This assembly is secured to the block by using a brad as a dowel, inserting this into both the apex of the lever and the center of the block. Finish as desired.

Homemade Ladder Hook

A ladder hook, attached to the upper end of a ladder as a means of holding it in place securely, is a measure of safety as well as convenience. One that is simple to make is shown in the illustration. It consists of two ⅝-in. steel rods and two collars. The largest rod is 4 ft. long and is bent at both ends, one end to fit the rungs of the ladder and the other end bent into a semicircle about 6 or 8 in. in diameter and ground to a point. The other rod is 2 ft. long and has one end bent to fit the ladder rungs. The collars are large enough to accommodate both rods, as shown in the cross section. After the rods are slipped into the collars and adjusted on the top rungs of the ladder as shown, the setscrews in the collars are tightened down to hold the rods securely. The hooks must clamp the rungs of the ladder firmly so that they will not slip sideways.

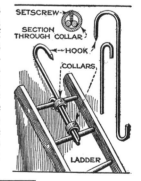

SETSCREW
SECTION THROUGH COLLAR
HOOK
COLLARS
LADDER

¶When lubricating broaches, direct the stream into the hole at the top.

Oil Can Spreads Stamp Ink

Applying ink to stamp pads by pouring some ink out of the bottle and then spreading it over the surface of the pad with a knife, is a slow and inconvenient task, and in doing this one is very likely to get the hands soiled with the ink, which is extremely difficult to remove. A much better method of applying stamp ink is to use an oil can with a short spout and a fairly large outlet.

Removing Burrs on Turret-Lathe Work

Half the time ordinarily required for filing off burrs on turret-lathe work can be saved on many jobs by using two files arranged as shown in the accompanying drawing. This method was employed in a shop producing a large quantity of brass collars, the wire edges on both sides being removed in one operation.

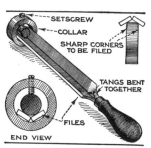

The files are held in proper position by a collar and a loose piece of rod, slipped through the collar as shown. The tangs of both files are bent inward and driven into an ordinary file handle. By varying the size of the rod and the diameter of the hole, the files can be set to suit different widths of work.

An Emergency Pipe Wrench

When unscrewing a cap from a gas pipe that projects through the wall, it frequently happens that the nipple turns instead of the cap. The nipple is usually so short that a pipe wrench cannot be used to hold it and therefore other means must be employed. Clamp a narrow iron bar and a nail set or punch on the nipple by means of a C-clamp as shown in the illustration, to hold the nipple securely, and the cap can then be unscrewed quite easily, and without any further difficulty.—Edwin M. Love, Alhambra, Calif.

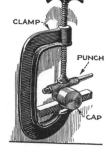

Field Protractor for Vertical Angles

Vertical angles for railroad fills and embankments, altitudes for topography, etc., can easily be determined by using a simple

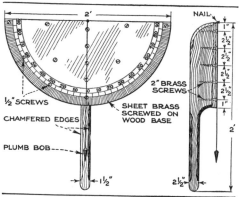

A Simple Homemade Hand Level Which Will Prove of Assistance to the Amateur Surveyor

protractor of the kind shown in the illustration. It is made from a piece of heavy sheet brass, cut to a semicircular shape having a radius of 1 ft., and graduated into degrees from 0 in the center to 90 at either side. The graduating marks and numerals are etched on, which is done by first covering the brass with a thick film of asphaltum varnish or wax, and, when dry, scratching through it with a sharp scriber. The brass is then etched by applying a solution consisting of 16 parts of nitric acid in 160 parts of water, and 6 parts of potassium chlorate in 100 parts of water, the two solutions being made separately and then mixed together. Whenever an acid and water are mixed the acid must always be poured into the water; never the water into the acid, in order to avoid accidents. Nitric acid also causes severe burns and its fumes are highly poisonous, which makes it necessary to handle it with extreme care.

After the brass is etched to the desired depth, the wax is removed and the plate is screwed firmly to a ½-in. wooden base of the same size and this is screwed to a wooden handle as shown. The handle also serves to prevent the base from warping or splitting. A nail is driven into the upper part of the handle and a plumb bob suspended from it. The wooden parts of the instrument are made of hard, tough wood, such as maple or beech, varnished or oiled.

In use the instrument is held so that the plumb bob will swing freely and when it is at rest the angle can be read by an assistant.—J. J. Brehm, Baltimore, Md.

Weeder for Small Crops

Homemade Weeder for the Early Cultivation of Small Crops Such as Soy Beans and Small Corn

A homemade weeder of the kind shown in the photograph has been found to be an excellent tool for the early cultivation of soy beans and small corn. It is made by joining together two weeders, side by side as shown, and hooking them to the frame of an old corn cultivator. With a team of horses hitched to this improvised weeder, and a small boy driving, a surprising acreage of ground can be cultivated in one day. It roots out the small weeds and grass without damage to the crop.

Cutting Circles with Torch

The cutting-torch attachment shown in the photo will be found useful when cutting off the corners of square plates and other similar work where the torch moves in a circular path. A piece of flat plate, bent over to fit the torch tubes, is drilled through the side and squared out for a nut, into which a pointed, headless screw threads. This completes the attachment with the exception of a piece of flat brass, bent over the top of the screw to prevent it from marring the tube. In operation, the work is laid out from a center as usual, and the end of the pointed screw placed on the center before commencing the cut. The attachment is slid along the torch tubes to the required position and locked by turning the screw.

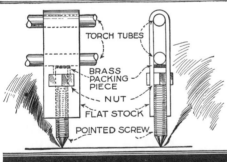

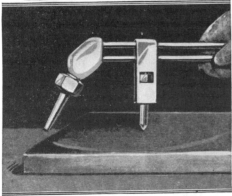

Simple Attachment for a Cutting Torch, Which Is of Great Assistance in Making Circular Cuts

An Adjustable Scaffold

Painters and paperhangers often use a scaffold made by extending a plank between the steps of two stepladders. As the height of ceilings varies, the plank can be raised or lowered one or more steps to suit the worker, but the change of a foot in the height of the scaffold is often too much. For this reason the hooks shown in the photo will be found very convenient, as with their use,

the scaffold can be raised or lowered to any desirable height. The hooks are made of ½-in. iron rod, bent as indicated, and threaded for almost their entire length. A 14-in. length of flat steel, ¼ in. thick and 2 in. long, is drilled at each end to fit loosely on the hooks, and nuts are screwed on, as shown, to hold the bar at any point. The hooks are hung on the steps and the plank is placed over the bars. Four hooks and two steel bars form a complete set.

¶A fine feed must be used on milling-machine work that is likely to be easily sprung.

Wood-Sawing Rig Made from Old Car

By L. B. ROBBINS

INSTEAD of spending from a hundred and fifty to two hundred dollars for a portable wood-sawing rig, a Cape Cod man made use of the power plant of an old car. It has been in use for several years, and will saw up the largest piece of cordwood with ease. The outfit, minus the saw and such parts, cost less than fifty dollars.

An old auto-truck frame with only the rear wheels left on was utilized for the portable foundation. The front cross member of the frame was sawed off, thus making a pair of shafts, into

rear cross timber, and the other to the cross member of the truck frame. The end of the shaft is threaded to take the flanges and retaining nut of an 18-in. circular saw. Spark, choke, and throttle rods are held under cleats on the timbers, and can be adjusted at will.

The saw table consists of a rectangular wooden frame, with deep notches cut in the top of the vertical members to take the sticks. The bottom is hinged to stakes which can be driven in the ground next to the saw, and the table is

DIAGRAM OF ASSEMBLY — CROSS TIMBER, ENGINE TIMBER, SAW, BEARINGS

NOTCH, HINGE, CHAIN, SAW TABLE

which could be hitched a horse for drawing the outfit around.

The engine, including radiator, transmission housing, dashboard, and gas tank, is mounted by means of bolts to heavy timbers attached to the chassis, as shown in the illustration. Low and reverse gears are removed, and the driving shaft run through two pillow-block bearings, one bolted to the

Details and Photo of Portable Wood-Sawing Rig Made from Old Automobile: Left, Plan of Assembly; Right, Details of Saw Table

then ready for use. A chain keeps it from swinging back too far when a heavy stick is being sawed up, besides holding it in position ready for the sticks to be placed on it and pushed over against the saw. The chain is securely attached, by means of a staple, to a stake driven into the ground on the side of the table away from the operator.

Micrometer Holder Keeps Oil from Spindle

When a micrometer is required for measuring work produced on a machine where cutting oil is used, it is a good plan

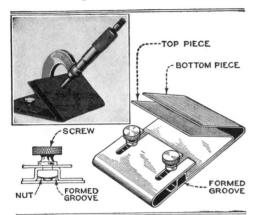

Simple Holder for Micrometer Used to Gauge Oily Work

to have some special device for holding it so that the oil will drain away from the spindle. As everything, including the operator's hands, is covered with oil, it is nearly impossible to keep the tool clean, but with a holder of the kind shown in the photo, the tool can be held in such a position that the oil will drain away from the thread, which would otherwise soon become inaccurate, due to the impurities that the oil contains.

The holder is made of two pieces of sheet metal, bent to the shape shown and held together with two thumbscrews, turning in nuts placed in a groove formed in the top piece. The bottom piece is slotted to make the holder adjustable, which is necessary to make the holder suitable for different settings of the micrometer on various jobs.

Increasing Orchard Yield

Farmers and orchardists in the United States are beginning to realize the necessity of restoring plant foods to the soil by applying concentrated fertilizers. Nitrogen is one of the foods that every plant needs and one that is soon exhausted from the soil, necessitating fertilizers, such as ammonium sulphate, sodium nitrate, and Chile saltpeter. Sodium nitrate is in such a form that it can readily be assimilated by the tree roots, while ammonium sulphate is slightly less soluble. When using these fertilizers in orchards the best results will be obtained if they are applied

to the soil in the spring, just when the season's growth begins. The amount of fertilizer applied to the soil under each tree varies, of course, with the condition of the soil, and with the kind, age and size of the trees. In recent experiments with apple trees on poor soil it was found necessary to apply ¼ lb. of fertilizer for each newly planted tree, and about 15 lb. for each mature tree that had been unproductive.

Cast Copper Vise Jaws

A large shop supplies its bench hands with copper vise-jaw pads to fit the different vises. They are cast from a metal pattern as shown in the illustration, and a good supply is always kept on hand so that a new set can be obtained when the old ones become badly battered and worn. The old ones are then returned to the foundry as scrap copper and recast. Any alloy metal, or even lead, may be used for this purpose, the lead being of special advantage for some classes of work. The pads are placed in the vise and the projecting ends are bent back over the jaws. Copper pads seem to stay in place much better than those made of sheet metal and they also last much longer.—H. L. Wheeler, Westwood, Mass.

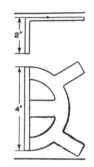

Gib-Head Key Guard

An effective guard for gib-head keys of the kind shown in the illustration not only prevents a loose key from coming out, but it also eliminates the danger of having the projecting head of a revolving key catch

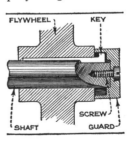

the workman's clothes, consequently causing injury. The guard consists of a cast-iron cap fastened on the end of the shaft so that it covers the head of the key. The cap is attached by means of a machine screw driven into a hole drilled and tapped in the end of the shaft. The hole in the cap is counterbored to take the screw head.

Hitching Wagon Train to Tractor

Hauling grain, corn and other products of the farm with trucks is the most modern method, but it is questionable whether a train of wagons drawn by a tractor is not a still more efficient one. Although the time consumed in making the trip with a tractor is much longer than if the trip were made with a truck, a tractor can draw a number of loads at once while the truck must make a separate trip for each load. The only objectionable feature in the use of a tractor for such purposes is its clumsiness, which makes it difficult, and in some cases im-

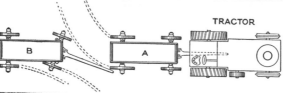

Above, Tractor Pulling 408 Bushels of Corn in Six Trailers; Below, Method of "Hooking Up"

possible, to pull the loaded wagons on the grain-elevator platform. Of course, much depends on the particular size and type of the tractor.

In the case shown in the photograph six wagons, loaded with shelled corn, having a total weight of 408 bushels, were drawn by the tractor. It was necessary to hitch the wagons as close as possible so that corners could be turned safely. To do this the tongues were securely fastened to the front axle support of the wagon ahead, instead of the rear one as is customary. In order to avoid the necessity of moving the wagons by hand the tractor was backed up in front of the first wagon, A, and its tongue was attached to the drawbar of the tractor, as indicated by the dotted lines of the detail. The first wagon was pulled up to a position directly in line with the second wagon, B, the tongue of which was cramped hard over. B was then backed until the tongue could be straightened, and A backed so that the two could readily be hitched as described above. This operation was repeated for each wagon which could not be hitched before it was loaded. A team of horses drawing another wagon load was taken along with the train so that it could be used to pull the wagons on the elevator platform separately after they were unhitched; this could not be done by the tractor, owing to its size.

Turning Bell Pattern to Size

In making a pattern for a large bell difficulty was encountered, after the inside was finished, in turning down the outside to the proper size, as no calipers that were large enough were available. The difficulty was overcome by drilling a number of holes through the pattern about 3 in. apart, and inserting plugs of a length equal to the desired thickness of the pattern at various points. The pattern was then mounted in the lathe

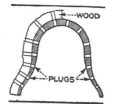

and the excess thickness turned down until the outer ends of the plugs were flush with the surface.—A. E. Holaday, Springfield, Massachusetts.

New Use for Sandblast

A novel application of the sandblast has been discovered by an English company— that of cleaning boiler tubes. It is claimed that the tubes of modern tubular boilers are rapidly cleaned of soot, etc., on the outside, and that the interior of each tube can be cleared of scale or other deposit thoroughly, and at a much greater speed than by any other existing method. This certainly has the merit of simplicity.

Homemade Drag for Leveling Orchard Land

After experimenting with several kinds of drags, the one shown in the illustration was found the most serviceable and convenient for leveling orchard land, which in this case, had been plowed the same way for several years with the result that the surface was formed in a series of ridges and furrows. Although a drag of this kind may not level the ground perfectly it will, nevertheless, help considerably. The work must, of course, be done when the soil is still loose from harrowing, before the winter rains pack it down.

The frame of the drag is made of two timbers of 2 by 8-in. pine or similar strong material, and four 2 by 4-in. crosspieces, two of which are bolted at each end, the upper one flat and the lower one on edge, as shown in the upper right-hand detail. The length of the drag, or rather the distance between the crosspieces at the ends, should be equal to the distance from center to center of the orchard ridges, and this depends, of course, on the distance between the rows of trees. About 3 ft. is the best width unless a tractor is used, and then the drag may be wider and

BOXES FILLED WITH ROCKS
1"X6" BRACES
2"X8"
2"X4" STEEL PLATE
2"X8"
2"X8"
2"X4"
DRAG SCRAPING SOIL FROM CRESTS OF RIDGES
LAND ORIGINALLY PLOWED IN DIRECTION AT RIGHT ANGLES TO MOVEMENT OF SCRAPER
DRAG DEPOSITING SOIL IN FURROWS

A Homemade Drag that Has Been Found Very Efficient for Leveling Orchard Lands

also much heavier. A 2 by 4-in. reinforcing block is bolted behind each lower crosspiece to prevent it from being torn off while dragging. Diagonal braces of 1 by 6-in. material or lengths of angle iron are bolted across the frame to prevent distortion, but heavier timbers, say of 2 by 4-in. material, would be better, as there is a considerable strain on the drag when it is turned. A box is nailed at each end and filled with stones to give the drag the necessary weight. Steel plates, $\frac{1}{4}$ in. thick, or lengths of angle iron are bolted to the edge of the lower crosspieces, as shown, so that the drag will take a good "bite" when scraping the soil. One horse can readily pull a drag of this size. If a team or tractor is used more ballast may be added.

In use, the crosspieces scrape soil from the crests of the ridges and deposit it in the furrows. Some difficulty in the use of this drag is encountered in turning, but this can be eliminated by making the drag "double-ended" so that it can be pulled back without turning.—H. H. Parker, Los Gatos, Calif.

Cutting Washers in Lathe

There are all sizes of washers on the market, but it is often difficult to get one to fit snugly, because the shaft or spindle on which the washer is to be used is sometimes worn down a trifle below the nearest standard size of washers, or the particular size of the washer needed may not be available, making it necessary to cut an emergency one. An excellent method of cutting washers accurately to any desired size and without much trouble, is to do it on the lathe.

The material from which a washer is to be cut, whether felt, fiber, rubber, leather, etc., or even thin sheet metal, such as brass, copper and tin, is tacked to a wooden disk about $\frac{3}{4}$ in. thick, which is mounted on the screw faceplate of the lathe. The tail center is then moved forward to mark the center on the disk and a pair of dividers are used to mark the inside and outside diameters, which is done in the following way: The diameter of the shaft is measured with a slide caliper and the dividers set to slightly less than half of this distance, to insure a tight fit. Then with one point of the dividers on the center mark just made on the disk a circle is carefully scribed on it, holding the dividers on the toolpost at an angle to the work, and revolving the faceplate slowly by pulling the belt. If the impression of the divider is not distinct enough, it can be brought out by running over it with a sharp-pointed pencil. The outside diameter is then scribed by setting the dividers to one half of this distance and proceeding in the same way. The lathe is set in operation and a sharp knife used to cut out the washer, the knife being steadied on the toolpost. It is obvious that the inner circle must be cut first. In cutting washers from soft materials such as felt, cork and rubber, which cannot readily be marked with the dividers and are not easy to cut, a stiff piece of cardboard is tacked over the surface and this surface used to mark on and cut through; the result will be that the material under it will be neatly cut to the same size. The size of the washers that can be cut in this way is limited only by the size of the lathe used to do the work. When cutting brass, copper and tin washers a regular metal-cutting tool must be used instead of a sharp knife.—J. E. Decker, Chicago, Ill.

Cold-Air Check for Chute

In a manufacturing plant where finished slabs are conveyed from the inside through a chute to the outside, a cold-air check was

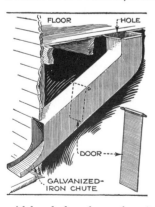

installed to prevent too great a loss of warm air in winter. The chute is made of galvanized iron and is nearly square in cross section. The check is also made of sheet iron and is slightly sm..ller across than the inside width of the chute, but is about an inch longer. The upper edge is bent over to hinge on a wire that is run through the chute and is fastened on both sides. When the check is at rest, the lower or free edge is a little further out than the top; this prevents it from swinging inward and effectively keeps out all cold-air drafts. Still it does not interfere with the passage of the slabs in any way.

Preventing Tap Breakage

It often happens that a small tap suddenly breaks after it has been used constantly on the same kind of work. The

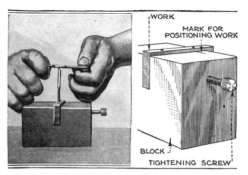

Left, Using Loose Block to Tap Small Work; Right, Details of Block

breakage is most likely due to too much torsional strain. Breakage of taps due to this cause can be eliminated by providing a loose block to hold the work; then if the tap binds in the work, the whole block will turn. The block is simply a piece of cast iron with a groove or slot cut in it to hold the work and a tightening screw to hold it securely. The block is placed on the bench plate and the friction between the block and the plate is sufficient to hold the former stationary while the tapping is being done. By moving the work so that the hole to be tapped is eccentric, the block can be adjusted to turn before the tap gets too great a strain. When this position is found a mark is scribed on the block so that the work can readily be placed in the correct position.

Drill-Press Clamp Bolts

Cheap and serviceable adjustable drill-press clamp bolts of the kind shown in the illustration can readily be made from suitable lengths of 1 by ½-in. iron. One end is cut down and threaded, while a series of holes to take a loose pin are drilled in line through the flat side as indicated. In use, the flat part is inserted into a slot of the drill-press table and the loose pin pushed through the hole that is nearest to the underside of the table. Then a nut is screwed in the threaded end to hold the work clamp.—John Harger, Honolulu, Hawaii.

MECHANICAL POWERS

By CARL W. MITMAN
Curator
DIVISIONS OF MINERAL AND MECHANICAL TECHNOLOGY UNITED STATES NATIONAL MUSEUM

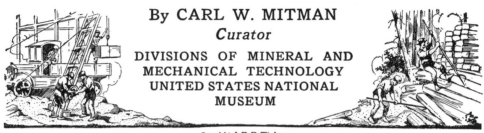

Copyrighted, H. H. Windsor

FOR many months the National Museum in Washington has been designing and building an unusual set of models of remarkable interest. These illustrate most simply and clearly the fundamental principles of the various Mechanical Powers. These models show at a glance, what textbooks have heretofore taken pages to describe. This is the second of a series of articles by Curator Mitman—who is himself an engineer of great ability—which not only explain in simple language what every mechanic and inventor who designs or builds a machine must know, but also tell how any one can exactly duplicate for himself the complete identical set of models in the National Museum. Mr. Mitman tells how to do this with ordinary tools and at practically no expense for materials.

For schools teaching physics or manual training, the opportunity is now presented for the first time of duplicating the set of these models in the National Museum. If one or more classes each year will build a few of the models, which should bear the nameplate of the class, in the course of two or three years the school will possess not only lasting monuments to the classes, but acquire, without cost, the full set for use of all future students, and which can be available to all local mechanics and inventors for all time.

If schools desiring to take advantage of this opportunity will communicate with us, we will be glad to furnish suitable nameplates, bearing the name of the class and year, free. Address Room 408, Popular Mechanics Bldg., 200 E. Ontario St., Chicago.

This series will run for many months to come; the third article will appear in the May issue, and, as this is the first time articles like this have ever been published, they should be preserved for future reference.

Photo No. 1, Completed Model of Compound Lever of the First Order; Photo No. 2, Model of Compound Lever Combining First and Second Orders

Part II—Moments and Compound Levers

A FORCE acting upon a lever tends to rotate it one way or another, depending first upon the magnitude of the force and second upon the perpendicular distance of the force from the fulcrum of the lever. These two factors taken together always determine the rotating or turning effect on the lever, and their product is called the moment of the force. In all questions involving levers and the work they are to do, the moments of the forces to be used must always be taken into consideration, and of greatest importance is the principle of moments. This states that when two or more forces act upon a lever and tend to rotate it about its fulcrum, then equilibrium will exist if the sum of the moments of the forces which tend to turn the lever in one direction equals the sum of the moments which tend to turn it in the opposite direction about the same axis. In other words, in the case of a first-order lever having two forces acting upon it on opposite sides of the fulcrum, as in Fig. 1, equilibrium will exist in the lever only when the moment of W (W times a) equals the moment of P (P times b). This is a very simple equation and is used to solve lever problems.

Should it be desirable, for instance, to know just how long a lever must be to accomplish a certain job or how much force must be applied to do that job with a lever of fixed length, the information is to be had by using the above equation. Fig. 2 illustrates just such a definite lever job, in that there is a force of 40

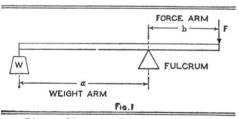

Fig. 1

Diagram Illustrating Principle of Moments

pounds available to bring into equilibrium three scattered forces acting on one arm of the lever and totaling 80 pounds pull. The question is, what length must the other arm of the lever be to permit the 40-pound pull to be effective. According to the principle of moments:

40 lb. × length of lever arm = 20 lb. × 40 in. + 50 lb. × 30 in. + 10 lb. × 25 in.

$$\text{Length of lever arm} = \frac{800+1,500+250}{40} = \frac{2,550}{40}$$

Length of lever arm = 63¾ in.

It will be noted that three calculations

have been combined into one in this example; that is, instead of figuring the moment of the weight arms separately, a short cut was taken.

The principle of moments is the underlying principle not only of levers, but of the whole subject of the action of forces in general. It is applied by the bridge designer in determining the type of structure necessary to support all loads and under all conditions; by the architect in the de-

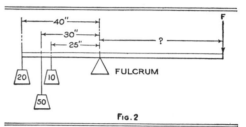

Fig. 2

Diagram Illustrating Problem in Design of Simple Lever

sign of buildings; and by the draftsman in the design of machines and machine parts.

When using levers to do work, and bearing in mind that the moments of the forces acting determine the effectiveness of the work done, it is quite easy to picture conditions in actual practice which would prevent the use of the simple order of lever, either due to the restricted space through which the applied force must act, the inconvenient location of the point of delivery of the power, or the prohibitive length of the lever arms. For such conditions combinations of the simple levers are used and these combinations are called compound levers. Of such mechanical powers there is an almost endless variety, beginning with combinations of two simple first-order levers; first and second-order combinations; first and third orders; two second orders; and so on. Then combinations of three, four and even five levers, some of which are first-order, others second and still others third-order. Thus the letter-printing action of one of the well-known typewriters is accomplished with a compound lever consisting of a second-order lever and two third-order levers. In the preceding chapter reference was made to that well-known saying, "What is gained in power is lost in speed." So, in the case of the typewriter action, speed is the object desired, but which must be produced with an available force of small magnitude (the fingers). The compound lever described above solves the problem.

Compound levers are sometimes rather difficult to recognize and even more difficult to devise for a specific piece of work unless the individual parts of the combination can be distinguished. In this connection, therefore, attention is directed to Figs. 3 and 4, which illustrate two types of lever combinations, conventionalized for

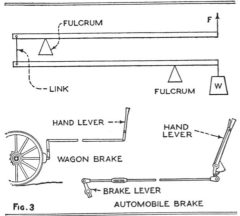

Fig. 3

Simplified Drawing of Compound Lever of First Order, with Examples of Its Use

simplicity. Fig. 3 is a simplified drawing of a compound lever consisting of two first-order levers. That it is a combination of two first-order levers is recognized from the relative location of the applied force, the fulcrum, and the resisting force respectively, and it will be observed that the fulcrum in both the upper and lower levers lies between the two opposing forces, hence they are of the first-order, as brought out in the preceding article. The fulcrum in the upper lever in the model, Fig. 5, however, takes a different form from that of the lower. While this lever combination yields a mechanical advantage, it is gained at a loss of speed and distance through which the resisting force (weight) is moved. Even so, there are undoubtedly occasions in practice where this characteristic is the one desired. Probably the most extensive use of two first-order levers combined is in the hand brake of a wagon and the emergency brake of an automobile. Simply by substituting a longer link connecting the two levers, and a brake shoe or one end of a brake band for the weight, the diagram shown in Fig. 3 illustrates this mechanism. Again, the throttle control on certain American-type locomotives is gained by the aid of a compound lever consisting of two first-order levers.

Another type of compound lever is shown by the diagram in Fig. 4. This type is a combination of a second-order lever above and a first-order lever below. The combination is to be found in foot

brakes both on wagons and automobiles, the difference between this type and type shown in Fig. 3 being the reversal of the position of the fulcrum and connecting link of the upper lever. This permits the applied force to be moved through a lesser distance to obtain the same work, and also in the opposite direction. Another application of this lever combination is found in some types of children's vehicles, especially those propelled by the child sitting on a platform and operating a vertical handle backward and forward.

For the compound-lever model, the first order, the following materials are required:

Base, 12-in. x 3-in. x ½-in.
Fulcrum block, 1½ in. square x ⅞ in.
Fulcrum, base ⅞-in. x ⅝-in., side 1-in. high.
Two lever arms, 11-in. long, ¼-in. wide, ¾-in. at apex.
Weight (resisting force), base 1¼-in. square, top 1¼-in. square, side 1½-in. high.
Pillar, 4½-in. x ⅞-in. x ½-in.
Arrow (applied force), 1¼-in. long, ¼-in. thick, ½-in. across barbs, ¼-in square shaft.

Square and face the base and block with a finish bevel on top of each. On the center line of the base, and 7 in. from the end, secure the block by gluing and bradding from beneath. On top of this glue and toe-nail the fulcrum with its longest dimension running parallel to the center line. 2¾ in. from the end of the base and 1 in. from its side, mortise a hole, ⅞ in. x ½ in., through the base. Connect the toe of one lever and the end of the other by the link, making the connection by drilling oversize holes in the ends of the levers and link, and inserting in these holes round-head brass screws. By a similar method pivot the

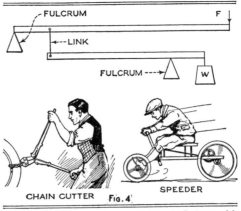

CHAIN CUTTER   **Fig. 4**   SPEEDER

Compound Lever of First and Second Orders, with Examples of Everyday Compound Levers

lever on which the toe is linked to the pillar, by a hole drilled through the center of the lever at the apex, to accommodate a screw. Fasten the weight to the toe of the lower lever by inserting the screw-eye, used as a handle, in a notch cut in the end of the lever. Attach the arrow to the end of the upper lever by inserting the point in a notch cut therein. Fasten this assembly to the base by inserting the pillar in the mortise, securing with glue, and pivoting the lower lever on the fulcrum below the apex, retaining it by an invisible brad. Finish as desired.

For the compound-lever model, 1st. and 2nd. orders, use the following materials:

Base, 12-in. x 3-in. x ½-in.
Fulcrum block, 1½-in. square x ⅞-in.
Fulcrum, base ⅞-in. x ⅝-in., side 1-in. high.
Upper lever arm, 11-in. x ¼-in., ⅞-in. at apex.
Lower lever arm, 6¼-in. x ¼-in., ⅞-in. at apex.
Pillar, 5-in. x ⅞-in. x ½-in.
Link, 2-in. x ⅝-in. x ¼-in.
Weight (resisting force), base 1¾-in. square, top 1¼-in square, side 1½-in. high.
Arrow (applied force), 1¼-in. long, ¼-in. thick, ½-in. across barbs, ¼-in. square shaft.

Square and face the base and block with a finish bevel on top of each. On the center line of the base and 6 in. from the end secure the block by gluing and bradding from beneath. On top of this glue and toenail the fulcrum with its longest dimension running parallel to the center line; ¾ in. from the same end of base and ⅞ in. from the side, chisel a mortise, ⅞ in. by ½ in. through the base. ¾ in. from one end of the pillar saw a cut across the

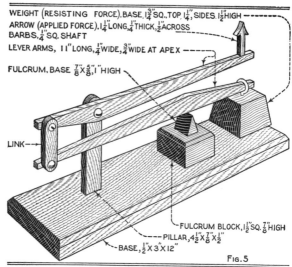

WEIGHT (RESISTING FORCE), BASE 1¾"SQ., TOP 1¼", SIDES 1½"HIGH
ARROW (APPLIED FORCE), 1¼"LONG, ¼"THICK, ½"ACROSS BARBS, ¼"SQ. SHAFT
LEVER ARMS, 11"LONG, ¼"WIDE, ¾"WIDE AT APEX
FULCRUM, BASE ⅞"X⅝", 1"HIGH
LINK
FULCRUM BLOCK, 1½"SQ. ⅞"HIGH
PILLAR, 4½"X⅞"X½"
BASE, ½"X3"X12"

FIG. 5

Dimensioned Drawing for Constructing Reproduction of Model of First-Order Compound Lever

width of the pillar ¼ in. deep, and remove the material from this cut to the nearest end. Insert the other end of the pillar into the mortise, gluing securely. Connect the apex of the upper lever and the end of the lower lever by the link, making the connection with screws inserted in holes bored in the ends of the link and the levers. Rest the screweye, used as a handle, in a notch cut in the toe of the lower lever. Fasten the arrow to the flat edge of the end of the upper lever by inserting the point in a notch cut therein. Fasten this lever assembly to the remainder of the model by pivoting the toe of the upper lever to the offset in the pillar with a screw and resting the lower lever on the fulcrum at a point under the apex, retaining it with an invisible brad. Finish as desired.

(Continued Next Month.)

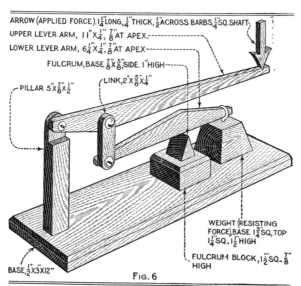

ARROW (APPLIED FORCE), 1¼"LONG, ¼"THICK, ½"ACROSS BARBS, ¼"SQ. SHAFT
UPPER LEVER ARM, 11"X¼", ⅞"AT APEX
LOWER LEVER ARM, 6¼"X¼", ⅞"AT APEX
FULCRUM, BASE ⅞"X⅝", SIDE 1"HIGH
PILLAR 5"X⅞"X½"
LINK, 2"X⅝"X¼"
WEIGHT (RESISTING FORCE), BASE 1¾"SQ., TOP 1¼"SQ., 1½"HIGH
FULCRUM BLOCK, 1½"SQ., ⅞" HIGH
BASE, ½"X3"X12"

FIG. 6

Full Details of Model of Compound Lever Combining Levers of the First and Second Orders

An Efficient Pen Cleaner

Most draftsmen and others using ruling or writing pens have the careless habit of allowing the ink to dry on the points. This soon accumulates and becomes very hard to remove. A good method of cleaning these pens is to allow them to stand immersed in a small bottle of common red writing ink for a few minutes. Even pens covered with a hard and crusted cake will look like new in a few minutes after being immersed.

Novel Valve Has No Packing

Users of compressed air will find the valve shown in the illustration of considerable utility. It was developed in a large machine shop, to eliminate the trouble due to gland leaks in the usual valves, and found thoroughly practical. The valve body consists of a thick steel disk, drilled as indicated for the air passages, one of the passages being reamed to form a valve seat. A spring-steel diaphragm is dished and welded to the disk, and a conical valve welded to its center, as shown. A cast-iron yoke fits over the disk, and carries a cam fitted with a lever. The cam bears on the valve stem and forces it into its seat, and the spring of the diaphragm opens the valve again when the cam is released. This valve, of course, can be adapted to liquids as well as air.—G. A. Luers, Washington, D. C.

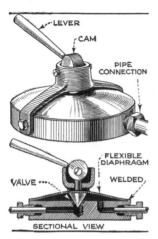

Attachment for Locating Template

Templates are usually the exact shape of the work they are used on and in many cases it is necessary to clamp them before marking off the job. If there are a number of pieces to be laid off, the locating and clamping of a template takes up considerable time. However, with the use of the clamp shown in the illustration the work can be greatly facilitated. Two studs, set on opposite sides, are riveted to the template as indicated and the heads are drilled to take a length of drill rod, which is doubled and bent to pass through the holes. In use, the template is placed on the work with the handle of the attachment in vertical position. The end of the template where the handle fits over should

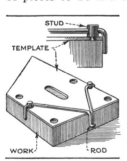

be slightly out of line, that is, showing the work beneath, so that the ends of the handle locate the sides when the handle is pressed down and the double part, which is bent slightly outward, pulls the template along until it is flush with the end. Locating is thus effected very quickly and the attachment grips the work securely enough to prevent any movement while the marking off is being done.

Measuring without Yardstick

In hardware stores where wire, rope, screen, and various other materials are constantly measured with yardsticks, the method shown in the illustration, which has already been adopted by a number of dry-goods stores, will be found to save considerable time. The scale is laid off on the edge of the bench top, or on the floor, brass tacks being driven in at 1-ft. intervals. If several yards are laid off in this way, numbered tacks can be used to designate the yards and ordinary brass-headed tacks for the foot intervals. This method of measuring is as accurate as any other and has the advantage of being much more convenient.

Gauge for Drift-Bolt Holes

Often in ship and bridge work and other heavy wood construction drift bolts are used for fastening. These bolts are without nuts and depend on friction alone for their holding power. When they are used for fastening two or more members together, they should never reach the bottom of the hole, and this makes it necessary to measure both the bolt and the hole accurately. The illustration shows a simple and convenient gauge for doing this. It consists of a length of wire, about No. 10 or 12, with a ring formed at one end, and a cork pushed on as shown. In use, the depth of the hole is measured by dropping

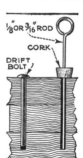

the wire down as far as it will go and then pushing the cork down until it touches the surface of the wood. The wire is then removed and a drift bolt selected that is a little shorter than the length indicated by the gauge.—J. A. Stevens, East Boothbay, Me.

Draftsman's Paper Cutter

Many T-squares and triangles are ruined by running a sharp knife or razor blade along the edge when cutting paper. This is a very careless practice and does not show good workmanship. It is much better to use a paper cutter of the kind shown in the photo.

This cutter was devised by a draftsman and found to facilitate the work considerably, without the danger of cutting into the T-square. It is made from two small pieces of sheet brass about 1⁄16 in. thick, bent and soldered together as shown, with the lower edge of the vertical piece projecting about 1⁄8 in. beyond the bottom piece to form a guide running on the edge of the T-square. The surplus solder is, of course, removed from the corner between the bottom piece and the projecting edge

Simple Paper Cutter for Draftsmen that Protects the T-Square

of the vertical piece, by means of a triangular file and all the edges and corners of the device are also filed down smooth. Two 1⁄8-in. holes are drilled in the vertical piece at the points indicated, and are extended with a round file to form slots. The distance between these slots must be the same as the distance between the two holes in a safety-razor blade, which is then attached by means of small screws, 1⁄2 in. long, fitted with thumbnuts. The blade can be adjusted to cut bristol board and drawing paper of various thicknesses, or even a number of layers of paper, and as it can be securely tightened to the holder, there is no danger of it breaking.

¶To tin brass and copper, boil the article with tin filings in a solution of caustic alkali or cream of tartar.

Tightening Tractor Belt

When using light tractors to fill a silo, or to run a thresher or any other farm machine, trouble often arises from the belt slackening. A simple method of preventing this is shown in the photograph. An automobile jack is set securely against a stone, or a stake driven into the ground, and it is then jacked up against the front axle of the tractor. If the tractor creeps, allowing the belt to slacken, it takes but a moment to jack it back enough to tighten the belt again.—J. C. Allen, West Lafayette, Indiana.

Preventing Damage to Steam Traps

In a heating system installed in a farm garage it was necessary to place a steam trap in a place where, at times, it was subject to frost, if neglected. This accident did occur a few times, and each time with the result that the outer shell, which was made of cast iron, was broken, making the purchase of a new one necessary. To prevent recurrence of this trouble two holes were drilled in the side of the

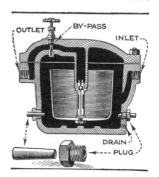

case as shown and tapped for 3⁄4-in cast-iron pipe plugs. A 3⁄8-in. hole was drilled through each plug and a tapered steel pin driven in just tightly enough to withstand the ordinary pressure of the water inside. When the temperature became low the pins contracted more than the cast-iron plugs, and, if the water froze, the pins were pushed out without any damage to the case.—G. G. McVicker, North Bend, Nebraska.

Recording Gauge Used as Watchman's Clock

In order to assure himself that the watchman of a large office building visited the boiler room at stated intervals, the superintendent made use of a pressure-recording gauge installed on the boiler, instead of purchasing a time clock. A ⅜-in. hole was drilled in the glass door of the gauge near its outer edge and on a line with the pen point. On each visit to the engine room the watchman inserts the inked rubber tip of his pencil through the hole in the glass and stamps a mark on the chart, thus indicating his presence in the engine room at that time. As the chart revolves a separate and distinct mark results at each visit, when the inked pencil rubber touches the chart. This device is "fool-proof" and the record cannot be faked unless the lock is opened. An ordinary stamp pad fastened to the side of the gauge enables the watchman to ink the rubber tip of the pencil. Simple individual marks are easily cut in the rubber tips.—John H. Schalek, Pittsburgh, Pa.

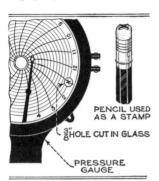

PENCIL USED AS A STAMP

⅜" HOLE CUT IN GLASS

PRESSURE GAUGE

Oil-Hole Covers

Insufficient lubrication is the root of many machine troubles and a frequent cause of this is the general custom of furnishing machines with oil holes that are simply plugged with short headless screws, which often become entirely covered with dirt and grease so that they cannot be easily located. In order to make oil holes easily recognized, a pattern shop uses the covers shown in the illustration. Each consists of a circular piece of sheet brass with two short slots cut in it as shown, and a pin driven tightly in the center, the other end of the pin carrying a short screw which also fits tightly. Space is left

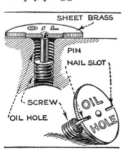

SHEET BRASS

PIN

NAIL SLOT

SCREW

OIL HOLE

OIL HOLE

between the cover and screw to allow it to be easily screwed down in the oil hole. which is tapped for this purpose. To place or remove the cover over the oil hole the finger nails are inserted in the slots. When stamped with plai nletters, this cover is easily noticeable, even in out-of-the-way places, and, being very thin, it does not foul working parts.

Counterweight for Pump

When pumping water from a deep well with a single-cylinder pump, the type mostly used, the upward stroke is very heavy as the whole column of water has to be raised, and the downward stroke is light. This uneven load causes a great deal of strain on the pump jack and engine and therefore the counterweight, shown in the illustration, was adopted. The size of the weight needed was found by turning the pump-jack pulley by hand and adding weights until the load was uniform, that is, when the downward stroke and upward stroke were equal. The counterweight used was an old hot-water tank, about 4 ft. long, partly filled with stones. It was suspended from a ¼-in. steel cable, run over a 14-in. pulley and tied to the top end of the plunger rod of the pump. It was found that, due to this arrangement, an engine of less power could be used to do the same work.

PULLEY

COUNTER-WEIGHT

However, as this engine was too small to do the work without a counterweight, a handle was attached to the latter, so that it could be made inoperative until enough water was raised in the well to counterbalance the weight. This is only necessary, of course, when an underpowered engine is used.—Jonas Byberg, Silverton, Ore.

¶Two parts of tallow and one part of neat's-foot oil, melted together, make a good belt dressing. Apply once a month with a brush.

Portable Power Plant for Farm

By J. V. ROMIG

Just as this article was being prepared for publication, we learned, with deep regret, of the death of Mr. Romig at his home in Allentown, Pa. Mr. Romig was one of our earliest and best contributors, and, through a long and friendly relationship, we had come to respect sincerely his ability as a mechanic, designer, and writer, so it is with a sense of real loss that we pen this brief tribute. His articles found many admirers among our readers, but for these friends of his and ours there is a measure of consolation, in that we have a number of his articles still unpublished; his constructive work will, therefore, not cease immediately.—Editor.

MANY old automobiles, the engines of which are in good and serviceable condition, are scrapped and broken up each year by junk dealers. Such an engine is good for many more years of stationary use, and would form the basis of an ideal portable power plant for the farm. Before purchasing any portable or stationary power plant, the prospective user should give the auto plant careful consideration.

The first cost is small, as these engines can be purchased as low as $20, depending upon their condition. Any power, and any speed within their range can readily be secured, and governors can be fitted to them readily and cheaply, to hold them to any speed desired. These governors usually operate on the gasoline feed, controlling the opening and closing of the throttle in the intake manifold.

The best engine to select for

Driving the Silage Cutter and Elevator with the Portable Auto-Engine Power Plant

a portable power plant is a four-cylinder water-cooled plant, of about 18 to 20 hp., with magneto ignition, and pump-operated water circulation. An engine with mechanical oilers should be shunned, as these are out of date, and a motor with a good constant-level splash lubrication is to be preferred, for this purpose, to one having a full force-feed system. If possible, the engine should be examined thoroughly before purchasing, to determine if the cylinders are scored or scratched; such a motor should not be bought, even though the cylinders can be reground, as regrinding is an expensive job. The water jacket should be examined for cracks and leaks, and, if any are found, the engine should be rejected. Loose pistons should also be a

cause for rejection, but if only the rings are worn, this is not important, as they can easily be renewed. Loose bearings can also be remedied easily, and, if the engine is good otherwise, may be overlooked.

Magneto ignition is very desirable, as it is a self-contained system. If the engine is of the magneto-ignition type, the starter and generator may be removed. If of the battery ignition type, discard the starting motor, but retain the generator.

To be portable, the engine must be mounted on a truck of some sort, and, while a suitable truck can be bought comparatively cheap, the writer advises that only the wheels and axles be purchased, and that the frame of the truck be built up of 5-in. channel iron, as shown in the illustration. The mounting of the engine on the frame need not be a very hard job, if the builder has a few hints to guide him in the construction.

Engines are supported in car frames in different ways, some having four supporting arms, like the unit shown, others but three, two at the rear, and a yoke or round journal at the front. In any event, a cross-mounted sub-frame will be found the best method of supporting the engine. This frame should be of 4-in. channel iron, and should project over the side of the truck, so that the radiator can be mounted in the same position as in the car. A crosspiece of the same material should tie the ends of the sub-frame, to support the cranking-handle bearing, and to stiffen the assembly. Cross-braces, made of ½ by 6-in stock, should be used wherever necessary, and be fastened in place by capscrews. It is recommended that the radiator used be one taken from a larger car than that from which the engine was obtained, or from a heavy truck, to provide the additional cooling capacity necessary for long runs under full load.

The drive pulley for general purposes can be built up of wood, bored out to fit over the clutch extension shaft, and fastened to the flywheel by means of long studs, screwed in place of the regular flywheel capscrews. This makes a strong and rigid driving pulley; for higher speeds,

the flywheel itself can be used as a pulley.

The gasoline tank should be a large one, of 15 to 20-gal. capacity, and should be mounted on flat-steel brackets high enough to provide a gravity feed to the carburetor. Care should be taken to obtain a tight tank, with well-soldered connections. A shut-off cock should be fitted between tank and carburetor.

The treatment of the exhaust is simple. A thin pipe section is bent and flattened, as shown in the drawing, then coupled to the end of the exhaust manifold by means of

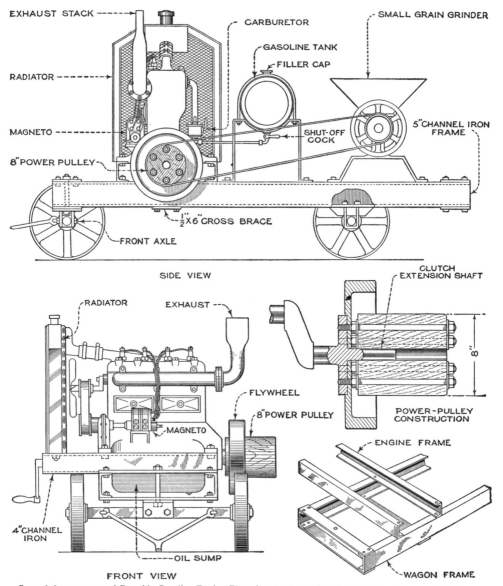

General Arrangement of Portable Gasoline-Engine Plant for the Farm, Showing Details of Frame, Sub-Frame, Drive Pulley, and Method of Mounting Engine

thin flanges, or a threaded coupling. The flat opening should be about ¼ in. wide; this will minimize the sound of the exhaust to some extent, while permitting free escape of the gases.

As large a fan as possible should be fitted, and the belt kept tight at all times. Use none but clean water in the radiator, and only the best grade of oil in the engine.

Besides driving the threshing machine, grain elevator, and other farm implements, the frame may be made to accommodate a small machine, as suggested in the illustration. Such machines as a water pump, sprayer, or an air compressor may readily be mounted on the frame. The length of the frame will, of course, depend on the machine that is to be mounted on it.

A power plant of this type will prove of considerable value on any large farm, as instead of trying to connect the machine to a stationary engine by long pipes or belts, the portable plant may be driven right up to the job.

Stamping Graduated Collars

In a small shop having a number of graduated collars to stamp from 0 to 9, it was found that the usual method of stamping each number separately was too slow, and that a quicker method would have to be adopted to make the operation profitable. A fixture that was found to facilitate the work considerably is shown in the illustration. It consists of a steel ring that fits over the collars, having ten holes drilled through from the outside, these being equal in diameter to the corner-to-corner dimensions of the stamps. To hold the stamps squarely in the holes and to prevent them from falling out, the ring is covered with a piece

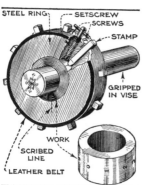

of 1-in. belt, fastened with a couple of screws, and square holes are cut in the belt to fit tightly over the stamps. A hole is drilled and tapped for a tightening screw, with which the fixture is tightened on the collar. After the collar is slipped on a short length of steel rod, which is held in the vise, the ring is turned so that the numerals on the stamps are brought in line with a mark already scribed on the collar and they are then impressed by tapping lightly with a hammer.

¶A 30 by 3½-in. clincher rim sometimes causes the casing to pinch the tube. This can be prevented by cutting from a scrap tube a strip of rubber, 1½ in. wide, and running this strip around the rim. One hole is cut at each end of the strip for the valve. An oversize tube should also be used.

Filing Crosscut Saws

Large crosscut saws used for sawing logs are, owing to their size, difficult to file when sharpening them without the aid of a vise. Experienced woodsmen employ the slot-and-wedge method of holding the saw, as shown in the drawing. A deep slot is cut across a log or heavy timber and the saw is

placed upside down in this cut. One or two small wooden wedges are then driven in the cut to hold the saw securely in position and it can then be filed readily. —G. E. Hendrickson, Argyle, Wis.

Improving the Ladle

When pouring a large number of small lead castings the writer was seriously handicapped by the necessity of frequently removing the dross from the surface of the molten lead, in order to obtain clean castings. After some experiments the method shown in the illustration was found to eliminate this trouble entirely. A short length of steel tubing was welded to the in-

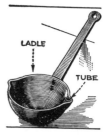

side of the bowl of the ladle, from the center of the bottom to the lip, as indicated, so that the metal would be taken from the bottom where it was free from dross. It was then no longer necessary to skim the metal at all, and the work could be accomplished with much greater speed. —R. H. Kasper, Philadelphia, Pa.

Removing Dust Caps from Hubs

Sometimes it is necessary to remove the dust cap from a front wheel of a Ford automobile, and this is usually done by

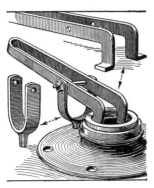

tapping the cap out of the hub with a hammer and punch. This method is objectionable, however, as it often results in damaging the cap. The tool shown in the illustration has been found very practical for this job. It consists of a length of flat steel, 1 in. wide and ¼ in. thick, bent to the shape shown and pivoted on a yoke made of the same stock. A short length of round-steel rod is welded to the bottom of the yoke to fit in one of the bolt holes of the hub flange. In use the frame of the tool is pressed together to allow the ends to be inserted under the cap, and pressure is then applied on the doubled end; this draws the dust cap out without damage.—R. M. Thomas, Denver, Colorado.

Two Kinks for Draftsmen

In making record drawings from customers' patterns it is sometimes necessary to know the contour of a groove. Of course, a paper template can be made by the "cut-and-try" method, but a quicker way is to light a candle and let the drippings build up in the groove as shown in Fig. 1. This is removed and cut with a knife so as to form a section at right angles to the groove if it is straight, or radial if it is circular. The cut face can then be laid on the drafting paper and the contour traced off direct.

In a manganese-steel foundry drafting room where it is often necessary to obtain the actual length of a shrink-rule dimension, the T-squares are ruled as shown in Fig. 2 of the drawing. A centerline is first drawn and on one side a standard 2-ft. scale is laid off by eighths of an inch. On the other side of the centerline, a shrinkage scale is laid off. This makes a convenient reference in determining the actual lengths of pattern dimensions. For example, if it is desired to know the proper length of a soft-steel insert that is to be cast in the manganese steel for convenience in machining, the distance between the ends of the prints on the pattern is noted on the shrink scale and then the correct length to cut the soft-steel insert, so that it will fit in the mold snugly, may be obtained by reading the standard scale at the point noted.—D. A. Price, Chicago Heights, Ill.

Brace Chuck for Round-Shank Drills

When small bits are used in an ordinary brace they are frequently broken. The shanks, however, should not be thrown away. Saw off the broken stem as shown in the illustration and slit it lengthwise with a hacksaw as shown, thereby dividing the shank into four pieces, save for a narrow strip at the small end. A small round-shank drill is inserted in the shank, which is then clamped tightly in the brace chuck. For larger sizes of round-shank drills, it is, of course, necessary to enlarge the hole in the shank,

BROKEN BIT
PART CUT OFF
HACKSAW CUTS
ROUND-SHANK DRILL

which may be done by filing or chipping off the four inside corners, which grip the drill. Another way is to place two hacksaws side by side in the saw handle and split the shank with two saws instead of one, or for fairly large drills, to drill a hole in the shank before slitting.—James F. Hobart, Dunedin, Fla.

Fig. 1: Accurate Method of Determining the Contour of a Groove. Fig. 2: A Standard Scale and a Shrink Scale Ruled on T-Square for Convenience

❡When painting a wire wheel it often happens that the valve stem is daubed, which makes it difficult to remove the valve nut after the paint is dry. To remove the valve nut, cut it with a chisel, or soak the stem in gasoline and light it to burn the paint off. It is usually necessary to repeat the latter operation a few times before the paint softens.

Raw Oil as Stain

While turning out a number of mahogany cabinets on a rush order the supply of mahogany stain became exhausted. As it would mean a considerable delay to have the order held up until more could be obtained, raw linseed oil was tried out as a substitute and the results obtained were highly satisfactory. It was rubbed into the wood until the desired shade was obtained and then rubbed down with a dry cloth. Coats of shellac were next applied and rubbed down, and the surface finished with a final rub-down of pumice and oil.
—T. W. Bean, San Pedro, Calif.

Improving Torch Air Pump

Nearly every mechanic has experienced the annoyance caused by the leather washer on the air-pump plunger of a gasoline torch drying out, especially after the torch has not been used for a long time. A good

method of eliminating this trouble is shown in the illustration. A groove is turned in the side of the piston for a single turn of a coil spring to fit in, the groove being just deep enough to allow the springs to project about .01 in. above the surface. The coil spring, which must be of slightly smaller diameter than the piston, will fit tightly in the groove, holding the leather skirt in place, and preventing any trouble even though the torch is not used for several months.

Measuring Pipe with Tape

Pipe workers will appreciate the spring shown in the illustration as it greatly facilitates measuring long lengths of pipe, when the work is done by one man. A length of spring wire is bent to the shape shown, and is inserted in the end of the pipe so that the tape measure can be hooked onto it. The spring should be sufficiently strong to take care of pipe ranging from ½ in. to 1 in. in size.

Backless Drawers Aid in Office

In a small establishment, where the office was located next to the shipping room, the drivers were in the habit of coming in constantly to get orders, and

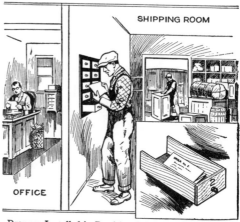

Drawers Installed in Partition Between Office and Shipping Room Found to Save Considerable Time

this was more or less disturbing to the office force. To prevent this annoyance, a number of small drawers were fitted in the partition between the office and shipping room, for the purpose of holding the orders in readiness for the drivers. The drawers were made of wood, and had no backs, so that the orders could be quickly inserted in them from the office side. A separate drawer was provided for each driver and this eliminated waste of time on the drivers' part in sorting the orders.

Hammer Used as Reamer Wrench

It is often possible to combine tools used constantly, to save time in handling them separately. The photo shows a combination tool consisting of a hammer and reamer. The hammer is an all-metal one with a hole drilled through the head for a reamer, which is driven in.

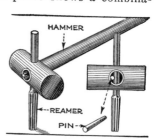

The shank of the reamer is ground flat so that a pin, driven in, holds it snugly and keeps it from turning. The tool was found to be a time saver, as it was first used to ream out holes for pins, which were then tapped in with the hammer.

A Self-Closing Rail Gate

Part of the contents of a warehouse were considered dangerous enough to be railed off, and in constructing the rail a novel gate was built in the center of it. With

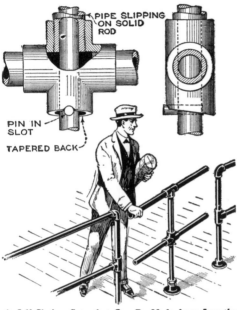

A Self-Closing Gate that Can Be Made from Lengths of Pipe and Fittings

the exception of one part, the gate is made up of iron pipe and fittings the same as the rail. In the center of the space left for the gate a piece of solid, round stock, with a pin driven in, is fixed vertically by screwing one end into a floor flange and screwing the latter to the floor. The gate proper is made from lengths of pipe, a cross and a tee. The vertical lengths of pipe between the fittings slide over the solid rod, as shown in the left-hand detail. A shallow slot is cut in the bottom of the cross to fit the pin driven through the rod. The edges of the slot are filed round, as shown in the detail, so that the gate can readily be pushed open without interference from the pin. The bottom edge of the cross is beveled toward the slot, as shown in the right-hand detail, so that the gate automatically turns to the closed position when released.

¶Screeching auto brakes are usually caused by particles of dirt and mud between the lining and the drum. Wash these out when washing the car, and the screeching will stop. The water also helps the lining.

Using Soap on Concrete Forms

Crude oil is usually applied to forms in concrete construction work to prevent the concrete from adhering to the wood. However, there is a disadvantage in using oil for this purpose if a finishing coat is to be applied later, as a thin film of oil will be left on the surface of the concrete and this prevents it from bonding properly with the finishing coat. Soap dissolved in water will serve the same purpose as the crude oil without the undesirable effect just mentioned. The soap solution should have the consistency of thin paste, and it can be applied hot by means of a whitewash brush or a broom. As soap is easily dissolved, even by cold water, the film can be washed away by means of a hose in a short time, leaving the concrete clean.

Fire-Extinguisher Mounted on Truck

A large automobile manufacturing concern doing a considerable amount of welding has provided a fire extinguisher on every truck carrying the welding equipment. A pair of heavy spring clips are attached to the crossbar of the truck near the handles to hold the extinguisher, which is of the hand-operated type, so that in case of fire it is within reach of the workmen.

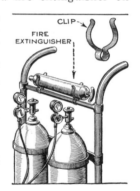

A Novel Turnbuckle

Turnbuckles are usually tapped for a right and a left-hand screw, but a good one can easily be made that is tapped for two right-hand screws, having different-size threads. About three-fifths of the body of the turnbuckle is tapped with a U. S. S.-thread tap; the rest with a S. A. E.-thread tap. Due to the greater pitch of the U. S. S. thread, when the body of the turnbuckle is turned, the screw with this thread travels nearly twice as fast as the other screw.

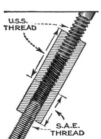

A Portable Drill and Grinder

By D. R. VAN HORN

THE little tool shown in the illustration is in use in a second-story violin-repair shop in Lincoln, Neb. The proprietor, who is an expert in his line—making and repairing violins and other string instruments—uses it for dressing down wooden parts, drilling, inlaying, etc. But it is in some degree a universal tool, and as it is made from odds and ends of material, it should be of interest to all small-shop mechanics. The power unit is an old ¼-hp., 60-cycle fan motor, picked up for a few dollars. But let the owner describe the construction.

"I wanted a tool," he said, "which would fit my own purposes well. What I most needed was a tool for grooving violin backs for inlaying, which would duplicate the good work of other methods and save a lot of time. With this device I can run a groove around in twenty minutes. Having the motor, I sought out a flexible

connection by which a chuck could be used, taking different tools. The part used, which, by the way, cost 75 cents, was found in a garage around the corner. This consisted of flexible housing, chain, and a steel shank from an old speedometer.

"The motor was set upon a wooden base, 2 in thick, 12 in. wide and about 20 in. long. The motor base proper is a second 2-in. piece, nailed to the larger base, and on one end of this is nailed a wooden piece as a sort of reinforcing or bearing for the end of the flexible shaft. On the other end of the main base is located a small grinder head. Here is also fitted a grooved rest, consisting of a short piece of 2 by 4-in. wood, which is used to do careful work with the grinder." But the chief point of interest lies in the method of producing a working unit on the free end of the flexible shaft. The chain

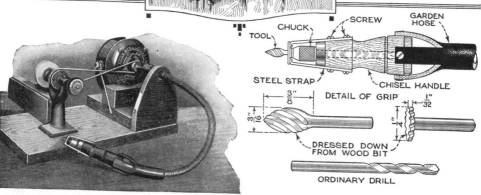

Made of Scrap Material, This Portable, Flexible Drill Can Be Built Very Easily, and Will Prove Valuable in Any Small Shop

was attached to a short steel shank threaded on one end. To this was fitted a small chuck of suitable capacity. The handle from a wood chisel forms the hand grip, and this is strengthened by a short length of rubber garden hose. One end of the hose is split into four sections. This is then slipped onto the shaft, the ends spread and screwed to the end of the chisel handle. This handle is hollow and permits the shaft to be passed through it.

Two flat steel strips are also attached in the manner shown to add strength to the outer end. The shaft is connected to the motor by a threaded sleeve. The motor shaft carries a short collar which is threaded on the inside. The shaft is also attached to a short steel rod, threaded, which screws into the motor shaft. A few of the tools used with the shaft are shown.

All told, this portable unit does not exceed twenty pounds in weight. It has been in almost constant service for several years, and seems good for many more.

Special Stencil Expedites Printing

The common stencil and daubing brush is both crude and slow in comparison with the special stencil shown in the drawing.

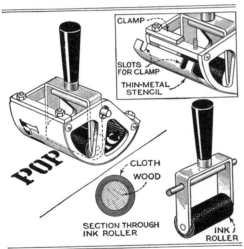

CLAMP

SLOTS FOR CLAMP

THIN-METAL STENCIL

CLOTH

WOOD

SECTION THROUGH INK ROLLER

INK ROLLER

Novel and Efficient Stenciling Machine for Labeling Boxes or Other Material

This was made up in a small shop to label boxes. The same idea can be used for stenciling any kind of material.

The drawing shows the details clearly. A frame of heavy sheet metal is made to hold the thin metal stencil. The side members of the frame are semicircular in shape, and are connected by crossbars, which carry the clamps used to fasten the stencil. The ink pad is a wooden roller, covered with several layers of soft cotton, and mounted in a U-shaped frame fitted with a handle and a pivot pin. The hole for this pin in the side frames is much larger than the pin, so that the roller can be pressed with sufficient force on the stencil.

The manner of using is evident. The roller pad is soaked with ink, and the frame rolled over the material to be stenciled, pressing firmly on the handle.

Stacking Fiber Cartons

Warehouse workers complain that it is difficult to stack fiber cartons, when filled with product, so that the stack will not bulge out. A method which gives satisfactory results is as follows: Stack the cartons five high and then cover the top of the pile as it stands with building paper, or discarded cartons that have been folded so as to lie flat, so that the adjacent stacks of boxes will be held together by the weight of those above the paper. After another layer of boxes has been placed over the paper, place common laths all around the edge of the stack, between the fifth and sixth layers of boxes. The building paper ties the whole stack together, while the laths serve to tilt the outside boxes a trifle toward the center. In this way fiber cartons may be piled to the warehouse roof without danger of bulging.

Repairing Ford-Axle Spindles

I have discovered a method of repairing Ford front axles when the spindle-body bolt holes are worn egg-shaped, and when the threads are stripped in the lower spindle bolt holes. I have repaired six cars in this way with excellent results. First remove the axle from the car, put it in a vise, and ream out both holes with an $\frac{11}{16}$-in. reamer. Then take a spindle-body bushing (part No. 2713), and force it into the

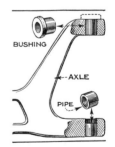

BUSHING

AXLE

PIPE

top hole. Force a short piece of $\frac{3}{8}$-in. pipe into the bottom hole, driving it in from the underside. This piece should go into the hole $\frac{5}{8}$ in. deep. Now tap the bottom hole with a $\frac{1}{2}$-in. 20-thread tap. This little job takes only 1 to $1\frac{1}{2}$ hours to do after the axle is removed from the car. — Allen Knapp, Collinsville, Ill.

Painting Over Calcimined Walls

Interior walls are often painted nowadays instead of being papered. In preparing old walls for painting it is first necessary to remove the paper, paste, and calcimine which was previously applied. This leaves the walls in poor condition for the application of paint, as small pieces of thin paper stick to the walls here and there, and the plaster is usually cracked in many places, making it almost impossible to apply the paint successfully. The cracks should be filled up with plaster of paris and the walls filled with a liberal application of shellac, which has the consistency of glue. This will bind together the loose segments of plaster and will span the numerous small cracks without being absorbed into them as would be the case if paint were applied without this preliminary coating. After the shellac has been allowed to dry for half a day or so the wall can be given two coats of oil paint, allowing the first to dry before applying the second, and it will be found that the surface will not have the numerous high spots and dull places that would result if no shellac were used.

Guide for Filing Saws

Saws can be filed much more accurately by providing a guide ruled, as shown in the illustration, with lines at the correct angle for the saw being sharpened. This guide, which is simply a strip of stiff paper, is tacked to a length of ¾-in. board fastened to the saw clamp. The surface of this board must be about 1 in. below the edge of the saw teeth when set in the clamp so that it will not be cut by the file. When filing, start at the heel of the saw in the customary way and the eye will automatically follow the lines of the guide. Most saw clamps are made to clamp onto the benchtop directly, but this makes it necessary for the worker to stoop over, which is very tiresome. To make the work more convenient the clamp should be mounted on a piece of 2 by 10-in. material, and this piece securely held in the bench vise.

STIFF-PAPER GUIDE

Automobile Fender Clamp

Every fender repairman has experienced the trouble of trying to keep a bar on hand to clamp to a fender in order to prevent it from spreading while shaping the edge.

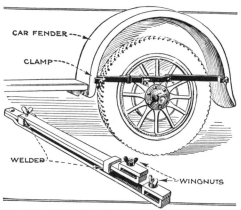

CAR FENDER

CLAMP

WELDED

WINGNUTS

An Adjustable Folding Clamp for Keeping Automobile Fenders True While Shaping the Edges

However, the folding bar shown in the illustration can be kept in the toolbox and is therefore not liable to be lost so quickly. It consists of two lengths of steel bar hinged together at the center with a rivet, and a third piece sliding on one of these. The sliding piece has a sleeve welded at each end so that it can only slide backward and forward and is held securely from moving any other way. A hole is drilled and tapped through the inner end of the sliding bar for a thumbscrew with which it can be tightened down, a number of spots being drilled in the other piece to take the end of the thumbscrew. Clamps of the shape shown are provided at the ends of the pieces to hold the edges of the fenders.—L. H. Candy, Bordeaux, Can.

Vacuum-System Kinks

The trouble frequently experienced with stationary vacuum-cleaning systems in that the pipes become clogged, is often due to the use of ordinary pipe fittings, as they are small and form excellent places in which matches, hairpins, and other objects may lodge. When installing a system of this kind it is therefore best to use pipes of large diameter and extra-large fittings. It is also a good idea to drill a ${}_{16}^{1}$-inch hole in the end of each pipe so that a little air will pass through the pipe all the time; this will dislodge any dirt that may have settled in a corner when the machine was shut down. Such a small opening will not affect the vacuum to any perceptible degree.

Barrel Hoist and Rack for the Garage

Oil drums in garages are usually placed on racks a few feet from the floor, but considerable difficulty is often experienced in

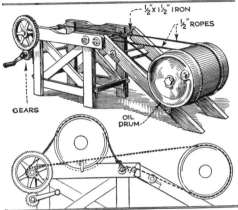

A Simple Barrel Hoist and Rack for the Garage that Can Be Operated by One Man

lifting the oil drums up on the racks. A simple hoist for this purpose, which can easily be operated by one man, is shown in the illustration. It consists of a winch arrangement attached to one end of the rack. A large gear is keyed on one end of the winch and a small gear, meshing with the larger one as shown, has a handle attached so that the winch can be turned.

A skid is hooked to the rack for the drums to be rolled on, which is accomplished by means of two $\frac{1}{2}$-in. ropes, attached at one end to the winch and at the other end to the rack. These ropes must be long enough to be passed around the drum when it lies on the floor close to the skid. Winding the winch then rolls the drums up over the skid and onto the rack. The top edges of the rack are notched for the drums to rest in, so that there will be no danger of them rolling off.

Rotating Crops

Nearly every farmer is beginning to realize the necessity of crop rotation as a means of restoring and maintaining the fertility of soils. Systematic crop rotation is the regular changing of crops on certain soils to prevent them from becoming exhausted of particular plant foods, as different crops require different kinds of food. By rotating crops the injury caused by insects and bacteria is also lessened considerably.

Due to the great variety of climates and soils, and crops that are particularly suited to them, it is impossible to adopt any standard system of crop rotation, and each farmer must, therefore, devise his own rotation system, as influenced by the above-mentioned factors, as well as the local characteristics of his farm. In general, a good rotation system is based on the regular alternation of three main classes of crops, namely; grain crops, grass crops, and cultivated crops. In the middle west, many farmers devote one-eighth to one-half of their farms to corn and the rest to grass one year and simply reverse the crops on these fields the following year, instead of growing the same crops on the same soil every year. Such rotation does not require much planning and will not reduce the income per acre, but will rather gradually increase the income by increasing the fertility of the soil.—E. R. Haan, Chicago, Ill.

Polishing Concave Work

Concave grooves and slots, bearings, and many other similar jobs, can be neatly finished off with emery cloth if the latter is held in a suitable manner. One method of doing this is shown in the drawing, where a hacksaw frame is used to hold the device, the emery cloth being held on a round piece of wood, as indicated. The piece of wood is grooved along its length; either a round or a V-groove will do. Two screweyes are driven tightly into each end and a round piece of steel, a little longer than the piece of wood, is

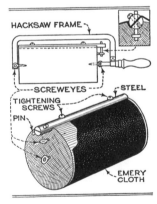

drilled and tapped for two round-head screws and is then split in two pieces. To tighten the emery cloth on the wood, one end of the cloth is inserted in the slot in the steel rod at one side, the other end at the other side, and the two screws tightened up securely. The overhanging part of the rod carries a pin, as shown, which fits loosely in the hole so that when the cloth is tightened it can be stretched tightly around the wood by giving this pin a quarter turn. To hold it in this position it is pushed down to enter the eye of the upper screw. The whole thing is then placed in a hacksaw frame and tightened.

A Toolmaker's Square and Test Block

A toolmaker's square, embodying a number of original features, is shown in the drawing. The square blade, of tool steel, is formed as illustrated, and finished to dimensions by grinding. The blade is supported in a steel block containing a slot into which the blade is inserted, and held by means of a pin passing through both members, so that the blade is, in effect, pivoted. The surfaces of the blade slot are recessed to make it easy to grind out the slot accurately; the recess is made with the side of a small end mill and is about ⅛ in. deep. Two holes are drilled through the center of the base, in line with the slot, and tapped to take the two adjusting screws by means of which the blade is lined up. It will be found necessary to drill a hole through the block at right angles to those drilled for the adjusting screws, in order to permit the tap to bottom. The blade should fit snugly in its slot without the least side play. The bottom of the base is recessed and the sides are checkered to provide an easy grip. The base can be finished by lapping with emery flour and oil to a high polish and the grooves in the sides can be filled with black enamel to accentuate the finish on the sides.

The test cylinder is recessed at each end for ⅜ in., bored to fit the arbor used, and the bore is undercut for a part of its length, so that the hollow cylinder thus formed is supported on the arbor only at the ends. After being placed on an arbor and between centers of a lathe, the sides and ends are rough ground, the grinding wheel being dressed as in the drawing, so that the ends and sides can be ground at the same setting. After the rough-grind operation, the wheel is trued up again and the work is ground to its finished diameter. By grinding the cylinder in the manner described, it is evident that if it is exactly parallel throughout its length and the ends are ground at the same setting the block will stand squarely on the surface plate.

To line up the blade of the square, both it and the test cylinder are placed on a surface plate and the adjusting screws turned in or out as may be required until the edge

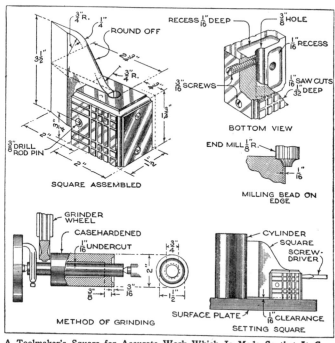

SQUARE ASSEMBLED

BOTTOM VIEW

MILLING BEAD ON EDGE

METHOD OF GRINDING

SETTING SQUARE

A Toolmaker's Square for Accurate Work Which Is Made So that It Can Be Checked and Adjusted by Means of an Accurately Ground Test Cylinder

of the blade is exactly parallel to the side of the cylinder. All parts should be made of tool steel, and casehardened.—Henry S. Laraby, New Haven, Conn.

Paper Edges on Wallboard Joints

It is customary to paste paper strips over wallboard joints so that the wallpaper to be laid over the board will not crack, which would greatly mar the appearance of the finished decoration. However, the edges of these strips will show through the wallpaper unless some method is used to make a featheredge. This is done by expert decorators in the following way: Before pasting on the strips turn up their edges on the outside about ½ in., making them U-shaped, then paste the strips on, applying the paste to the bottom of the U. After the adhesive is thoroughly dry tear off the turned-up edges, pulling them down and slightly toward the inside. This will remove all the paper that is not stuck to the wall, and leave a featheredge which will not show through the wallpaper.—James Ryan Haydon, Chicago, Ill.

Angular Attachment for Drill-Press Vise

In small shops a special vise is of considerable usefulness when drilling holes on an angle, which must otherwise be done by using packing on the regular vise. By

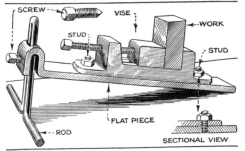

SCREW — VISE — WORK
STUD — STUD
FLAT PIECE
ROD — SECTIONAL VIEW

Attachment for Converting Common Machine Vise into Angular Vise for Drill Press

using the simple attachment shown in the illustration any ordinary machine vise can be used conveniently for this purpose.

First a length of flat stock is heated at one end and bent to the form shown. Then a piece of round steel is heated, doubled, and the ends bent at right angles. The flat piece is drilled and tapped in two places and studs screwed in tightly to hold the vise on the attachment. The top of the bent part is slotted to take the doubled rod, and drilled and tapped so that the point of the screw enters between "legs" of the doubled rod. To set the vise at the required angle the screw is loosened and the flat base is slid up or down and the screw tightened again, which causes the doubled rod to spring apart slightly below the slot.

Supporting the Parting Tool

When cutting off bars of large diameter, especially brass stock in the screw machine, a good deal of chattering and digging in of the tool results from the need of having the parting tool extend well out

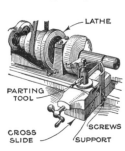

LATHE
PARTING TOOL
CROSS SLIDE — SCREWS SUPPORT

and supported by the holder at a point where support is most needed. When a situation of this kind arises, the tool can be supported by the simple method illustrated. Take a piece of ⅜ by 1½ or 2-in. flat steel, bend it into a vee and then bend the ends to fit down over the cross slide. In the center

of the vee, drill and file and finally broach out a hole with a piece of the parting tool used on the job; then caseharden the hole only. Fasten the supporting pieces to the cross slide by means of four screws—two on each side. The supporting piece is fastened to the bottom of the cross slide, leaving the top free to work back and forth as usual; this can be attained by packing out with washers, if necessary. The parting tool is held in a regular toolholder, and set to move freely in and out of the broached hole in the supporting piece. In this manner the tool is well supported from the beginning of the cut, eliminating all chattering and digging in, and cutting a clean, smooth groove clear through.

Drop Lamp Adjusted with Tape Measure

In a workshop where it was necessary to adjust the height of an electric drop lamp over the bench frequently, a simple and novel arrangement was employed that may recommend itself to home mechanics. When extended to full length the cord of the lamp was long enough to lower the lamp to the best position for close work. To adjust it instantly to a higher position an automatic spring - winding tape measure was attached as illustrated. A hook

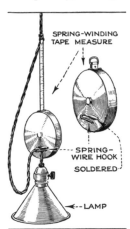

SPRING-WINDING TAPE MEASURE
SPRING-WIRE HOOK SOLDERED
LAMP

made of spring wire was soldered onto the outside of the drum inclosing the tape so that it could be attached to the lamp cord just above the lamp itself. The tape was then drawn out and the end attached by means of soft-iron wire to the lamp cord near the ceiling. To raise or lower the lamp with this arrangement it was only necessary to press the button of the tape measure, and release it when the lamp was at the desired height.—G. E. Hendrickson, Argyle, Wis.

¶To find a hidden rivet in a cast-iron handle apply some muriatic acid on the handle. This will cause the rivet to turn brown so that it can be plainly seen and driven out.

MECHANICAL POWERS

By CARL W. MITMAN
Curator

DIVISIONS OF MINERAL AND
MECHANICAL TECHNOLOGY
UNITED STATES NATIONAL
MUSEUM

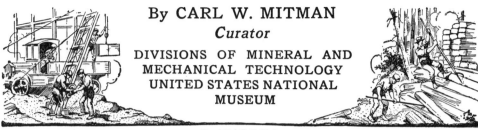

Copyrighted, H. H. Windsor

Part III—Friction: Wheel and Axle

THE discussion in the preceding chapter did not take into consideration any of the resistances met with in all machines. The chief one of these is friction. It was deliberately left out of the discussion, for the reason that its effect is realized under so many and variable conditions that were it considered in with the application of the principle of moments, for instance, no formula that could be applied to all cases could be arrived at. Furthermore, friction exerts such an important influence on the practical working of machines that theory is not of much actual use.

Mechanically speaking, friction is the enemy of efficiency. On the other hand, without friction it would be equally impossible to make or use machines, for nothing could be screwed or nailed or tied together or grasped securely in the hand, so that the ad-

and the degree of lubrication. To illustrate: To move a block of stone weighing 1,080 pounds over a rock surface required a force of 758 pounds; when placed on a wooden sled, it was drawn on a wooden floor by a force of 606 pounds; when both surfaces were greased a pull of 182 pounds was sufficient; and when mounted on wooden rollers, 3 inches in diameter, a pull of 28 pounds was all that was required to move it. Friction during the movement of surfaces in contact is:

Proportional to the pressure exerted upon the sliding surfaces; independent of the extent of the surfaces in contact; independent of the speed of movement; greater between like than between unlike materials; greatest between rough surfaces, and greater with soft than with hard materials. Also that friction at starting is: Propor-

Photo No. 1, Finished Model of Spanish Windlass; No. 2, Differential Hoist, and No. 3, Model of Capstan

vantages arising from friction are vastly greater than the loss of power that it occasions. Friction is the resistance to motion which takes place when one body is moved upon another. Two kinds are generally recognized, termed sliding friction and rolling friction; these are quite distinct in themselves and vary with conditions, especially with the composition of the two bodies, the conditions of loading,

tional to the pressure; independent of the extent of the surfaces, and generally decreased by polishing the surfaces.

Friction at starting and during movement is the same when the sliding surfaces are hard, but if they are compressible like wood, starting friction is much greater.

Rolling friction is quite distinct in character from sliding and very much less in amount. Investigation has shown, for instance, that the relationship of friction to pressure of wood sliding on wood is as 36 to 100, whereas the rolling friction in the same case

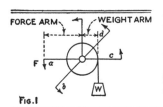

is as 6 to 1,000. That is to say, it is 36 per cent of the pressure in the former case, while in the latter the percentage is only .6. As said before, friction between machine parts lowers the efficiency, that is, the ratio of the power it is possible to take out of the machine and that put into it. In this connection, therefore, the following average values of efficiency in per cent are of interest: Ordinary bearings, 95 to 98; roller bearings, 98; ball bearings, 99; spur gears with cast teeth, 93; spur gears with cut teeth, 96; belting, 96 to 98; silent power transmission chain, 97 to 99; roller chains, 95 to 97.

Diagram Illustrating Action of Wheel and Axle: Below, Example of Its Use

The Wheel and Axle

As a machine, the simple lever has its limitations, especially in raising weights,

SPANISH WINDLASS

for after the weight has been raised it must be supported in its new position until the lever and its fulcrum can be again adjusted to repeat its action. To avoid this defect, engineers early decided that the fulcrum must be stationary and the lever must be made to revolve about it. The result is a machine or mechanical power known as the wheel and axle, in which the center of the axle corresponds to the fulcrum of the lever, the radius of the axle corresponds

to the short arm of the lever, and the radius of the wheel corresponds to the long arm of the lever. To do work power is applied to the wheel rim and the weight is attached to a rope wound around the axle in the opposite direction. There are a great many applications of this mechanical power, altered more or less to suit a variety of conditions. For instance, instead of using a whole wheel, one or more spokes only are inserted in the axle or attached to it in some other fashion, the machine that results being the common, everyday windlass used in digging wells, raising water, in mine prospecting, in small derricks, and for numerous other purposes. Although the wheel and axle is a development of the simple lever, its action is not at all times that of a single type of lever, for at some points in a complete revolution of the wheel the action is that of a straight lever, while at other points it is that of an angular lever. This fact is made apparent in Figure 1, where there is represented in section a horizontal axle to which a single spoke of the wheel is attached. When the spoke or long arm of the lever is in position a, the work done compares with that done by a straight lever of the first order. The instant the spoke moves

Left, Capstan as Used on Shipboard; Right, Modern Motor-Driven Car Mover

away from this position, the action of the machine is that of an angular lever or bell crank, as shown at position b, yielding less mechanical advantage than at a. By the time the spoke has made one-half a complete revolution the action has become that of a straight lever of the second order, as seen in position c, and with the least mechanical advantage. After passing this point, angular-lever action again comes into play, as at d and e, with an increase in mechanical advantage that reaches its greatest value again at position a.

An interesting modification of the wheel and axle is that shown in Figure 3, which is a reproduction of a model of the so-called Spanish windlass. This machine was devised primarily for use aboard ship for tightening rigging, and is therefore defined as "a wooden roller turned by a rope with a rolling hitch, and a handspike in the bight." It will be observed that this nautical definition fully describes the model illustrated. Off ship the device is used to a certain extent on overtruck frames for suspending loads, and also for lifting heavy building materials for transportation. The similarity of its action to that of the common windlass is so apparent that further discussion is believed to be unnecessary.

Placing a windlass on end, that is, fixing the axis of the axle in an upright position, results in a machine known as a capstan. This machine likewise had its origin on board ship, as illustrated by the model reproduced in Figure 4. The coming of the steam windlass has, however, brought about the abandonment of the capstan for weighing anchor. In proportion to the men employed, the windlass is more powerful than the capstan, for a man can exert a force of about 150 pounds on a windlass spoke, but only about 35 pounds on a capstan bar. A greater number of men, however, can be used about a capstan, nor do the bars have to be disengaged as the machine revolves. To prevent backlash, a simple ratchet and pawl are attached.

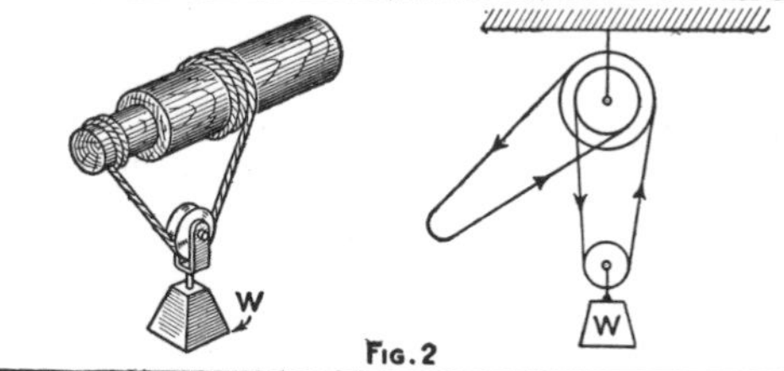

Fig. 2

Above, Diagram of Principle of Differential Hoist; Below, Example of Use of Hoist

Capstans were used by the ancient Romans in transporting the Egyptian obelisks, and by the English, French and Spanish on ships of the fifteenth century, and up to the end of the nineteenth. Today they may be seen in use in heavy haulage such as moving buildings intact, operated either by man or animal power, and, motor-driven, for moving freight cars.

Another useful application of the wheel and axle is that shown in Figures 2 and 5, the latter being a model of the Chinese windlass. This machine is also called a differential windlass. It consists of an axle of two diameters, the rope winding off one part of the axle and onto the other, and the amount of lift being governed by the difference in the diameters

of the two portions of the axle. The combination of forces secured by this device gives extraordinary power, and at the same time the power is obtained without making the axle so small as to be too weak for its work. The use of a single pulley permits ease of attaching the load but does not increase the power. In use, the pulley and load are raised a distance equal to one-half the difference in the circumference of the two parts of the axle for each turn of the crank. If the rope is wound on to the larger drum and off the smaller, the load is raised; if the reverse, it is lowered. The effect is to make the weight arm of the lever very short, without the disadvantage of a weak axle, as mentioned above. Based upon this principle, Thomas A. Weston invented the differential hoist or chain block in 1854, substituting an endless chain for the windlass rope and iron sheaves for the wooden drum. The endless chain passes over a double sheave, as shown in the diagram, Figure 2, and around a single sheave beneath it having a hook to which the load is attached. The double sheave has two chain grooves, the diameter of one being somewhat greater than the other. Because of this variation a greater length of chain will pass over the larger groove at each revolution than over the smaller one, so that when pulling downward on that side of the chain which is on the larger sheave, this loop will be lengthened, but the loop around the lower or single sheave will be shortened and thus raise the load. By pulling downward on the side of the chain which leads to the smaller sheave the load is lowered.

For the model of the Spanish windlass, the following material is required:

Base, 8" x 4" x ¾".
Two pillars, 4" x 1" x ¾".
Two arms, 3" x ¾" x ½".
Beam, 9" x 1" diameter.
Lever, 4½" x ½" square.
Weight, base 1¾", top 1¼", side 1½".

Square and face the base with a finish bevel

on top. Bevel the pillars on four sides, ⅜ in. from the ends, and, on the center line of the base, erect the pillars and secure

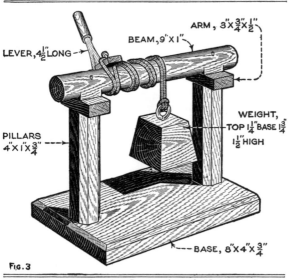

ARM, 3"X¾"X½"
BEAM, 9"X1"
LEVER, 4½"LONG
PILLARS 4"X1"X¾"
WEIGHT, TOP 1¼"BASE 1¾" 1½"HIGH
BASE, 8"X4"X¾"

Fig. 3

Detailed Drawing for the Construction of Model of Spanish Windlass

them with glue and screws from beneath. On top of the pillars secure the arms with screws and glue, forming a T. To the screweye, used as a handle for the weight, attach a loop of cord. Lay the beam across the arms and wind the loop about the beam. The lever is fashioned with a handle and a shank with a slight offset near the end forming the heel. Place the toe of the lever in the extremity of the loop. Finish as desired.

In constructing the capstan model any suitable form of base may be used, it being necessary, however, that it be large enough to provide ample bearing surface for the axle of the capstan. In the original model, the capstan was mounted on the bow of a model ship as in actual practice, but a flat base will serve equally well for illustration. The materials given below are required:

Base, 4" x 3" x ¾".
Coarse hacksaw blade.
Pawl, ½" long.
Six bars, 2" long, 3-16" diameter.
Blank, 3" long, 1½" diameter.

Turn from the blank a narrow-waisted barrel with 1½-in. base, ¾-in. waist, and 1¼-in head, to the shape shown in the drawing. Drill the head with six radial holes, ³⁄₁₆-in. diameter. Attach the capstan to the base, using a No. 12 screw of sufficient length to pass through the base, which is drilled oversize, and well up into the capstan. Anneal the hacksaw blade

and with it form a ring 1⅝-in. inside diameter. Place this over the capstan and secure to the base with fine staples, permitting the capstan to turn within this ring. A pawl is a comma-shaped piece of metal, drilled through the round portion. Secure the half-inch pawl to the base of the capstan at such a distance above the toothed ring that the tail will engage with the teeth, permitting rotation in one direction but stopping it in the other. Insert the capstan bars into the holes at the top. The capstan may exert its pull upon the end or the middle of a rope. The former method is adopted where the amount of rope in use is too great to be wound upon the barrel, in which case the rope extends from the point where the pull is applied, thence several times around the capstan barrel, the extra rope being coiled or stored in a locker. The latter method is used where the amount of rope is not excessive and may be stored upon the barrel. In the former case the rope winds at the waist and slips upward. Finish as desired.

Use the following materials for the Chinese windlass, or differential hoist:

Base, 8½" x 6" x ¾".
Two uprights, 10½" x 1½" x ½".
Two corner blocks, base ⅞", altitude 1¼", width 1½".
Blank to be turned, 2½" diameter, 10" long.
Crank arm, 6" long, ¾" wide, ¼" thick.
Two pulley sides, 2½" long, ½" wide, 3-16" thick.
Weight, base 1¾", top 1¼", side 1½".
Small wire hook, with cross eye, 1½" overall.
Two ½" washers.
Two 1½", 6-32 machine screws, with nuts.
Two dozen washers No. 6.

Square and face the base with a finish bevel

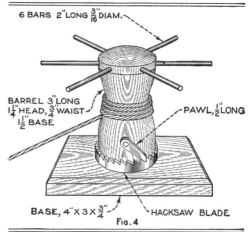

6 BARS 2"LONG ³⁄₁₆"DIAM.
BARREL 3"LONG 1¼"HEAD, ¾"WAIST 1½"BASE
PAWL, ½"LONG
BASE, 4"X3X¾"
HACKSAW BLADE
Fig. 4

Working Drawing for Model Capstan, with All Dimensions

on top. The differential axle, the pulley and the crank handle are turned from the blank to the dimensions shown in the drawing. The uprights are drilled with ½-in. holes, with the centers of the holes ¾ in. from the ends and from each side. The uprights are then placed on opposite ends of the differential axle, with the ½-in. washers between the axle faces and the uprights. This assembly is secured to the base by screws from beneath and by gluing the uprights on the center line of the base one and one-quarter inches from each end. The corner blocks are placed outside of the uprights to strengthen their position, and are fastened with glue and small brads. Holes are drilled in each end of the pulley sides. The pulley assembly is built up with a machine screw passing through the sides of the pulley, washers being used between the pulley face and the pulley sides. The hook is fastened to the lower ends of the pulley sides by inserting a machine screw through the holes in the pulley sides and the eye of the hook, retaining it in the center by washers. These machine screws are retained in position by nuts. Connect this pulley assembly to the differential by a cord passing through the pulley and wind over the drums of the axle in opposite directions, each end being fastened. Place the screweye used as the handle of the weight on the hook. To one end of the crank arm attach the handle by screwing through the arm into the handle. The other end is fastened to the projection of the axle by any secure method. Finish as desired.

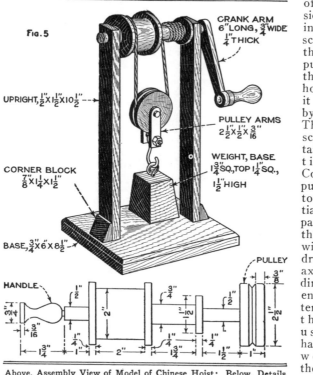

CRANK ARM 6"LONG, ¾"WIDE ¼"THICK

UPRIGHT,½"X1½"X10½"

PULLEY ARMS 2½"X½"X³⁄₁₆"

WEIGHT, BASE 1¾"SQ.,TOP 1¼"SQ., 1½"HIGH

CORNER BLOCK ⅞"X1¼"X1½"

BASE,¾"X6X8½"

PULLEY

HANDLE

FIG. 5

Above, Assembly View of Model of Chinese Hoist; Below, Details of Barrel, Pulley, and Crank Handle

This is the third article of a series by Curator Mitman, explaining in simple language what every man who builds or designs a machine must know, and showing in detail just how to build a set of models of the mechanical powers that will exactly duplicate the set in the National Museum at Washington, D. C. The first articles of the series appeared in the March and April issues, and the next will appear in the June number.

Keeping Dairy Barns Sanitary

There is no excuse for permitting the accumulation of manure in and around barns, especially dairy barns. The labor and time spent in keeping the barns clean are rewarded by a more sanitary condition, which insures better milk and offsets the danger of originating contagious diseases directly traceable to barnyard filth. An excellent practice, which is followed by many farmers, is to sprinkle hydrated lime over the floor every day. This not only tends to keep the stanchions dry, as the lime absorbs moisture, but also prevents undesirable odors and combats bacteria. Moreover, as the lime is removed with the manure it is spread out over the land where it is highly valuable as a soil fertilizer. If it is impossible to clean the barn thoroughly every day the bulk of the manure should be removed outdoors to a manure pile located at least 50 ft. from the barn.

Whitewashing walls and ceilings is also a step toward sanitation. This should be done not less than twice a year.

Double "Shank" for Handling Crucibles

Handling crucibles and ladles in the foundry is made much easier by using the double "shank" shown in the illustration.

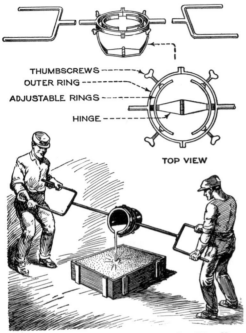

THUMBSCREWS
OUTER RING
ADJUSTABLE RINGS
HINGE

TOP VIEW

Double "Shank" for Carrying Heavy Crucibles Has Been Found Convenient in Foundry

It is made of steel rod, of a suitable diameter to bear the weight of the crucible. Each separate shank is forged to one of two semicircular steel rings, which are held together by means of a heavy hinge, as shown in the upper detail, so that they can be opened to grip the crucible. The outer rings are drilled and tapped for four thumbscrews, holding two adjustable inner rings, which are screwed up against the sides of the crucible to hold it firmly and prevent it from upsetting while pouring. When adjusted to any size pot, the latter is gripped or released instantly by raising or lowering the handles.—J. R. Master, San Quentin, Calif.

Cementing Celluloid

An excellent method of cementing celluloid battery jars or other articles is to use glacial acetic acid. The surface to be mended must first be made perfectly clean by scraping lightly with a penknife, and the acetic acid applied with a fountain-pen filler. It is allowed to stand for a few minutes and then the two parts are pressed firmly together, being left under pressure for 4 or 5 minutes. In this way patches have been applied to the bottom of the battery jars while they were being charged. —G. E. Jones, Mussoorie, India.

Novel Hook Hangs Metal Sheets

In a concern where sheet-metal covers are used on a bench operation it is necessary to clean and repaint the covers on both sides frequently. The most convenient method of holding the covers while the paint is drying is to hang them up on the wall on the hooks shown in the photo, which were especially devised for this purpose. To hang up a cover the hook is first passed through the hole in the top, and the other end is slipped into a screweye driven into the wall. The weight of the cover causes the end of the hook to press against it, thereby forcing the

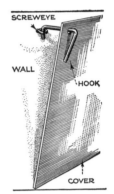

SCREWEYE

WALL

HOOK

COVER

bottom tightly against the wall. Before hooks of this kind were used, the covers were loosely hung up clear of the wall and consequently any draft of air through the room caused them to swing about and become marked, but since the hooks were used this trouble has been stopped.

Quick Method of Tightening Wire Fence

It often happens that fence wire stretches considerably and sags, due to various reasons. A quick and effective method of tightening the wire consists merely of drawing up the wire on a post by doubling it and then nailing it down securely by means of a staple, as indicated at point A of the illustration. Another method is to make a number of sharp bends in the wire by means of a short length of wood having two nails driven through the end.

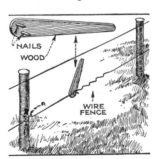

NAILS
WOOD
WIRE FENCE

Pipe-Cleaning Tool

In cleaning an underground pipe, the regular jointed-wooden sticks that are made especially for this kind of work were not at all satisfactory. The work was, however, quickly accomplished by means of a length of telephone-post guy wire, which was stranded and somewhat flexible. A ball of solder about 1½ in. in diameter was wiped on the end and this end then pushed through the clogged pipe, with the result that the obstructions were easily dislodged. The guy wire was stiff enough to be pushed forcibly against the obstruction and still flexible enough to go around quite a bend, although it could not pass an elbow. It works best in 4 and 6-in. tile pipe.—A. S. Jamieson, Springfield, Mass.

Hand-Operated Chamfering Fixture

It is sometimes possible to do a job much more quickly by hand than by machine, in cases where a small amount of metal is to be removed. This is clearly illustrated by the device shown in the drawing, which was

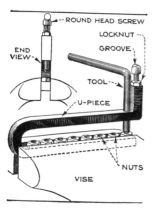

made to chamfer or remove the sharp edge on the back side of brass nuts after they are cut off by machine. A length of square - steel rod is bent to U-shape, and one end bent up at right angles. This part is drilled and tapped in the end for a special round-head screw with a groove filed on the top. The chamfering tool is made of tool steel, fluted on one end and bent at right angles to form a handle. This passes through a hole in the U-piece. The whole fixture is gripped in the vise and operated in the following way: As many nuts as possible are placed in the slot formed by the vise jaws and the U-piece, and the nuts fed under the tool. One revolution of the tool is sufficient to chamfer a nut. The purpose of the round-head screw is to hold the tool clear of the nuts at the end of each revolution. This is done semi-automatically as the handle rides easily up the screw head, and with the tool out of the way, the next nut is pushed beneath it.

Creeper with Adjustable Feet

Although a creeper is an indispensable piece of garage equipment, many auto mechanics prefer a piece of old carpet or

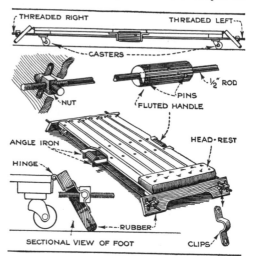

Auto Mechanics' Creeper Provided with Rubber-Tipped Feet that Can Be Let Down to Make It Immovable

robe, as this gives a much more steady support to lie on while pulling nuts tight; it allows them to pull hard without the danger of slipping and injuring themselves.

A creeper that has the advantageous features of a robe in this respect, and still can be pushed around on casters is shown in the drawing. It is provided with four rubber-tipped feet, which are hinged on the ends and can be lowered or raised by means of two ½-in. iron rods, passing through them as shown, a fluted handle being provided on each rod to turn it. The ends of the rods are threaded right and left for nuts pivoted on the feet, and the feet are drilled to fit loosely on the ends of the rods. Turning the rods thus raises or lowers the feet.

Ordinary casters are provided at the four corners, allowing the creeper to be rolled into any desired position. When it is necessary to tighten nuts or do similar work requiring a steady support, the feet are simply drawn down to the floor and the creeper becomes immovable.

❡Denatured alcohol, squirted into the cylinders through the spark-plug holes at night, when the engine is warm, will loosen up the carbon deposits, and the carbon will be blown out of the exhaust when the engine is run the next morning. On starting, the engine should be raced a few times with the spark retarded.

Making a Hydraulic Ram

By L. B. ROBBINS

WHERE there is a natural fall of water a hydraulic ram is an ideal means of elevating water to a storage tank some distance away. The hydraulic ram is a self-acting pump which utilizes the momentum or energy of a slight fall of water to force a part of the water to a height many times that of the fall. The simplicity, durability, and effectiveness of this device make it one of the most useful as well as the most economical of the machines used for pumping water to elevated points. Its main advantage is that its operation necessitates no labor or expense, as, once started, it continues to pump day and night without attention, as long as the supply of water is sufficient.

The principle of operation of the ram may be understood from a study of Fig. 1. It consists simply of an air chamber or dome, fitted at its bottom with a valve opening upward, and connected, below the valve, to the supply or drive pipe leading from the river, pond, or other source from which the water supply is obtained. The continuation of the drive pipe is closed at the end, but a side outlet is provided, which is fitted with a check valve opening inward. The water flows down through the supply pipe, and out through the check valve until the velocity, or constantly increasing pressure, closes the latter. This, of course, stops the stream suddenly, and the shock caused by this sudden stoppage forces the dome valve open, this being the only other outlet. Through this valve, some of the water passes into the dome and delivery pipe. When sufficient water has passed into the chamber to relieve the pressure, the dome valve closes, the outlet check valve opens, and the cycle of operations is repeated. The air in the dome acts as a cushion, absorbing the shocks, and keeping up a steady, even flow through the delivery pipe.

It is obvious that a portion of the water is wasted to operate the ram, through the outlet valve, but, as this water is obtained at no cost, and no attention is required, the low efficiency of the ram may be ignored.

Such a ram can be made by the handy man from pipe fittings. The one illustrated in the drawing is designed to deliver only a maximum of one quart of water a minute, but, considering the fact that it works 24 hours a day, that is quite sufficient to store a considerable supply against the drain by an ordinary household. In other words, one quart a minute means 360 gal. in 24 hours. This is approximate, of course. As a ram delivers about one-seventh of its supply this one will require about 2 gal. of water a minute; a quantity which should be found in the smallest stream. It will elevate about 7 ft. for every foot of fall from the head of supply to the ram, but a fall of less than 2 ft. will not operate it.

By consulting the drawings the construction will be found quite simple. The air dome consists of an 8-in. piece of 6-in. pipe, capped at each end. The top is tapped and furnished with a plug for cleanout purposes, while the bottom cap is tapped for 1¼-in. thread. A 1¼-in. close nipple is threaded into this hole, then a 1¼-in tee with a ¾-in. side opening. The bottom of the tee is then fitted with a 1¼-in. close nipple, fitting into a 1¼ by 2-in. bushing.

The supply valve is composed of two 2-in. pipe flanges bolted together on each side of a circular leather valve similar to a pump-deck valve. This is shown in Fig. 3. The leather should be arranged to lift up and admit water to the dome but close tightly by the pressure from above when the flow relaxes and also by addition of a small weight attached to the flap as indicated. Thread the top flange into the bushing above and then fit a close 2-in. nipple into the bottom flange. It is best to force a ring into the upper end of the lower flange, to form a seat for the valve to rest on, if the 2-in. nipple does not come up flush with the flange. In any event, the ring will form the better seat.

The supply line consists of the following from right to left: One 1¼-in. 45° elbow and a 1¼-in. tee with 2-in side opening, connected by a 1¼-in. close nipple. A long 1¼-in. nipple connects the opposite end of the tee to a second 1¼-in. tee with a ¾-in. side opening. This second tee is then closed with a 1¼-in. close nipple and cap. Arrange the side openings in each tee in exact line and also in line with the 45° elbow. Thread the 2-in. nipple into the large tee and a ¾-in. elbow fitted with two close ¾-in. nipples, into the opening of the smaller tee. Point the elbow toward the cap.

If a ¾-in. safety valve is available it wall save some work, but if not, then a common ¾-in. horizontal check valve will suffice. Arrange the valve so that the gate closes toward the pipe end. The make and type of the check valve determine its installation. It may be found necessary to install it tilted, so that the valve will hang open until the pressure builds up sufficiently to close it, or it may be found necessary to fit a spring to it to aid it in closing, or in staying open. Fig. 3, which shows how the spring may be fitted so as to be adjustable, is not to be taken literally, but only to illustrate the attachment of the spring, should this be necessary. The type of valve shown would not need a spring, in fact, it might be necessary to tilt the valve to make it stay open.

Mount the completed ram on two heavy timbers set at the tall. This latter can consist of a slight rapids, waterfall, flume or

sations should be steady and constant. To start the ram, all that is necessary is to press inward on the check valve to open it, then permit it to close. After repeating this a few times, the ram should start operating automatically; if it does not, the fault is most likely in the check valve, and various adjustments should be tried, increasing or decreasing the spring tension, or the angle of valve tilt, until it does start. Should the ram become water-bound, it may be found necessary to drill a very fine hole through the 2-in nipple, below the

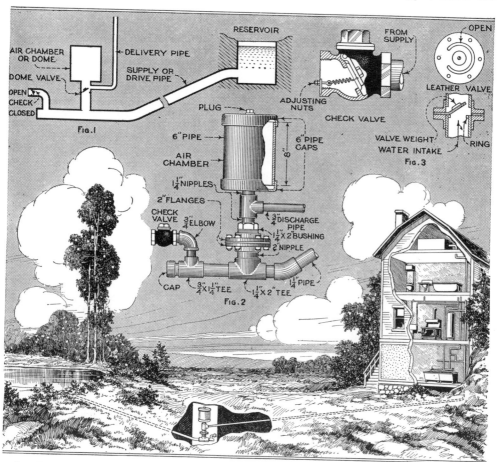

Any Handy Man Can Make this Hydraulic Ram, Which Will Supply the House with Water at All Times without Labor or Expense, and with a Minimum of Maintenance

other means of conveying a quantity of water in a steady flow down a length of 1¼-in. pipe threaded into the 45° elbow. The ram can be secured by metal straps and should rest horizontally and plumb. Use red lead in all the joints, and paint it for security against weathering, if desired. When properly built and installed the pul-

valve, to admit a small quantity of air with each stroke of the ram.

The ram may be housed in a pit, as indicated in the lower illustration, if necessary, to get the proper amount of fall.

A strainer should always be placed in the inlet end of the drive pipe, to prevent the ram from becoming choked with dirt, twigs, etc. It is also a good plan to surround this strainer with large wire netting, to prevent it from being choked also. Wherever possible, turns should be avoided in both drive and discharge pipes, and, where turns must be used, the elbows should be as large as practicable, so that there will be the slightest possible obstruction to the flow of the water.

Paperhanger's Level

In order to do a good job in wallpaper hanging it is necessary to get the first strip hung accurately; hanging the other strips will then be found comparatively easy. The customary method of doing this is to set a straightedge such as a trimmer up against the wall, level it with an ordinary carpenter's spirit level, and run a pencil mark on the wall along the straightedge. This necessitates carrying a large level around constantly just for this purpose, which means additional bulk and weight in the worker's grip, and is therefore not desirable. A much more convenient level, due to its small size and adaptability on the standard Ridgeway trimmer, is shown in the illustration.

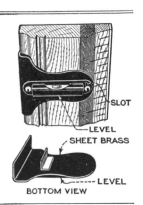

Such a level can easily be made by anyone who is mechanically inclined or it will cost only a few cents to have one made by a local tinsmith. The level consists of a small plate to which a spiri-level vial is attached. The plate is made of $\frac{1}{32}$-in. sheet metal such as brass or copper, with one edge bent over at right angles and a short angle piece soldered onto the back as shown. It can then be clipped solidly in the groove and over the edge of the trimmer. Another piece of copper is bent to a cylindrical shape to hold the vial; this piece is soldered to a narrow strip, which, in turn, is riveted to the plate as indicated. The vial, which can be obtained at any hardware store, is cemented in the cylindrical sleeve with plaster of paris; this holds the vial securely and also provides a white background against which the marks on the glass and the air bubble inside can

clearly be seen. The strip on which the vial is mounted is not riveted tightly to the plate, but one rivet is passed through a small slot cut in the strip as shown, so that the level can be set accurately. The method of setting the level correctly is as follows: Clamp it on the trimmer and set the trimmer up vertically against the wall, using a regular spirit level to get it plumb; then if the small level does not read according to the other level, the strip is tapped lightly up or down as necessary.

Etching Steel

One disadvantage of using nitric acid for etching steel is that the gas given off "lifts" the wax or other ground, causing very ragged edges on the lettering, if not making it unreadable. Another is that the fumes will rust near-by tools. These faults are not found in an etching solution of copper sulphate and common salt, made with equal quantities of fully saturated strength, and the solution is just as satisfactory as the acid.

Keeping Drawings Clean

An improved method of keeping a drawing from becoming soiled by the shifting of a long T-square, is shown in the drawing.

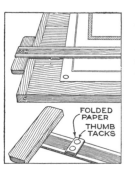

Fold a sheet of paper a number of times to form a pad about $\frac{1}{8}$-in. thick, and fasten it to the underside of the T-square, about 4 in. from the head, with two thumbtacks. When the draftsman places his hand on the head to shift the T-square, the weight of the hand will raise the straightedge from the paper; when the weight on the head is removed the blade drops down again.—Frank Harazim, New York City.

Preventing Decay of Fence Posts

A cheap, simple and effective method of preserving the ends of fence posts against decay is to char them. The ends are heated in a fire until the surface is well burnt and they are then immersed in water, with the result that a layer of charcoal about ½ in. thick is formed all over the surface. Charcoal is a form of carbon and, as carbon does not combine readily with other elements, it is very resistant to decay, protecting the wood underneath for a long time. Creosoting fence posts is, of course, an excellent method of preserving them, but is expensive and somewhat inconvenient, while charring the ends as described above can be accomplished anywhere and at any time, at practically no cost; it is only necessary to build a fire and have some water handy.

Gauge for Setting Boring-Bar Cutters

When using the boring bar, either on a horizontal boring machine or a lathe, it is often necessary to change cutters for different sizes of bores and counterbores, and much time is usually lost in trying to reset tools to just the right radius. Measuring the distance with a scale is slow and not very convenient. A handy little tool that has been found very satisfactory for resetting is shown in the illustration. The base of the tool is a 120° V-block, on top of which is mounted a plate that extends over one end of the block. A hole is drilled and tapped in line with the vee, and a screw is fitted, as shown, with a locknut. The bottom of the screw is perfectly straight and smooth and acts like a spindle of a micrometer on the straight face. Before removing a tool, which has sized a hole to its correct diameter, register the setting with the gauge by bringing the screw down so as barely to touch the highest part of the tool's cutting edge, and then lock the setting with the nut. Swing the screw point over the tool so that its center engages with the cutting edge as indicated. The tool can be made double-ended so that it can be used on two cutters.

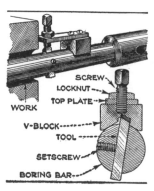

Increasing Capacity of Small Wagon

Loads of merchandise, which are light in weight but large and bulky in size, can easily be carried on small wagons by pro-

Side Supports on Small Wagon Increase Its Capacity for Holding Bulky Loads

viding two side supports of the kind shown in the drawing. The supports are made by nailing a 10-in. board to two lengths of 2 or 3 by 4-in. wood, as shown in the upper right-hand detail, and the supports are then arranged on the wagon box, as shown in the left-hand view, with the 2 by 4-in. legs crossing each other. The legs should be bolted together to keep the supports in position securely, so that heavy loads will not displace them. Large loads of hay and straw, and shocks of wheat, oats, etc., can readily be carried with the assistance of such a rack, and, as it is light in weight, it can be set up by one man.

Flume Lining

In order to reduce the water losses in a flume as much as possible we lined it with heavy roofing paper, sometimes called "rubber roofing." The joints of the lining were made waterproof by overlapping them about 3 ft. in the direction of flow. The weight of the water seals the joints and holds the paper securely in place and, therefore, it does not have to be nailed down. The inside of the flume should be fairly smooth, as pronounced projections will puncture the lining. A lining made of this material will last for several seasons if rolled up and protected during the winter.
—Robert T. Pound, Lavina, Mont.

A Spruce-Limb Humidity Indicator

The photograph shows a spruce limb which is so sensitive to moisture changes that it might almost serve to indicate the humidity in the room where it is located. This limb is fastened to a door of the wood identification office of the U. S. Forest Products Laboratory at Madison, Wis. During the months when artificial heat is used the limb bends over to the left, and during the warmer months when the windows are kept

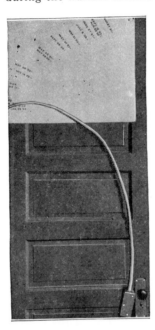

open it straightens and extends nearly vertically. In the course of its gradual changes the tip moves through a distance of 30 in., describing an arc of about 80°. The dates along the arc show its position at different times for several years. The interesting action of this limb cannot be traced to any freak condition of growth, but rather to the normal presence of what is known as "compression wood" along the underside of the limb, and on the lower side of the leaning trunks of all coniferous trees. Situated as it is, this wood must act as a sort of prop or stiffening for the trunk or limb, and as a result it differs somewhat from the rest of the wood of the tree. It is the action of this kind of wood that causes the standing limbs of dead trees to curve downward during long periods of dry weather. It is harder than most wood, but the remarkable difference is that it shows considerable shrinking and swelling along its length with loss or gain of moisture, whereas normal wood shows almost no change in length.

In the case of the limb shown in the photo, the compression wood shrinks and pulls it over to the position shown, when the air about it dries out, as when artificial heat is used. In the spring and summer when the windows are kept open the compression wood swells and this causes the limb to straighten out. Timbers or dimension stock that have been cut to include compression wood are very apt to bend excessively in seasoning and become worthless except as fuel. When they are weighted down in the pile so that bending cannot take place, enough tension is sometimes produced longitudinally to cause the wood to pull apart and show breaks or cracks across the grain—Forest Products Laboratory, Madison, Wis.

Improving T-Squares and Triangles

The edges of T-squares and triangles are always made vertical, and this makes it necessary for the draftsman to keep the side of the pen away from the lower edge to avoid getting the ink underneath it and smearing the work. A simple method of preventing this is to trim the edges of the triangles to a blunt V-shape. T-squares can also be improved considerably by gluing a strip of blotting paper or heavy drawing paper to the underside; this strip must be narrower than the width of the blade.

Tool Stand with Movable Holes

A tool stand of the kind shown in the drawing is especially useful around a drill press doing repetition work. It holds all the tools required on a job in a convenient manner and in the order in which they are used. Commonly a flat piece of wood is used for this purpose with a row of holes of various sizes, drilled to hold the tools, but this is in most cases rather clumsy because the holes being fixed cannot be adapted to suit the requirements of different jobs. The adjustable stand illustrated is made of wood and a piece of sheet metal. Two side pieces of wood are fastened with screws to a bottom piece, and a num-

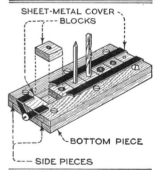

ber of square blocks, drilled in the center with different-sized holes, are fitted between the side pieces. The blocks, when in place, are equal to the length of the stand, and are held in place by the sheet-metal cover, which is fastened to the wood by screws at each end.

Shop Notes

A Drinking Fountain for Small Stock

By L. R. BUTCHER

IT is a well-known fact that swine make faster gains and are much healthier if fresh water is available at all times. However, some farmers dislike to buy the number of watering devices necessary to install one in each feed lot. This should keep no farmer from using them, for, in odd moments or on rainy days, he can make watering devices that serve every need just as well as the manufactured ones. They can be made in the farm shop at little cost.

The completed fountain, as shown in the illustrations, is connected directly to the farm watering system. The lever and float arrangement allows the device to be used on any system of ordinary pressure. Once

installed, the fountain requires no attention save an occasional cleaning. If desired, it is as readily attached to a stock tank or a supply barrel.

The box for the fountain consists of two parts: a drinking compartment and a float

Automatic Fountains for Small Stock May Easily Be Made by the Farmer at Home, and Will Quickly Repay Him for the Time Spent; Insert, Arrangement of Float

chamber. Water flows from the float chamber to the drinking compartment through small holes drilled through the partition. These holes should be about 2 in. above the bottom of the box. Located in this manner, little dirt or trash will find its way from the drinking compartment into the float chamber. The detail drawing gives all general dimensions necessary to make the box; the sides are of 2-in. material, and all other parts of 1-in. stock. The cover is held in place by two buttons—one at each end—such as are used to fasten window screens in place.

The float and lever arrangement is shown in the insert. A bracket is fastened to the inside of the float compartment and forms a pivot point for the lever. One end of the lever carries the float, while the bent end presses against the leather valve placed over the end of the supply pipe. As the float rises, the leather is pressed against the end of the pipe, cutting off the water supply until the water level is lowered. The supply pipe should project through the end of the box about ¹⁄₁₆ in., providing a firm seat for the valve. One-eighth-inch pipe has a large enough opening for the supply, and if the hole for the pipe is bored slightly smaller than the outside diameter of the pipe, the threaded end of the pipe

can be screwed into the wood. A liberal coat of white lead will keep the joint from leaking. The float shown in the photograph is attached almost directly to the lever, but a better arrangement would be to connect the two with a short chain. The water level of the fountain may then be changed by changing the float level, and adjustment may be made for any desired level. The detail drawings require but little explanation. Galvanized metal should, of course, be used for the float; scraps of sheet metal may be used, if large enough. The bracket is cut from a sheet of ⅛-in. metal and bent to shape before drilling. Bending can be done cold, although the work will be easier if the metal is heated. The float lever is made from ⅛ by ½-in. strap iron. Heat will be necessary to make the bend at the pivot point. The quarter-turn is made by clamping the piece in the vise and bending with a heavy pair of tongs. A heavy cotter pin or a stove bolt serves as a pivot. One caution should be observed in installing the fountain—it must be fastened firmly in place. If this is not done, the swine will shove and lift the fountain until leaky joints develop. If very small pigs are to drink from the device, it is well to cover part of the compartment as shown.

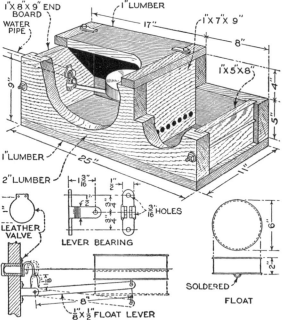

Details and Dimensions of the Automatic Fountain, Showing the Inlet Valve and Float Mechanism

---

Mirrors Useful in Garage

Small mirrors have been found very useful in an automobile repair shop when repairing cars. They are used for reflecting light into such places as the differential. The mirrors can also be used for reflecting light upward when working behind the instrument board. Handles should be provided on the mirrors so that they can be inserted in narrow places.

Melting Metal for Alloys

In making alloys first melt the metal of the highest fusing point, and when this is melted, drop in the other metal, broken into chunks. Cover the surface of the molten metal with salt or other flux, or with charcoal, in order to prevent oxidation. The metals should be stirred well with an iron or graphite rod before pouring from the crucible.

Supporting Long, Slender Work in Lathe

A very efficient method of supporting slender work required to be turned down in a lathe is shown in the drawing. When turning work of this description, if the diameter is small, a center in the end is not of much value unless a number of very light cuts are taken, as the work will spring away from the tool when near the center. When a number of such pieces require to be turned, get a piece of stock large enough to give it strength. Turn one end to fit the tailstock spindle and bore out to the diameter of the stock to be turned. A V-slot is next cut the length of the bore. This slot should be just wide enough to clear the tool at the bottom and allow for the escape of chips at the top. In this manner the work is well supported throughout its length and can be finished in one cut.

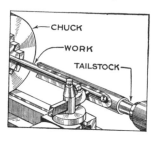

Heating Water with Steam

In many shops no provision is made for hot water for toilet purposes, although the buildings are heated with steam. In such cases, a steam line is often run to a point near the sink, and a hose run from the end of the pipe into the water. This heats the water quickly enough when the steam is turned on, but it is accompanied by an annoying noise, and the steam is apt to burn a careless user. A much neater arrangement is shown in the photo. Here the steam line is connected to the water pipe before the latter enters the sink, and is fitted with a globe valve to control the steam pressure. When the valve is opened full the steam heats the water to the boiling point. It is advisable in an arrangement of this kind, of course, to have the water turned on before opening the steam valve, especially when the steam pressure is low.

Vacuum Cleaner Furnishes Torch Blast

For soldering jobs that require higher temperatures than usual and for light

Hot Brazing Flame Produced by Using Ordinary Gas and Compressed Air from Vacuum Cleaner

brazing work, a mixture of forced air and ordinary cooking gas may be used to produce the desired heat. A compressor was thought to be too expensive in one case, and therefore the method of providing air by means of an old vacuum cleaner, as shown in the drawing, was resorted to and found satisfactory. A small hole was cut in the dust bag and a $\frac{1}{4}$-in. pipe nipple inserted, with washers and nuts on both sides to hold it in place. A length of gas tubing connected the nipple and the brazing nozzle, which was also connected to the gas outlet on the wall. The heat of the flame was varied by properly regulating the air and gas supplies. With some cleaners, an attachment can be had that locks on the outlet of the fan in place of the bag. If an attachment of this kind can be obtained, and the air hose attached to it instead of to the bag, a much neater and better job will result.

Patching Auto Tops

When patching auto tops it is a good plan to place a board across the top bows under the covering to provide a firm surface on which to work. After the patch is applied a weight should be placed on it and left until the cement is dry, so that the patch will not curl up at the edges.

MECHANICAL POWERS

By CARL W. MITMAN
Curator

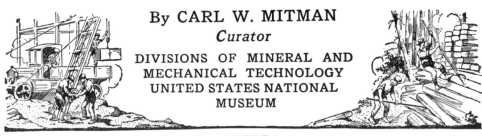

DIVISIONS OF MINERAL AND
MECHANICAL TECHNOLOGY
UNITED STATES NATIONAL
MUSEUM

Copyrighted, H. H. Windsor

This is the fourth article of a series by Curator Mitman, explaining in simple language what every man who builds or designs a machine must know, and showing in detail just how to build a set of models of the mechanical powers that will exactly duplicate the set in the National Museum at Washington, D. C. The first articles of the series appeared in the March, April, and May issues, and the next will appear in the July number.

Part IV—Gravity: Revolving Levers

NO consideration of mechanics would be complete were it to avoid a discussion of that prevalent natural force, gravity. This unseen attractive force exists between the earth and all other bodies and is endeavoring constantly to pull them downward to the earth. The measure of this pull is called weight. For instance, it is commonly stated that a man weighs 150 pounds, which simply means that he is being drawn to the earth by a force equal to that which pulls downward 150 standard 1-lb. weights. This pull is greatest at or near the earth's surface, but decreases with increasing depth beneath the surface, and also with increasing altitude above the surface. Furthermore, it varies for different localities upon the earth's surface, depending upon the distance of each place above or below the equator. This is due to the fact that the diameter of the earth through the north and south poles is 26 miles shorter than the diameter through the equator, in other words, the earth is not a perfect sphere.

Gravity pulls all bodies toward the earth's center, but as each body is made up of many particles, each of which has weight, the gravity of that body acts in the direction of lines (as many as there are particles composing the body) converging and meeting at the earth's center. The

length of these lines, however, in proportion to the dimensions of the body, is so great that they are always assumed to be parallel. Furthermore, by one of the fundamental laws of mechanics, these parallel-acting forces can be compounded into a single force equal to the sum of the weights of the particles composing that body, and whatever may be its position, there is always one point in the body through which this single force will pass; this point is called the center of gravity. It is the point at which the weight of a body is concentrated and thus may be defined as that point about which a body will balance in any position.

The importance of taking into consideration the center of gravity in the design and construction of every machine or other structure has resulted in making available many formulas and directions for finding the center of gravity of lines, areas and solids, and the reader is referred to this literature for the solution of specific problems.

The term revolving lever is not one of common usage to describe any particular type of machine

but is the selection of the writer as a name for a class of mechanical powers which operate on the principle of the wheel and axle, but which are quite distinct in appearance from the commonly accepted form. The distinctive feature of the so-called revolving lever is the axle, which, instead of being elongated as in the several types of windlasses, is short and, in fact, is more like the hub of the wheel than anything else. As an aid to raising heavy loads, a rope is usually attached to the load and to the hub or axle and power is applied to the wheel through another rope which fits into a groove in the wheel. By applying the power to the wheel through a rope rather than directly to the wheel a wider range of positions for the applied force is obtained. For instance, if manual power is used, applied through a rope or chain attached to the wheel, the pull may be directed downward, upward or horizontally, and at any convenient distance from the machine. The principle involved is, of course, one of the lever arms, and as in straight levers, three classes or orders of revolving levers are recognized, depend-

ing upon the relative positions of the fulcrum, applied force and resisting force. As in the case of the wheel and axle, the center of the revolving lever corresponds to the fulcrum, the wheel to the long arm and the hub or axle to the short arm of the simple lever. A revolving lever of the first order is shown in Fig. 1, reproduced from a model. The applied force acts downward, as does the resisting force, but the two forces are on opposite sides of the fulcrum. The mechanical advantage gained in this machine is the same as in a straight lever of the same order with the added advantage that the action is continuous. By reversing the direction of winding of the rope on the wheel, the applied force will be in an upward direction, as shown in Fig. 2. By this arrangement, however, the action becomes that of a second-order lever, having both applied and resisting forces on the same side of the fulcrum but with the same mechanical advantage. Still another arrangement that can be made is that shown in Fig. 3, illustrating a revolving lever of the third order.

More power is required to raise a given load than with the first or second-order forms, but if speed of raising the load is of first importance, this arrangement will bring about the desired result. In all the various types of lever actions discussed so

Model of Revolving-Lever Train

far in this series, the principle of moments has been considered, and it is undoubtedly realized that the relative lengths of the two arms of each lever influence the work which can be done. So, in the case of revolving levers, their efficiency can be augmented by diminishing the diameter of the hub or by increasing the diameter of the wheel. But the amount of increase in efficiency of a single machine is limited, for, if a very great power is required, either the hub would become too small to support the weight or the wheel would have to be made inconveniently large. For a case such as this a combination of revolving levers may be used, resulting in a system of machines which corresponds to the compound lever and which is governed by the same law.

A system such as this is illustrated in Fig. 4. The pull exerted on the first wheel transmits its effect to the axle or hub of that wheel, this acts by friction on the second wheel, which transfers the effect to the second hub, and so on, until the original applied force transmitted through the series in this order arrives at the last hub where the resisting force is encountered. According to the principle of moments, the applied force in this machine multiplied by the continued product of the radii of all the wheels, is equal to the resisting force

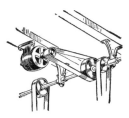

multiplied by the continued product of the radii of the hubs. In actual practice compound revolving levers are extensively used but not exactly with the transmission form described above. Instead, for some purposes, both the wheels and hubs are toothed, and for others they are connected by belts. When so arranged, the series is called a train; a wheel which imparts motion is called a driver and one which receives motion, a driven wheel. Where the toothed-wheel arrangement is met with, calculations as to size of wheels, necessary applied force, etc., are figured by using the number of teeth in the wheels, since these are proportional to the circumference and also the radii of the wheels, and the principle of moments is stated thus: The applied force multiplied by the product of the number of teeth of all the wheels, is equal to the resisting force multiplied by the product of the number of teeth in all the hubs or pinions.

In the discussion of the single revolving levers, the fact was brought out that with one order of lever speed could be obtained by sacrificing power and with another order great loads could be moved with a small force. Similarly wheel trains are employed either to do heavy work with

Fig. 4. In the second case, this arrangement is reversed; the available force is applied or exerts itself on the hub or pinion of the first wheel and thus produces the rapid revolution of the last wheel. Cranes of all kinds for hoisting materials do their work by a wheel train of the first kind, and the wheel train of a watch is an example of the second arrangement.

For a model of a revolving lever of the first order, the following materials are required:

Base, 10-in. x 4½-in. x ¾-in.
Pillar, 8½-in. x ¾-in., 4½-in. at widest end.
Round blank, 6-in. diameter, 1½-in. thick.
Weight (resisting force), base 1¾-in. square, top 1¼-in. square, side 1½-in. high.
Arrow (applied force), 1¼-in. long, ¼-in. thick, ½-in. wide across barbs, ¼-in. square shaft.

Square and face the base with a finish bevel on top. Construct the pillar with concave shoulders 1½ in. from the bottom. Narrow the upright shaft to 1½ in. wide. Turn from the blank (using a faceplate) concentric double pulleys, with V-grooves, of ¾-in. thickness and 6 and 3-in. diameters, drilling in the center for a pivot screw. Attach by the pivot screw to the

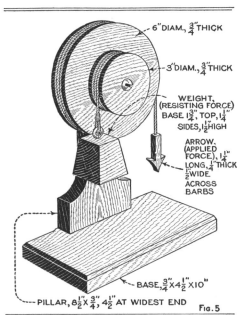

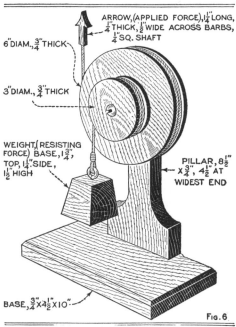

Left, Details of the Construction of a Model of a Revolving Lever of the First Order, with all Dimensions; Right, Working Drawing of Model of Second-Order Lever

little force or to produce great speed with considerable force. In the first case, the available force is applied to the first wheel of the series and is transmitted in the manner described earlier in connection with

top of the pillar. Secure one end of a piece of cord, about 6 ft. long, to the groove of the 6-in. pulley, winding the cord clockwise about the rim and permitting the free end to swing from the right side;

then attach the arrow by inserting the cord in a hole drilled in it. Attach the end of a piece of cord, about 3 ft. long, to the groove of the smaller pulley, and wind in a counterclockwise direction about the rim; then fasten the free end to the screweye used as a handle for the weight. Attach this assembly to the base by fastening the bottom of the pillar to the center of one side of the base by screws from beneath. Finish as desired.

For the revolving-lever model, second order, use the following materials:

Base, 10-in. x 4½-in. x ¾-in.
Pillar, 8½-in. x ¾-in., 4½-in. at widest end.
Round blank, 6-in. diameter, 1½-in. thick.
Weight (resisting force), base 1¾-in. square, top 1¼-in. square, side 1½-in. high.
Arrow (applied force), 1¼-in. long, ¼-in. thick, ½-in. wide across barbs, ¼-in. square shaft.

Square and face the base with a finish bevel on top. Fashion the pillar with concave shoulders 1½ in. from the bottom, narrowing the upright shaft to 1½ in. wide. Turn from the blank (using faceplate) concentric double pulleys of 6 and 3-in. diameters, with ¾-in. rims and V-grooves, drilling in the center for a pivot screw. Attach by pivot screw to top of pillar. Secure one end of a cord, about 6 ft. long, to the groove of the large pulley, winding in a clockwise direction, and allowing the end to extend upward from left side and securing to the end the arrow, by means of a hole bored in the shaft. Attach to the groove of the 3-in. pulley one end of a cord, about 3 ft. long, winding in a counterclockwise direction, and fasten the screweye used as a handle for the weight to the free end. Attach this assembly to the base and fasten the pillar to the center of one side of the base with screws from beneath. Finish as desired.

For the model of the revolving lever of the third order, the following material is required:

Base, 10-in. x 4½-in. x ¾-in.
Pillar, 8½-in. x ¾-in., 4½-in. at widest end.
Round blank, 6-in. diameter, 1½-in. thick.
Weight (resisting force), base 1¾-in. square, top 1¼-in. square, side 1½-in. high.
Arrow (applied force), 1¼-in. long, ¼-in. thick, ½-in. wide across barbs, ¼-in. square shaft.

Square and face the base with a finish bevel on top. Shape the pillar with concave shoulders 1½ in. from bottom, narrowing the upright shaft to 1½ in. wide. Turn from the blank concentric double pulleys of 6 and 3-in. diameters, with ¾-in. rims, V-grooves, and pivot hole in center. Attach by the pivot screw to the top of the upright shaft. Attach one end of cord, about 6 ft. long, to the groove of the large pulley, winding the cord in a clockwise direction, and attach the weight by the screweye used as a handle to free end. Secure one end of a cord, about 3 ft. long, to the groove of the small pulley, winding in a counterclockwise direction, and permitting the end to extend upward; then fasten the arrow by a hole drilled in the shaft. Attach this assembly to the base by screwing the pillar to the center and one side of the base. Finish as desired.

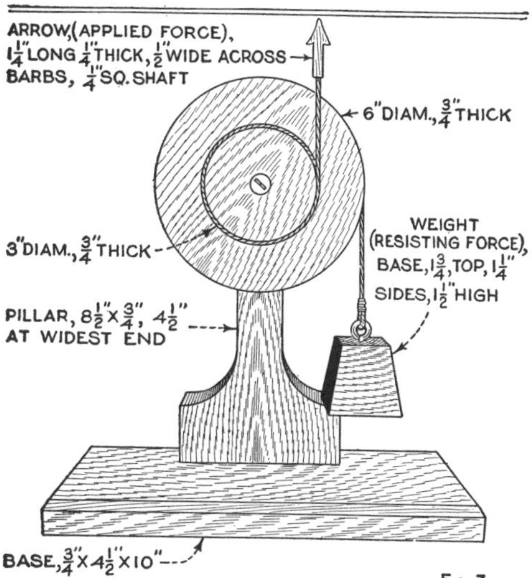
ARROW,(APPLIED FORCE),
1¼" LONG ¼" THICK, ½" WIDE ACROSS BARBS, ¼" SQ. SHAFT
6" DIAM., ¾" THICK
3" DIAM., ¾" THICK
WEIGHT (RESISTING FORCE), BASE, 1¾, TOP, 1¼" SIDES, 1½" HIGH
PILLAR, 8½" X ¾", 4½" AT WIDEST END
BASE, ¾" X 4½" X 10"
FIG. 7

Model of Third-Order Lever: Note Positions of Force and Weight as Compared with Figs. 5 and 6

For the compound revolving-lever model, the following material is used:

Base, 12¼-in. x 5-in. x ¾-in.
Six uprights, 6-in. long, tapering from 1½-in. at one end to 1-in. at the other, ½-in. thick.
Blank, 6-in. diameter, 1¼-in. thick.
Blank, 4-in. diameter, 1¼-in. thick.
Blank, 3½-in. diameter, ⅝-in. thick.
Blank, 1¼-in. diameter, ¾-in. thick.
Two ½-in. dowels, 2½-in. long.
½-in. dowel, 3⅝-in. long.
Six ½-in. washers.
Cordage, 3 ft.
Old automobile inner tube.
Weight (resisting force), base 1¾-in. square, top 1¼-in. square, side 1½-in. high.
Arrow (applied force), length 1¼-in., ¼-in. thick, ½-in. wide across barbs, shaft ¼-in. square.

Square and face the base with a finish bevel on top. Round the small ends of the uprights and drill a ½-in. hole, with its center ½ in. from the top and sides. Turn from the 6-in. blank two concentric double pulleys, with diameters 6 and 3 in., and rims ⅝ in. Turn in the larger pulley rim a square-shouldered groove, ⅛ in. deep and ½ in. wide. Drill a ½-in. hole in the center of the pulleys. Turn from the 4-in. blank two concentric pulleys with diameters 4 and 2½ in., and rims ⅝ in. wide, with square grooves 3/32 in. deep. Drill a ½-in. hole in the center of the pulleys. Turn from the 3½-in. blank a pulley 3½ in. in diameter, with a square-shouldered groove ³⁄₃₂ in. deep and ½ in. wide. Drill a ½-in. hole in the center of the pulley. Turn from the 1¼-in. blank a pulley 1¼ in. in diameter with a square-shouldered groove ¼ in. deep and ½ in. wide. Drill a ½-in. hole in the center of the pulley. Cut the inner tube into several strips ½ in. wide, using a wet, sharp knife and a straight-edge. Glue strips of sufficient length in all the grooves of the pulleys. Construct an assembly of the 4 and 2½-in. diameter pulleys upon a 2½-dowel, the ends of the dowel being fastened in two of the uprights. Center this assembly crosswise of the center line of the base, at a point 6¼ in. from the end of the base, securing it with glue and screws from beneath. Construct another assembly of the 6 and 3-in. diameter pulleys, placing this on the remaining 2½-in. dowel and supporting the ends upon two of the uprights. Fasten this assembly across the width of the base in a position that will permit contact between the 4 and 3-in. pulleys, with the smaller pulleys on one side, and secure to the base with glue and screws from beneath. Construct an assembly of the 3½-in. pulley upon the

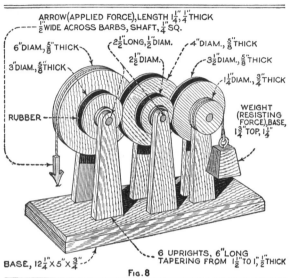

ARROW(APPLIED FORCE),LENGTH 1¼",¼"THICK
½"WIDE ACROSS BARBS, SHAFT, ¼"SQ.
2½"LONG,½"DIAM.   4"DIAM.,⅝"THICK
6"DIAM.,⅝"THICK   2½"DIAM.   3½"DIAM.,⅝"THICK
3"DIAM.,⅝"THICK   1¼"DIAM.,¾"THICK
RUBBER   WEIGHT (RESISTING FORCE),BASE, 1¾"TOP, 1¼"
6 UPRIGHTS, 6"LONG TAPERING FROM 1½"TO 1,"½"THICK
BASE, 12¼"X5"X¾"
FIG. 8

Model of Compound Revolving Lever: Force Applied to the Left-Hand Pulley Raises the Weight at the Right

3⅝-in. dowel with the protruding ends running freely through the remaining two uprights, the pulley being glued to the dowel, and glue the 1¼-in. pulley to the projecting end of the dowel in such a position that there will be 1 in. of dowel between the inner pulley face and outer face of the nearest upright. Secure this assembly to the base across the width in such a position that the 3½-in. pulley will make contact with the 2½-in. pulley and the small pulley will be on the same side as the other small pulleys. Fasten with glue and screws from beneath. Attach an end of a piece of cord, about 1 ft. long, to the smallest pulley. Wind the cord clockwise, and fasten the end to the screweye used as a handle for the weight. Fasten an end of cord, about 2 ft. long, to the largest pulley, winding it on the drum in counterclockwise direction, and gluing the end in a hole drilled lengthwise in the shaft of the arrow. The ½-in. washers are used as bearings between the pulleys and uprights. Finish as desired.

Part V of this series of articles will be published next month.

Figuring Water Required on a Farm

A certain quantity of water is required as the daily output of every water-supply system, whether it is pumped by wind or other power and a storage tank must be provided for holding the water until it is used, and for caring for the surplus. If a windmill is used to pump the water a tank large enough to hold a three-day supply of water should be provided in order to furnish water over a period when there is little or no wind. If engine-driven pumps are used the tanks need only be large enough to hold a single day's supply, as the engine can be operated at any

time regardless of weather conditions. The amount of water required for all purposes from isolated water-supply plants, is, on the average, as follows: For all household and toilet purposes allow 25 gal. for each member of the family; allow 10 gal. for each horse, 10 gal. for each cow, 2 gal. for each hog, and 1 gal. for each sheep. Applying the rule, the minimum allowance for a family of five persons for household purposes only will be 125 gallons. In order that ample pressure will be obtained at all cocks the storage tank should be elevated at least 10 ft. higher than the highest tap and the higher the tank the greater will be the pressure.

Meat Grinder Fills Bottles

An ordinary motor-driven meat grinder of large size from which the cutting disks have been removed, is used in a plant manufacturing preserved-fruit products, for filling bottles with relish and similar products. No other change has been made in the grinder, save the provision of a tapered spout at the outlet to fit the mouth of the bottle snugly. The relish is fed into the top of the grinder and the screw at the bottom forces the product out through the spout and into the bottles about as fast as the latter can be placed in position and removed by the operators. Formerly this work was done by hand, each worker filling bottles over a little wooden bowl. Twelve workers were then required to accomplish the work now done by four using the machines.—Orin Crooker, Elgin, Ill.

A Poppet-Valve Gauge

A valve tester similar to the one shown in the drawing provides a set standard that should form a part of the garage tool equipment for setting the machine in grinding up a set of valves or a valve-re-

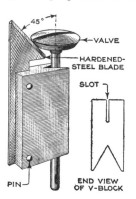

seating tool. Whenever both the valve face and the valve seat are machined to the same angle, only a small amount of grinding in will be required to obtain a perfect seating. The tester should be accurately made from two pieces of machine steel pinned together. The blade should be hardened and accurately ground so that a line parallel with the V-block forms a 45° angle with the blade line. Most valves are ground to an angle of 45°, but a 60° tester can be made along the same lines. To test a valve place the stem in the V-groove and slide it down until the face touches the blade; light showing between the valve face and edge of the blade will show the variations, if any. The valve-reseating tool is tested in the same manner.—Geo. Alexander, Pittsburgh, Pa.

¶To close the sides of a used cotter pin, hold one of its legs on the edge of a vise and tap the head with a hammer.

Homemade Pneumatic Punch

The illustration shows how a very useful pneumatic punch for the shop where compressed air is available can be made at little expense. The size or strength of the material used in its construction will, of

Pneumatic Punch Made in a Railroad Shop for Piercing Quarter-Inch Plate

course, vary with the thickness of the material to be punched. Plate steel up to ¼-in. thick can be punched very effectively with the one in the photo; the cylinder is 10 by 12 in., and is operated at a pressure of 50 lb. per sq. in. This machine was built only as an experiment, and therefore looks rather rough, but it is perfectly satisfactory in operation.—A. H. Keys, Baltimore, Md.

Increasing Capacity of Lumber Wagon

When a wagon box is removed so that a load of lumber can be carried the lumber is usually piled to a width equal to that of the wagon box. However, it is possible to increase the size of the load considerably by laying crosspieces over it when it reaches the height of the wheels, so that the wheels will have plenty of clearance, and then continuing to pile the load on top of the cross-

pieces, as shown in the illustration. Crosspieces up to 8 ft. in length can be used, as this is the maximum width of a vehicle allowed on public roads. The size of the load can be more than doubled in this way.

Emergency Wheel Puller

Pulling the wheel from a semi-floating axle is sometimes a very difficult task, especially after some strong-armed mechanic

Pulling Off a Wheel by Means of a Steel Bar, Chain and Sledge Hammer

has sent the retaining nut home with a 24-in. wrench. However, the work can easily be done by two men with a crowbar, a short length of chain and a sledge hammer.

The bar is placed with the flat end resting on the axle, and the handle held toward the rear, close to the tire. The chain is strapped tightly around the bar and two or three spokes, these, of course, being protected by wrapping a piece of burlap around them. The bar is then pulled outward at the end by one man, while the other strikes the bar with the sledge hammer squarely over the axle; this will usually start the wheel immediately. In stubborn cases it may be necessary to lengthen the bar with a piece of pipe on the end.

Welding-Rod Holders

Every acetylene welder who does heavy work on large preheated jobs knows how disagreeable the work is when ordinary short welding rods are used. As a makeshift, lengths of short rod are often welded together, but this is not entirely satisfactory because the workman cannot then hold the end of the rod on the weld so steadily. In order to overcome this trouble welding-rod holders of the kind shown in the illustration have been made in one shop and found entirely satisfactory.

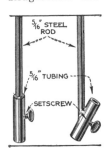

They are made from lengths of ⁵⁄₁₆-in. round steel rod and short lengths of ⁵⁄₁₆-in. tubing having a ¹⁄₁₆-in. wall, the tubing being welded to the end of the rod, either in line with it or at an angle to it as indicated; one type of holder will be found suitable for one class of work, the other for work of another kind.—Edwin Kilburn, Spring Valley, Minn.

Pouring Lead into Holes in Concrete

Occasionally it is necessary to pour melted lead or babbitt into holes drilled into damp concrete floors for the purpose of holding lag screws or leveling a machine. When the hot metal is poured into the holes it usually "flies" and numerous particles spatter up against the worker. This trouble is due to the dampness of the concrete; when the hot metal touches it steam is formed and the pressure of the steam blows the metal away. An excellent remedy is to pour a little kerosene on the floor and into the hole. The kerosene turns to a gas when the hot metal touches it, and escapes gradually.—A. S. Jamieson, Springfield, Mass.

Lifting Tongs for I-Beams

In shops where many I-beams are handled on hoists or cranes it is customary to hold the beams by means of chain slings, but it takes considerable time and labor to attach these slings so that they will not slip. In one shop the work was greatly facilitated by the use of the tongs shown in the drawing. These could be attached and detached in a fraction of the time consumed in ad-

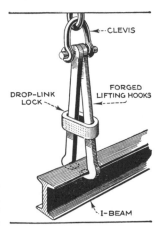

justing the sling, and they were just as safe as the latter, as they were self-locking. They consist of two forged lifting hooks having holes drilled at one end to slip on the pin of a heavy clevis, which is attached to the hoist, and having the other end bent over at right angles to grip the I-beam. A drop link holds both hooks on the beam.

Making Wagon Beds Last

The bottom of a wagon bed is the first part to wear out and usually has to be renewed two or three times before the sideboards and endgate are discarded. A good method of preserving it is to cover it with a piece of No. 20 sheet iron, 3 ft. wide and about 3 in. longer than the bottom. This piece is screwed down with heavy roundhead screws so that about 3 in. project at the rear. The projecting portion is bent down and screwed to the underside. Such a sheet-iron cover costs only a few dollars and is well worth the investment.

Portable Motor-Driven Saw

Operations such as sawing interior wood trimmings, cutting out floor boards when installing steam or water pipes and electric conduit, as well as other work in awkward places, are greatly facilitated by the use of

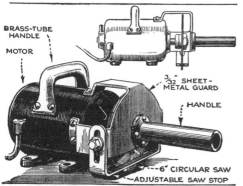

Portable Motor-Driven Saw which Can Be Made in the Home Workshop and Has Many Uses

a portable motor-driven saw that can be made in the shop.

It consists of a ⅙-hp. electric motor of the kind generally used for driving washing machines, fitted with an extension shaft on which a 6-in. circular saw is securely mounted. For the sake of safety, a guard is cut out of a piece of sheet metal, bent to shape and fastened as shown. A stop is attached to the guard. It is slotted in the bottom for the saw and at the ends to allow depth adjustments by means of the fastening bolts. A 6-in. length of brass tubing, with the end flared to permit its attachment to the guard with small stove bolts or rivets, is provided for use as a handle and another similar handle is fitted on the top so that the saw can be handled with ease. Feet are provided on the motor, so that it can be bolted down solidly to the workbench whenever desired.

A Gardener's Basket

Carrying baskets of garden truck from one end of the row to the other by hand is needless work when it can be made much easier by the use of a simple wheelbarrow

Large Homemade Wheelbarrow Which Is of Considerable Convenience to Truck Farmers

of the type shown in the photo. The body resembles a ladder and is built of 2 by 4-in. wood. The crosspieces are cut from 1-in. material, and the length of the body is determined by the space required by four bushel baskets set in a row, plus the additional length for the handles. The width of the body is also made to conform to the space required by the baskets. The crosspieces are spaced to provide openings for dirt to fall through, and also to reduce the weight. The wheel is mounted about 18 in. from the front end. The axle is held by means of four iron braces, which can easily be made of heavy tire iron. Wooden legs, braced securely, are provided near the handle to keep the top level.

A Handy Hardy

As a substitute for the usual blacksmith's hardy held in the hole provided for it in the anvil, the hardy shown in the illustration has been found very useful. It is welded to a length of ⅝-in. round or square iron rod, which is bent to fit over the top of the anvil and is hinged to the anvil block so that it can be swung down and out of the

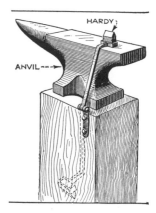

way when not in use. When wanted for use, the blacksmith reaches down with his hammer and pulls it up.

Roller Protects Barn Corner

Farm buildings sometimes are so arranged that when hay is hoisted into the barn the team must be driven around a corner of one building in order to avoid

Iron Pipe Arranged Vertically Along Corner of Building Protects It from Hoisting Rope

another. This causes the rope to rub hard against the corner, not only wearing it out quickly but also bruising the corner.

In one case injury to both corner and rope was prevented by arranging a steel roller vertically along the edge of the building as shown. The roller consisted of a 4-ft. length of 2-in. iron pipe, turning on bolts fitted into the ends. The bolts were in turn held by short pieces of 2 by 4-in. wood, nailed securely to the barn. The roller has been in use for two or three years and has never failed in its purpose.

Removing Auto-Spindle Bushings

After a few months of continual service there is always more or less play in the steering-spindle bushings of automobiles, which can readily be detected by shaking the front wheels. When these bushings are worn badly it is, of course, necessary to replace them, but it is sometimes a difficult task to remove the old bushings. In one case the spindle bolt was used as a punch in an attempt to drive out the bushing, but the latter could not be budged.

Heating and thereby expanding the spindle boss in which the bushing is located is the first solution a mechanic would naturally think of. This can be done by means of a blowtorch, but if a

blowtorch is not handy an improvised alcohol torch, which consists of a strip of asbestos cloth rolled up and set in the cover of a large tin can, and saturated with alcohol, will serve the purpose just as well. The asbestos acts as a wick and the burning alcohol generates considerable heat.

Often the new bushings are too small for the spindle boss, and fall out of themselves. An excellent method of fitting them in snugly is to apply strips of solder to the outside, lengthwise, and then tap the bushing into place. The excess solder will readily scrape off while the bushing is being driven in.—J. E. Dekker, Chicago, Ill.

A Belt-Shifter Lock

A common trouble on standard countershafts is that the belt shifter will not stay in position on either the tight or the loose pulley. There are several methods of overcoming this trouble, such as the setting of the shifter lever and the use of spring-clamp bolts, but the writer has not found any of these as simple and practical as the lock shown in the illustration. It consists of a link, attached to the end of the shipper rod and to a ceiling joist as shown, and a coil spring to hold the link in the positions indicated. That end of the link which is connected to the shipper rod is slotted so that it will not bind when being moved

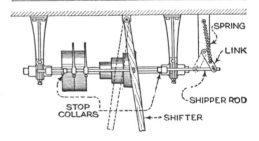

Simple Lock that Keeps the Belt Shifter in Position

from one position to the other. One end of the coil spring is attached directly above the point where the link pivots on the joist and the other end is fastened to the link just below its center. Two stop collars are fastened on the shipper rod at the points indicated, to limit its travel in either direction.—W. Burr Bennett, Honesdale, Pa.

¶By soldering the holes in the corners of the top of the coil box of a Ford car, a water-tight dipper is formed that will serve for filling the gasoline tank when no other receptacle is available.

Making Wood Dowels

By H. H. PARKER

HARD and soft-wood dowels are used to a large extent both in pattern-making and general woodworking, and while they may be purchased ready to cut up, there are times when none is available and they must be made by hand. A fairly good job may be done by planing and sand-papering from a square rod, but the best way is to prepare a dowel plate of the type shown in the illustration.

The stick is planed to an octagonal shape and driven through the plate, the result being an accurate round rod, true to size, and made in a fraction of the time required to shape the pin entirely by hand. The plate is drilled with a series of holes of the diameters most-ly used for dowels; a thin plate will do, but one made of 1-in. square stock will pro-duce smoother and straighter work. For con-tinuous work,

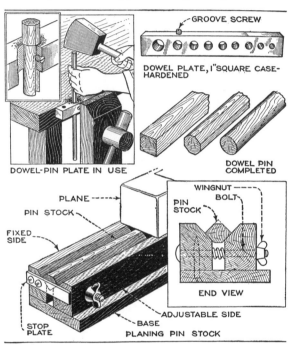

Above, Dowel Plate, Rough and Finished Dowels, and Method of Grooving; Below, Fixture for Planing Stock

hardened and tempered tool steel is best, or casehardened cold-rolled steel, but for occasional use, a cold-rolled steel bar, drilled and left soft, will answer the purpose very well. If a good assortment of twist drills is at hand, a good plan is to make up three plates, one with standard-size holes, the others having corresponding holes 1/64 in. larger and smaller than standard. This will allow the production of dowels for drive and push fits in holes bored with fractional-size wood bits.

At times it is of advantage to use a dowel having a groove along one side, to allow the escape of air and glue from the hole as the dowel is driven down. Such a groove is readily made by drilling and tapping a hole through the side of the plate for a small pointed setscrew; the point projects into the dowel hole, and as the wood is driven down through the plate, a groove will be formed.

To make a dowel, first plane a wood strip square, each side being a trifle wider than the required diameter, then plane off the corners, making the stick octagonal. After pointing one end slightly, drive the stick through the plate with a mallet, while hold-ing the plate firmly in a vise or clamped over a hole in the bench.

A special bench fixture will be found of service when planing the strip octagonal. The simplest form is a wood block with a 90° groove planed along its top surface, in which the stick rests while the corners are be-ing planed. Some form of end stop will, of course, be necessary. A better form of fixture consists of a strip screwed to a base block, and with another parallel to it, and adjustable in or out by means of two or more bolts provided with thumbnuts, as shown in the illustration. The inner upper corner of each strip is beveled at an angle of 45° to form a chan-nel for the dowel stick to rest in; the mov-able strip is let out so that when the upper corner of the stick is planed down far enough, the plane will just touch the top surfaces of the fixture strip, thus making the fixture serve also as a gauge. A steel plate is screwed to one end to serve as a stop for the sticks.

¶Do not use paint containing compounds of lead about stables or outbuildings where the fumes of decaying organic matter arise, as these gases are likely to darken the color of lead paints.

Convenient Box for Nails and Screws

The handy box illustrated is made up into as many compartments as desired, all but one being provided with an individual cover, when in use. This makes it possible to expose only the contents in the

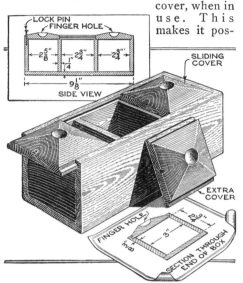

A Box of This Type Will Prove a Special Convenience to Patternmakers and Other Woodworkers

compartment in use. Also, the contents of one compartment can be dumped out without emptying the whole box. The covers are pyramidal in shape, with a depression in the top for moving them conveniently with the finger. In case it is desired to carry the box in a tool chest, where it might be upset, covers are provided for all the compartments; the extra one is slipped on just before the box is packed, and all the covers are locked in place by dropping a nail into a hole drilled through one cover and the end of the box, as in the side view.

Damming Irrigation Ditches

It is often necessary in irrigating fields to dam a ditch temporarily in order to divert water into other ditches. This can be done by means of an improvised sheet-iron dam. The sheet iron is cut about 1 ft. longer than the width of the ditch and about 1 ft. wider than its depth, and then cut to a semicircular shape. A stout piece of 2 by 4-in. wood is securely bolted along the straight edge of the sheet iron. This piece of wood should be a couple of feet longer than the sheet iron so that the projecting end can be used as a handle. A length of iron rod is bent to a U-shape and fastened at the center of the 2 by 4-in. piece to facilitate pulling the sheet iron out of the ditch. In use, the device is forced down into the bed and sides of the ditch so that it dams the water effectively. It can be put in place or removed in a few moments whenever necessary.

Wrench Made from Connecting Rod

A useful socket wrench can readily be made from an old drop-forged connecting rod. The rod is cut off at the point indicated and the end ground smooth. The bushing is removed from the other end and the eye heated until it is red-hot. A bolt head of the size for which the wrench is to be used is driven into one side of the eye while it is hot and the metal hammered down to fit against the flats. If desired, the other side can be similarly treated to fit bolts of larger or smaller size. — Sebastian Vierengel, West Palm Beach, Fla.

Round-Shank Drill Chuck for Brace

The ordinary carpenter's brace will take only square-shank drills, and it is occasionally desirable to use round-shank twist drills in it. This can be done if an adapter of the type shown in the drawing is made; the tool does not take up much room in the tool kit, and will be found very handy. It is made of round steel, turned down at one end to form a shank, and drilled at the other end to suit the shank of the drill, then a slot is

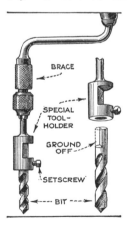

milled or filed across the body as shown, and the lower part drilled for a setscrew. The shank is squared and tapered to fit the brace chuck. The drill to be used in the adapter has a flat filed across the shank, as indicated, so that it will bear against the flat at the bottom of the slot in the adapter.

Repairing Leaky Gasoline Tanks

When repairing leaky seams on gasoline tanks, the gasoline is, of course, always drained out of the tank first in order to prevent accidents. However, the film of gasoline left on the sides and bottom evaporates rapidly, and forms gas fumes which may explode and cause considerable damage. As a precaution against such accidents it is advisable to fill the tank with water after the gasoline has been removed, and allow the water to overflow, thus removing the residual gasoline. Another method of preventing explosions that are due to fume-filled tanks is to squirt a little liquid from a fire extinguisher inside the tank.

Shaft Holder for Light Babbitting

A couple of shaft holders made like the one shown in the drawing are handy to use on light babbitted bearing work. Most repair shops have to do this kind of work at times and the process of lining up, which is generally the longest part of the job, can be shortened to a great extent by means of the shaft holders. In making the holders no particular accuracy is required and the only materials necessary are a couple of short pieces of round solid stock, two sleeves to go over these, some ½-in. round rod, and half a dozen setscrews. The sleeves are drilled and tapped in three places, two screws being tightened up in line on each sleeve and a third screw in the center between them on the opposite side. The pieces of round stock are then drilled close to each end of the sleeve to take the ½-in. rod, which is driven in tightly after bending to the V-shape shown. When using, the blocks or caps to be babbitted are laid on the bench and, if necessary, wooden blocks are placed at each end to rest the holders on. The shaft is then laid in the vees and adjusted for height at both ends by moving the latter around, which raises or lowers the shaft. When properly set both tightening screws are tightened and the two screws in each sleeve support the work.—Harry Moore, Montreal, Can.

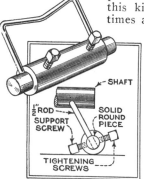

Boat Propeller Washes Tomatoes

Canners of tomatoes wash the fruit in large tanks to remove dirt and mold. A fairly rapid circulation is necessary in these tanks, but it is rather difficult to at-

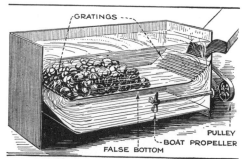

Motorboat Propeller Used to Wash Tomatoes. A False Bottom Protects the Fruit

tain without bruising the tomatoes unnecessarily. In one plant in Indiana, an ordinary motorboat propeller has been pressed into service for this purpose, with very satisfactory results.

To prevent the fruit from coming into contact with the propeller, the latter is placed at the bottom of the tank and covered with a false bottom. The propeller drives the water toward one end of the tank, where it strikes an inclined section, which deflects it upward through a grating into the upper part of the tank, where the tomatoes are dumped. A similar grating at the opposite end allows it to flow back into the bottom of the tank to be circulated over again.

A Soldering Kink

When resoldering the square brass base of an electric table lamp, it was found difficult to hold the loose corners together. After several unsuccessful attempts, a stout cord was looped over two opposite corners as shown, and twisted by means of a small pair of pliers until the corners were sufficiently tight to permit soldering. After twisting the cord, the pliers were drawn out until the nose rested against the inside of the lamp base so that the cord could not untwist. The job was thus easily done without help.

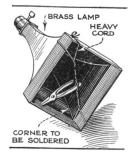

Device Starts Boxes Along Roller Conveyor

Wire-bound shipping boxes often get stuck on roller conveyors unless the drop of the conveyor is sufficient to overcome

Endless Wire with Hook Located over Roller Track Gives Obstinate Boxes a New Start

this tendency. To eliminate this trouble a large gum-manufacturing concern has equipped the conveyors in its shipping department with a device which gives the obstinate boxes a new start. The device consists of an endless wire suspended on grooved pulleys over the center of the roller tracks, with an iron hook attached to the wire at the point where the two ends are joined. A handle on one of the pulleys allows the operator to bring the hook to any point over the track; the back of the hook does not catch the box but readily passes over it. Then by reversing the direction of movement the hook catches behind the box and pulls it along.

A Planer Kink

When called upon to plane a flat spot on a number of castings that were not provided with a raised finishing pad, as is usual in such cases, I knew that the stroke of a belt-driven planer varied considerably, due to belt slippage, and that the usual result is a series of ragged, uneven cuts. To do a first-class job, therefore, I proceeded as follows: I marked off the spot to be finished,

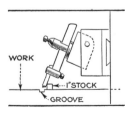

and chipped a groove, 1/8 in. deep and 3/8 in. wide, the width of the spot to be planed. I then clamped a piece of 1-in. square stock back of the groove, and bolted the job on the planer in the usual way. I set the table stroke with plenty of length, so that the

stroke would go as far as the 1-in. square piece each time. In case the stroke was long the tool simply lifted, as shown, and, on the forward stroke, settled into the groove.—A. F. Loeffler, Sheboygan, Wis.

Making Announcement Slides

After trying several different methods of making announcement slides for screen projection, I found the following method neat, simple and economical: A piece of unused black typewriter carbon paper, placed over a sheet of ordinary white paper, is fed into the typewriter and the ribbon key set to the position for stenciling. This allows the type to hit the uncoated side of the carbon paper directly, and transfers some of the carbon on the white paper. When finished, the effect can be seen clearly by holding the carbon paper closely in front of an electric lamp; there will be a contrast of nearly white and black that will be still more distinct when projected on the screen. The carbon paper is trimmed to fit the slides and is bound between them in the usual way.—Charles N. Shaw, Chattanooga, Tenn.

Increasing Capacity of Small V-Blocks

To eliminate the necessity of carrying around heavy V-blocks, a mechanic devised the auxiliary pieces shown in the photo so that a small pair of V-blocks could be used on light work of a diameter much larger than the blocks were intended for. The auxiliary V-blocks are made of flat-finished stock and they are held to the regular blocks by means of two pieces of round steel, drilled in the center to clear round-head screws, which

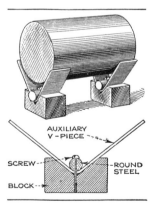

thread into tapped holes in the center of the blocks. The auxiliary pieces can be attached or removed in a moment; for light work they are just as handy as heavy blocks, and, of course, the difference in bulk and weight makes them most desirable when they have to be carried around in a tool kit from one job to another.

Making Hay Loading Easier

By J. M. COLLINS

ANY device that reduces the work in harvest time is a boon to the farmer, even if it takes a little time to make. The wagon attachment shown in the illustration, which is used on the farm of Mr. J. E. Myers, Pataskala, Ohio, has been found very convenient when loading hay, and does away with a great deal of hard work.

The device consists of an extra half-section frame, mounted upon lengths of iron pipe, fastened lengthwise on the bed of the regular hayrack. In front of the rack

attached to the windlass by means of ropes. When loading, the frame is first set at the rear of the rack, as shown at the lower left; when it has been loaded, it is drawn to the front by means of the windlass, as shown at the lower right, and the rear half of the rack loaded. This does away with the hard work of forking the hay to the forward part of the rack by hand, which, as anyone who has tried it knows, is hard labor. The hay on the rack being thus separated into two bunches, is also

Lower Left, Frame Drawn to Rear Ready for Loading; Lower Right, Drawing the Frame Forward; Insert, Loading Rear Half of Rack

is fitted a simple windlass, also made of pipe and fittings. The extra frame is

much easier to load into the hay fork, when drawing it up into the barn.

Auto Gearbox Used in Machine-Tool Drive

The transmission and speed-changing gear of an automobile can be successfully used for giving different speeds, including reverse, to the lineshaft in a small shop. In one instance, the transmission device was set upside down over a lathe, in such a manner that the handle was within convenient reach of the operator. With work on the machine, the operator could change speeds and reverse without taking his hand from the handle, or shifting belts. For a small shop, the gearbox could be so arranged that the speed and direction of rotation of the entire shaft could be changed. The stub shaft, which is ordinarily connected to the crankshaft in the automobile, was connected to the main shaft, which was driven by an electric motor, and the

machine to be driven was belted up to the jack shaft from the opposite end of the transmission. The gears were oiled frequently with heavy gearbox oil and a special drip pan was made to catch the waste.—James B. Hays, Boise, Idaho.

Cleaning Files

A good method of cleaning files that have been used on wood or soft metal such as lead, is to rub the end of a brass or copper strip over the file in line with the grooves. This cuts notches into the brass corresponding to the grooves on the file and will clean the file of foreign substances more effectively and quickly than a steel brush or any other method. A thin piece of stock, about $\frac{1}{4}$ or $\frac{1}{2}$ in. in width, will do the work best.—H. Olsen, Park Ridge, Illinois.

Portable Support for Vise

On jobs where it is necessary to make use of a vise it is quite often a problem, especially in the absence of a workbench or table, to

find a convenient and stable place to attach it. But if some 2-in. lumber and a few heavy nails can be found near by, a simple and sturdy support can readily and quickly be knocked together. A support of this kind, which has the further advantage of being portable, is shown in the drawing. It consists of two 4-ft. lengths of 2 by 6-in. material with both ends sawed off at suitable angles so that the support can be set up steadily against the wall. Three crosspieces are nailed on, the lower one serving as a step for the worker, whose weight gives additional stability, and the upper one as a backrest, permitting the support to be set against studdings, while the center piece holds the vise.—G. A. Luers, Washington, D. C.

Grinding Hardened Lathe Centers

The usual way of truing hardened lathe centers when they become worn is to anneal them, turn them down to the proper angle and re-harden, all of which takes considerable time, particularly when there is a rush job waiting. Unless there is a toolpost grinder handy, as there generally is, there is nothing else to do but take the time and anneal the centers. However, the drawing shows how the centers of a lathe were ground with an old emery wheel. The wheel was carefully trued up to a level and sharp-cutting surface. Then, removing the toolpost, the wheel was laid flat

on its side and bolted in position on top of the compound rest, which had been turned around to the 60° angle. The belt was next placed on the high-speed cone and the wheel fed back and forth along the center, the cross-feed screw being used to force the wheel against the center. This method proved rapid and successful. The tailstock center was next ground in the same manner. If no old emery wheel is at hand a clamp can be made to hold a coarse-grained emery or carborundum stone.— W. S. Standiford, Youngstown, Ohio.

A Handy Polishing Wheel

The method of securing strip emery cloth to a wheel shown in the drawing is both novel and safe and will probably be interesting to anyone who uses this type of wheel for polishing or smoothing down articles of wood or leather. The wheel is made of clear hardwood, drilled in the center to fit the machine spindle and about 1 in. from the edge to take a wooden plug; a slit is also cut from the latter hole to the outside of the wheel. The plug, which is 1½ in. in diameter for an 8-in. wheel, has a flat on one side into which four headless nails are driven; two of these are driven straight and the others are bent slightly. The

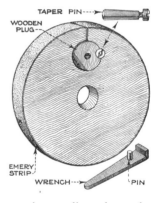

plug in all cases is smaller than the hole by the double thickness of emery cloth or paper used on the wheel. The wrench used to tighten the plug is made from a piece of flat steel or iron bent over at one end and having a pin that engages in a hole drilled in the center of the plug. To determine the length of the strip of emery cloth to use, place it around the wheel, bring the two ends through the slit and tear off, leaving enough to press over the nails in the plug when in place. Next, pull the plug around with the wrench until the emery is drawn tight on the wheel; clamp in this position and drill a taper hole, half the diameter of which is in the plug and the other in the wheel. The job is completed by fitting a taper pin, threaded on the end for a fillister-head screw, and counterboring for the screw head. When fitting new strips of emery on the wheel, tear off the correct length, using the old piece as a guide, and press both ends over the nails in the plug, then insert the latter in the hole and press the two ends above the plug through the slit at the same time, tighten with the wrench until the two halves of the taper hole come together, then slip in the taper pin. The wrench is then removed and the screw on the pin tightened, thus binding the plug firmly against the emery.

A Kink for Paperhangers

When hanging wall paper on a side wall it is necessary to see the edge of the paper from top to bottom in order to get the correct lap. This is very difficult to do when wearing spectacles, for it is impossible to see through them as well as with the naked eye. I have found that this difficulty can be eliminated to a great extent by driving a small lath nail slightly into the wall on the edge of the paper as far from the edge as is necessary to get the correct lap, and at a point about one-third of the length from the top. The nail can readily be seen and the paper hung against it. Only the slightest fraction of an inch lap is needed in lapping, and this lap can be rolled down so as to present the appearance of a perfect butt joint.—A. A. Kelly, Paoli, Pa.

Traveling Lamp Illuminates Gauge

When large tanks are located in dark places or their gauges have to be read at night, the latter should be well illuminated.

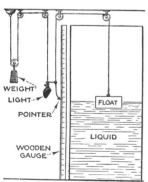

The illustration shows a novel installation of this kind. It consists of an electric lamp which is rigidly connected to the pointer of the gauge and hence travels up and down with it illuminating the scale. An extra long lampcord is used so that a suitable counterweight can be arranged as shown, causing the lamp and gauge pointer to move smoothly together. A distant switch may control the lamp.—Kenneth Coggeshall, Webster Groves, Mo.

Lunches Checked at Special Trucks

A Chicago factory permits its employes to bring lunches but does not allow them to be kept in lockers or carried into the operating department because left-over food thrown into wastebaskets, corners or on the floor, attracts rats, mice and other

Checking Lunches at Special Lunch Truck in Chicago Factory

pests. To take care of the packages several trucks with numerous pigeonholes were provided. In the morning the employes leave their lunches in the truck, receiving numbered checks from the attendant. Shortly before noon, the truck is moved to the company's restaurant, where the worker checks out his lunch and is permitted to eat it. Screen doors with padlocks are provided for the trucks to prevent pilfering and mix-ups.—Orin Crooker, Elgin, Illinois.

Transparent Flap Protects Drawings

From several standpoints it is highly desirable to present finished drawings to a client or prospect protected by a sheet of transparent paper, so that the completed work presents a clean, crisp, and dressy appearance. Glassine paper, which can generally be obtained from art and stationery stores, is preferred for the purpose. One edge of the transparent paper is pasted on the back of the drawing at the upper edge and folded over the face of the work. Where the flap is to be used for a long time the bottom edge can be reinforced by pasting it between a folded strip of tough paper. Where additional protection is desirable or necessary, an additional flap of craft paper can be used.—C. Nye, New York City.

Homemade Centrifuge for Farmers

By L. B. ROBBINS

EVERY farmer knows that the fat content of milk can be determined accurately and quickly by means of a "whirler" or centrifuge of the kind shown in the drawing. However, the cost of a manufactured machine often keeps the dairyman from using one, and this has led one farmer to design and construct a simple centrifuge at home. The device is made from old machine parts that were picked up around the farm workshop. It consists of a rectangular wooden frame, holding a horizontal and a vertical shaft, each with a bevel gear mounted on it as shown, a whirling arm, hand crank and two test tubes. The frame is built about 12 in. high and 3 in. wide, of 1-in. hardwood stock

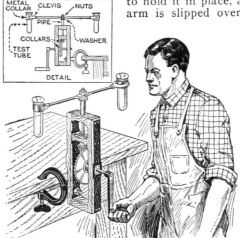

about 1 or 2 in. wide. The long pieces are screwed to the ends of the short ones, and may be braced with angle irons, if desired. Two bearing holes are drilled through the sides, to take the horizontal shaft on which the large bevel gear is mounted, and bushed with short lengths of brass tubing. A hand crank is attached to one end, and two washers and a collar are used to keep the gear in close mesh with the smaller one on the vertical shaft; this shaft is similarly mounted in two holes, drilled through the crosspieces and bushed. The shafts and

bevel gears of an old ice-cream freezer were found satisfactory for this purpose. The whirling arm can be made from a 12-in. length of ⅜-in. round steel rod, flattened and drilled in the center to fit the vertical shaft. A pipe nipple, washer and nut are fitted on the upper end of the shaft to hold it in place, and after the whirling arm is slipped over the end, the nut is screwed on tightly. On the threaded ends of the whirling arm two Ford brake-rod clevises are attached, and a short piece of thin metal tubing is mounted loosely inside of each clevis, by means of pins soldered to the sides, to permit it to swing freely without binding. The tubing should just be large enough to receive a glass test tube as indicated. An old washing-machine or wringer clamp can be fastened to the frame so that it can be attached to a bench or table. In use, the test tubes are filled about three-fourths full of milk, set in the tube holders on the whirling arm and the hand crank is then operated at a high rate of speed; this will cause the bottom end of the test tubes to swing outward due to centrifugal force. All solids in the milk go to the bottom, and this makes it comparatively easy to determine the fat content accurately; the device also allows the test to be made much more quickly than by any other method.

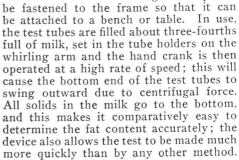

Inexpensive Homemade Centrifuge Made by a Farmer to Determine the Fat Content of Milk

---

Repairing the Faucet

It often happens when repairing a compression faucet that the screw holding the washer on the stem is stripped, making it necessary to purchase a whole new faucet, as the parts are not usually sold separately. A repair can readily be made by the handy man, however. The old screw is clipped off and the end of the stem filed down smooth. A hole, large enough to receive the end of a dry-cell binding post, is then drilled in this end, and the binding post sweated in place, screw end out. The

thumbnut of the post is cut in half so that it will not interfere with the seating of the washer, then used like the regular nut; the projecting end of the screw is also sawed or filed off.

Blueprint Signs without Tracing

Instead of printing signs and notices on tracing cloth and then making a blueprint from the tracing cloth, much time can be saved by stenciling the sign out of drawing paper, which costs much less. After printing, the letters will stand out in blue.

Making a Small Electric Hoist

By J. V. ROMIG

THE electric hoist described in this article was designed for a small ice plant, to speed up and lighten the work of pulling the ice cans out of the tanks, but the same type of hoist can be used for many other purposes.

The cross frame of the hoist is made of two channels, with tracks screwed to the lower flanges, as shown in the drawing. Through the center of the channels runs the carriage, which is simply built up from flat-steel stock. The hoisting apparatus consists of a worm and worm gear, a sprocket and a length of block chain. The gear and sprocket are keyed to the same shaft, the latter running in brass bushings carried in the carriage side members. The worm is pinned to a shaft at right angles to the gear shaft. On the projecting tops of the carriage side members two angles are bolted, and to these is fastened the ¼-hp. motor that drives the hoist. The motor is fitted with a flanged pulley, which is directly over a similar pulley keyed to the worm shaft. A pulley ratio of three to one gives ample power to lift the cans at a good rate of speed. The connection between motor and hoist

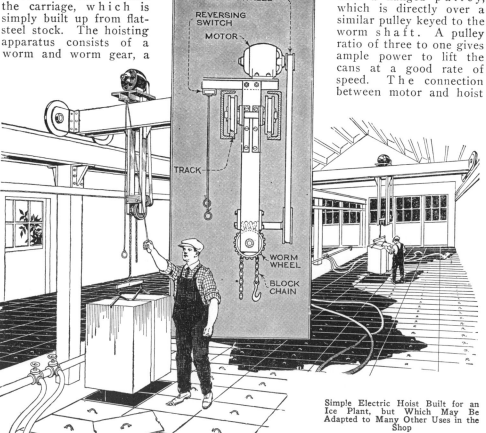

MOTOR WHEEL

REVERSING SWITCH

MOTOR

TRACK

WORM WHEEL

BLOCK CHAIN

Simple Electric Hoist Built for an Ice Plant, but Which May Be Adapted to Many Other Uses in the Shop

is made by a 2-in. belt, which provides a safe and powerful drive, but one that will slip should a can stick in the tank when being pulled.

While the method of connecting the

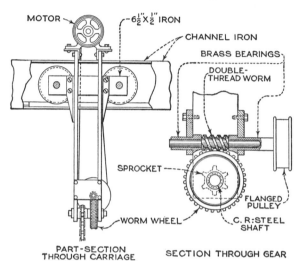

MOTOR — 6½"×½" IRON
CHANNEL IRON
BRASS BEARINGS
DOUBLE-THREAD WORM
SPROCKET
FLANGED PULLEY
WORM WHEEL
C. R. STEEL SHAFT
PART-SECTION THROUGH CARRIAGE   SECTION THROUGH GEAR

Details of Motor Mounting and Trolley of Carriage; Right, Section Through Worm-Shaft Bearings, Showing Method of Fitting

motor to the power line is not applicable in all cases—nor can it be recommended for use in places where some one is likely to come in contact with the wires—a short description may prove interesting. Three wires are stretched the full length of the track, and a short vertical length of angle iron is fitted to the end of the channels. This carries three brushes, which make contact with the wires. Three wires are similarly stretched along the channel frame, on the opposite side to the pulleys, and three roller brushes mounted on a bracket bolted to the carriage make contact with them. From the brushes, connection is made to the motor, through a reversing switch; two handles are attached to the latter, and extend down to within a convenient distance of the operator.

Truing Brake Bands

A brake band works efficiently only when the total friction area is utilized, which is not the case when the band is slightly out of true. A good method of truing up external brake bands is to first mark on a large piece of wood having a perfectly flat surface, a circle with a radius equal to the radius of the brake drum plus the thickness of the brake lining. This circle must not be made by running the pencil along the edge of the brake drum with the lining laid

around it, as this not being perfectly circular would result in inaccuracy, but the circle should be scribed by means of large compasses. The circle indicates the correct circumference of the inner edge of the brake band, which is then laid over it and compared with it. In many cases the lower edge of the band will not touch the surface of the board at all points and this is the first defect to be corrected. After the band has been made to lie flush on the board it is laid with its inner edge on the circle and the portions where it departs from the true line are carefully noted. These are bent inward or outward until the band is perfectly true to the circle. A small square is then set up against the side of the band to see if it is also true across its width; if not, it must be twisted until square. The correctness of the band s h o u l d be carefully checked by g o i n g through the above-described operations again, and the brake lining can then be riveted on, taking care not to throw the band out of true again. Internal brake bands are trued in a similar manner.

Storage-Battery Post Cleaner

Those who handle many storage batteries, either automobile or radio, must keep some tool at hand to clean the terminal posts. A simple little tool for this job, which can be carried in the pocket or the t o o l box, is

4"
4½"
METAL
EMERY CLOTH

s h o w n i n t h e drawing a n d can be made at very small cost. Cut a piece of metal to the shape shown in the upper detail; t h i s should be about 1½ in. wide, and curved as indicated. Now rivet or cement a p i e c e of coarse emery cloth to one side, rough s i d e out. B e n d the metal in the shape of a cone, slightly larger than the posts, then bend the ends out to form finger grips. The emery, of course, should be on the inside. To use the tool, slip it over the post, and grasping it between the fingers, tighten it and turn back and forth until the post is clean.

Eliminating Static in Camera

In film cameras, particularly motion-picture cameras, it sometimes happens that static sparks occur within the cameras, ruining the film. This is likely to happen especially in cold, dry weather. In taking some photos in a large electric power house, an entire roll of films was ruined in this way before the trouble was discovered. As a means to eliminate the static, the metal frame of the camera was grounded. This was done by means of a flexible copper wire attached to the camera and to the ground, and the result was as anticipated—no more trouble.

Combined Drawer Pull and Handle

A combined drawer pull and handle is a novel feature on workshop drawers which was found useful by a Wisconsin mechanic. A length of ½-in. iron rod was bent to the shape shown and attached to the sides of the drawer in the inside at the center, slots being cut in the front of the drawer to receive the rod when the drawer is slid under the

bench. Two shallow ½-in. holes are drilled directly under the screws on which the handle pivots, to catch the ends of the rod when it is set up for use. These ends are, of course, rounded to prevent cutting a groove in the side of the drawer.

Truck for Handling Logs

When short logs, telephone poles or even sections of large water mains must be moved short distances and the use of horses is impossible or unprofitable, a serviceable truck of the kind shown in the drawing, will prove worth the time required to construct it.

It consists of the wheels and axle of a light wagon and an ordinary wagon tongue mounted across the axle to serve as a lever. At the short end of the tongue a pair of steel tongs are suspended to swing freely in any direction. The truck

is loaded by pushing it in the position shown with the axle near the center of the log to be carried. The lever is raised so that the tongs grip the log and is then

Handy Truck for Transporting Short Logs, Telephone Poles and Sections of Large Water Mains

pulled down, raising the end of the log above the ground. A length of chain, attached to the tongue as shown, is then passed around the log and one of its links caught over a hook on the side of the tongue. For handling small, straight logs, a hook, made as shown in the detail, can be used instead of the chain.—G. E. Hendrickson, Argyle, Wis.

Simple Iodine Swab

The glass rod of a burnt-out electric lamp makes an excellent iodine swab. The bulb of the lamp is broken off and the wires carefully removed, those at the end of the rod being bent back and forth until they break. If sharp edges still project these should be filed down. Ordinary tape, or better still, rubber tape, a piece of which can be obtained at any electrician's shop for a few cents, is wrapped around the glass rod near the base to form a stopper. The base is left on to serve as a handle.—F. D. Brooks, Toledo, Ohio.

Repairing Concrete Tank

Concrete tanks often crack in the manner shown in the illustration, which makes it necessary to replace them with new ones. However, in one case where the

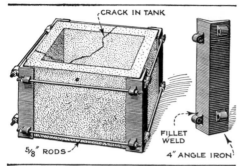

Cracked Concrete Tank Effectively and Permanently Repaired by Clamping Sides Together

tank was in constant use and making a new one meant too long a delay, an effective and permanent repair was made by filling the crack with neat cement and then clamping all four sides together as indicated. Four corner pieces were made of 4-in. angle iron, which were just as long as the tank was deep. To the sides of these angles were welded lugs, consisting of 2-in. pieces of 1½-in. cold-rolled steel drilled for ⅝-in. rods; the rods were threaded at both ends and fitted with nuts, to permit drawing up the corner pieces tightly.—A. S. Jamieson, Springfield, Mass.

Small Boring-Tool Holder

With the ordinary boring-tool holder, held in the toolpost in a position parallel to the direction of cut, it is necessary not only to adjust the tool centrally, but also to clamp it in a position parallel to the lathe bed each time it is placed in the toolpost, after sharpening. Otherwise the tool is liable to bear on the end of the hole being bored and thus push the point of the tool away from the cut. A boring tool held in the holder illustrated is always parallel, the adjustment being made after the holder is tightened in the toolpost by moving the eccentric around and tighten-

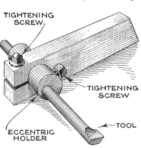

ing both screws This holder is made from ⅞ by 1½-in. stock, drilled and reamed for a 1-in. hole, after which the front end is slit and tapped for a tightening screw. Next, a piece of 1-in. cold-rolled rod is drilled with an eccentric hole to take the boring tools and a hole is drilled at right angles to this and tapped for a tightening screw which holds the tool. Both tightening screws should have the same size head to facilitate handling. Only the round tool is removed for sharpening, the holder remaining in the toolpost.

Jack Acts as Arbor Press

Having some rush work to do when the regular arbor press was out of order we rigged up one of our heavy-duty jacks as shown in the illustration to serve as an emergency arbor press. A U-bolt with a flat crossbar across the ends was hooked under the base of the jack as indicated. The bolt was made of ¾-in. round stock, with the ends threaded for a length of about 8 in., and the crossbar was a piece of flat steel 3 in. wide and 1½ in. thick. A short piece of flat steel was laid on the foot of the jack and the work—in this case a connecting rod that had to be fitted with a bushing—was placed on it. By raising the jack so that the work was pressed against the crossbar the bushing was forced into place.—Frank N. Coakley, Buffalo, N. Y.

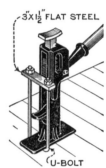

Improving Bearing Lubrication

The lubrication of a small bearing on a high-speed motor was improved considerably by turning the end of the shaft down to a taper. The taper extended ⅛ in. inside of the bearing to give the oil free access to its inner surface. When the shaft is rotating, the ring tends to climb up the taper, and upon touching the side of the bearing, feeds it with oil. Before tapering the shaft the bearing ran hot frequently, but since this was done the trouble was entirely eliminated.

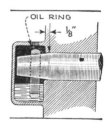

Pumping Water with Light Truck

By J. V. ROMIG

DURING a drought in the eastern states, a farmer was caught without any water for his stock, his cisterns all being dry. Some two miles distant, however, was a roadside spring, which ran strongly all the time, and he decided to haul his water from this source with his truck. Milk cans were used to carry the water, but he soon found that filling these by hand was a very arduous task, also that it consumed considerable time. He therefore looked around for a quicker and easier way.

A gear pump, found in a local plumber's shop, was bolted on the running board of the truck. The hub cap of the left rear wheel was removed, and a small wooden pulley, fitted with a threaded

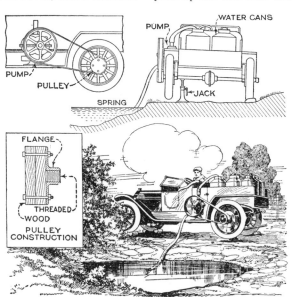

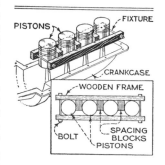

Pumping Water from a Spring with the Aid of a Truck and a Plumber's Gear Pump, During a Drought

flange, screwed onto the extending threads of the axle.

When the spring was reached, he would jack up the left rear wheel, and throw on the emergency brake, which only gripped the right wheel, as the left side was temporarily disconnected. A ½-in. belt was then placed on the wheel and pump pulleys, and the clutch let in. A length of hose, attached to the suction side of the pump, was thrown into the spring, and the discharge hose placed in each of the cans in turn, until all were filled. Upon arriving at home, the suction hose was placed in the cans, and the discharge hose in the open top of his cistern pump.

Replacing Cylinder Block

When overhauling automobile engines it is an easy matter to pull the cylinder block off the pistons, but it is a difficult task to get it back in place again, as the pistons usually tumble over in every direction. However, by the use of the simple fixture shown, this work becomes comparatively easy. The fixture consists of two lengths of wood held together at the ends by bolts. A number of small spacing blocks are screwed to one of these to hold the pistons properly

alined and spaced. The device is well worth making in a garage where repairing is largely confined to one type of car, and, in larger shops, it might pay to make such fixtures for several different engines.—G. A. Luers, Washington, D. C.

Serviceable Welding Goggles

On small jobs the worker with an acetylene torch usually dislikes to put on heavy goggles due to the difficulty of seeing the work clearly, but working without them is a severe strain on the eyes. For such cases a special pair of goggles can be made by removing the glasses from another pair, grinding off about a third of the upper part and then reinserting them in the frame. For setting up and adjusting the work, the operator looks over the top of the lens, but when using the flame he looks through the glass as usual.—Harold E. Benson, Boulder, Colo.

MECHANICAL POWERS

By CARL W. MITMAN
Curator
DIVISIONS OF MINERAL AND MECHANICAL TECHNOLOGY UNITED STATES NATIONAL MUSEUM

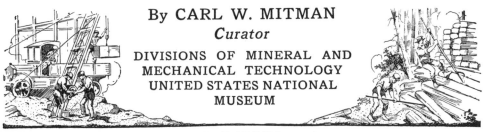

Copyrighted, H. H. Windsor

This is the fifth article of a series by Curator Mitman, explaining in simple language what every man who builds or designs a machine must know, and showing in detail just how to build a set of models of the mechanical powers that will exactly duplicate the set in the National Museum at Washington, D. C.

Part V—Pulleys and Pulley-Block Systems

WHILE the applied forces and resisting forces encountered in levers are quite easily discerned, and, therefore, easily analyzed, the same cannot be said of a more complicated mechanism such as a locomotive. This does not alter the fact, however, that the lever and locomotive are basically the same, in that each is an arrangement of parts in an apparatus by which force is transmitted from one point to another, generally with some modification of its intensity or direction, and resulting in the performance of mechanical work. Both function under the principle of work, and in each the principle of moments applies equally. In the case of the lever, however, the relationship of the contending forces is that of a small applied force and a great resisting force, while in the case of the locomotive a great applied force is used to move a small resisting force.

As a matter of fact, the use of any machine is to adapt the applied forces to the resisting forces. This adaptation is brought about solely by the construction and arrangement of the parts composing the machine and the al-most endless varieties and types of machines illustrate the ingenuity with which applied forces have been regulated, modified and adapted to the varying conditions and requirements of the resisting forces. Thus, wherever a small force is required to move a great resistance; where a force acting in one direction is required to impart motion in another or a velocity greater or less than its own; where a force having reciprocating motion is to produce continuous motion, or one having rectilinear motion is required to produce circular motion—in all these instances, a machine can be obtained or designed which will modify the effect of the applied force in the desired manner.

The simplest form of pulley is that of a grooved wheel turning within a frame to which a hook, eye or strap is fastened. To do work, a rope is fitted into the grooved wheel, and the "block," as it is then called, is attached to some object by means of the hook or strap. This simple block has no mechanical advantage except that which may arise from its ability to change the direction of the pull of the applied force. Whatever force is exerted at one end of the rope is transmitted without increase or decrease (except from friction and the rigidity of the rope) to the resisting force at the other end. This is quite evident from the fact that the machine is nothing more than

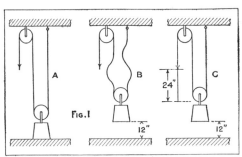

Diagram Illustrating How the Mechanical Advantage of a Pulley-Block System May Be Ascertained

a revolving lever of the first order with the fulcrum midway between the applied and resisting forces, and therefore in equilibrium or balance.

From the foregoing it will be seen that to gain mechanical advantage and therefore to constitute a mechanical power, more than one pulley must be used. The simplest of such combinations is that shown at A, Fig. 1. It will be observed that one pulley is attached or fixed to a support and the other is movable and has the resisting force or load suspended from its axis. One end of the rope is also attached to the support, passes under the movable pulley and over the fixed one. By this arrangement it is plain that the load is supported equally by the supporting beam and the applied force. But the fixed pulley does nothing more than permit the applied force to be directed downward so that, except for this advantage, it may be disregarded in the matter of work performed. Now, to raise the load 12 in., as shown at B, it is plain that each side of the rope around the movable pulley must be moved 12 in. This means that the applied force acting at the free end of the rope must then move downward 24 in., that is, the applied force acts through twice the distance traveled by the load or resisting force, as at C. Therefore, by the principle of

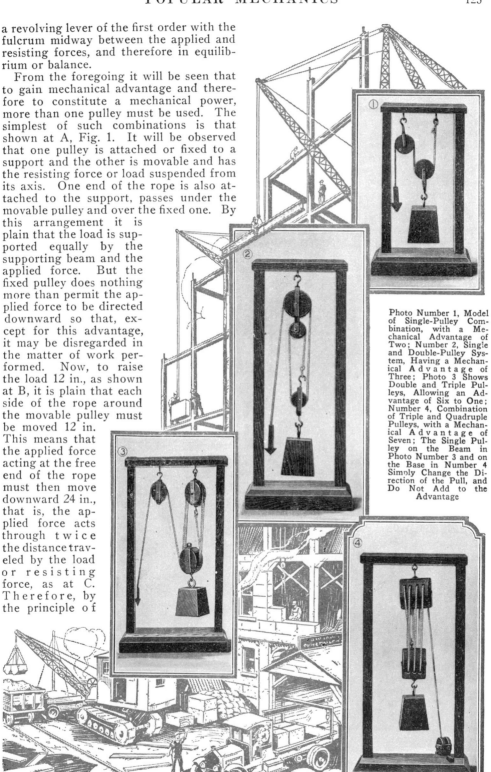

Photo Number 1, Model of Single-Pulley Combination, with a Mechanical Advantage of Two; Number 2, Single and Double-Pulley System, Having a Mechanical Advantage of Three; Photo 3 Shows Double and Triple Pulleys, Allowing an Advantage of Six to One; Number 4, Combination of Triple and Quadruple Pulleys, with a Mechanical Advantage of Seven; The Single Pulley on the Beam in Photo Number 3 and on the Base in Number 4 Simply Change the Direction of the Pull, and Do Not Add to the Advantage

work, that the applied force times the distance through which it moves must equal the resisting force times the distance through which it moves, the load in the case in point is equal to twice the applied force. In other words, an applied force of 1 lb. is sufficient to lift a load of 2 lb., which is the same thing as saying that this pulley arrangement has a mechanical advantage of two. A reproduction of a model of a pulley system of this character is shown in photo No. 1 and Fig. 2.

Photo No. 2 and Fig. 3 represent a combination of a single and a double-pulley block. By the same process of reasoning as before, each of the three ropes that engage the movable pulley must be shortened 1 ft. to raise the weight 1 ft., so that by the principle of work, the force applied at the arrow will have to move 3 ft. to lift the weight 1 ft. Accordingly this combination has a mechanical advantage of three. From these two examples it is evident that whatever the arrangement or number of pulleys, the weight that can be raised can be calculated by observing the relative distances passed through by the applied force and resisting force; also, that the resisting force that can be overcome is always equal to the applied force multiplied by the number of parts of the rope that engage with the movable block. This is a simple and convenient rule to follow in calculating the power of pulley combinations.

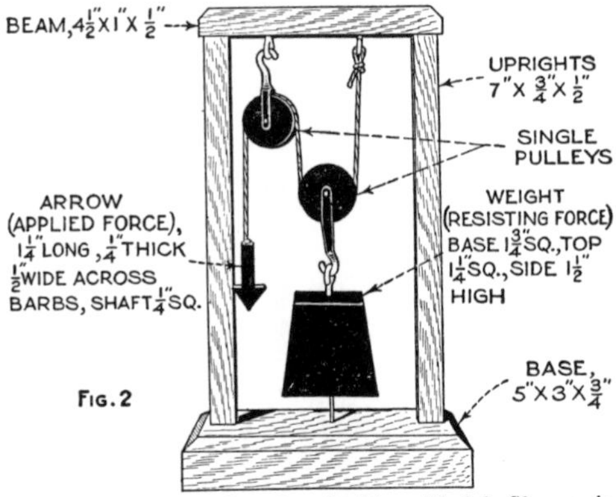

The block and fall illustrated by the model shown in photo No. 3 and Fig. 4 is a combination of a double and a triple pulley with a single draw pulley. The pulleys of each block turn freely upon the same axis and are of the same diameter. From what has been said of the single pulley, it is easily seen that the force required at the arrow is just the same as would be required at any point of the rope between the movable pulley and the single draw pulley. Furthermore the load is equally divided among the pulleys of the lower block, and, of course, among the parts of the rope passing around them, so that by the rule just given, the mechanical advantage of this arrangement is six, there being six parts of the rope which engage

the movable pulley. Another way of arriving at the solution of the relation between applied and resisting forces in pulley systems is by considering that the applied force produces a uniform pull throughout the length of the rope. Each part of the rope engaged with the movable pulley is in tension in an amount equal to the applied force so that the total upward force supporting the load is equal to the applied force times the number of parts of the rope supporting the load. Thus in Fig. 5 it is evident at a glance that there are seven parts of the rope supporting the load and that therefore 1 lb. of applied force will support a load of 7 lb., or that if 350 lb. are to be lifted, an applied force of one-seventh that weight, or 50 lb., is sufficient to do the job. The single pulley attached to the base of the model in Fig. 5 permits a change in the direction of pull of the applied force.

In constructing these models of pulley systems, standard pulleys may be used. They may be purchased in various styles suitable for this work from makers of model ship fittings. However, should the constructor be unable to obtain standard fittings, he may make them similar to the ones illustrated. These are made from turned metal pulleys and soldered strip-copper faces. In the case of the multiple combination, the large assemblies are readily built up by alternating pulleys and pulley faces, connecting all with a shaft of sufficient length.

For the model shown in Fig. 2, the following material is required:

Base, 5 by 3 by ¾ in.
Two uprights, 7 by ¾ by ½ in.
Beam, 4½ by 1 by ½ in.
Two single pulleys.
Weight (resisting force), base 1¾ in. square, top 1¼ in. square, side 1½ in. high.
Arrow (applied force), length 1¼ in., ¼ in. thick, ½ in. wide across barbs, shaft ¼ in. square.
Necessary cordage.

Square and face all wooden parts with a finish bevel on the top of the base and beam. Secure the uprights to the ends of the beam with glue and brads. Center this frame on the base, securing it with glue and screws from beneath. Attach small screweyes to the underside of the beam, one on each side, ¾ in. from the

BEAM, 4½" X 1" X ½"
UPRIGHTS 7" X ¾" X ½"
SINGLE PULLEYS
ARROW (APPLIED FORCE), 1¼" LONG, ¼" THICK, ½"WIDE ACROSS BARBS, SHAFT ¼" SQ.
WEIGHT (RESISTING FORCE), BASE 1¾"SQ.,TOP 1¼"SQ.,SIDE 1½" HIGH
BASE, 5"X 3"X ¾"
FIG. 2

Dimensioned Drawing for Making Model Shown in First Photo

pillars. Hook a single pulley to the left-hand screweye. Hook the other single pulley to the screweye used as a handle for the weight. Fasten an end of a cord, about 10 in. long, to the remaining beam screweye. Reeve it under the weight pulley and over the hanging pulley, attaching the end to the arrow by gluing it in a hole drilled lengthwise in the shaft. Secure the arrow and weight in their proper positions by invisible brads. Finish as desired.

For the single and double-pulley model shown in Fig. 3, use the following material:

Base, 5 by 3 by ¾ in.
Two uprights, 10 by ¾ by ½ in.
Beam, 4½ by ¾ by ½ in.
Single pulley.
Double pulley.
Weight (resisting force), base 1¾ in. square, top 1¼ in. square, side 1½ in. high.
Arrow (applied force), length, 1¼ in., ¼ in. thick, ½ in. wide across barbs, shaft ¼ in. square.
Necessary cordage.

Square and face all wooden parts with a finish bevel on the top of the base and beam. Insert a small screweye in the center of the underside of the beam. Fasten the uprights to the base with glue and screws from beneath. Fasten the beam across the uprights, securing it with brads and glue. Hook the double pulley into the eye on the beam. Hook the lower pulley to the weight. Insert an end of the cord in a hole drilled lengthwise in the arrow. Reeve the cordage over one wheel of the large pulley, under the wheel of the lower pulley, over the second wheel of the

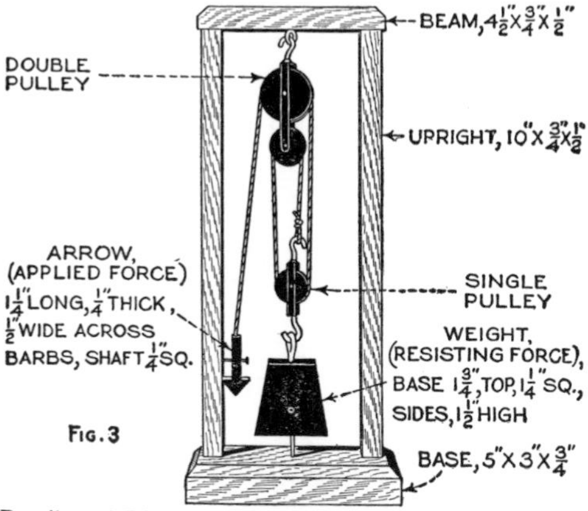

Fig. 3

Details and Dimensions of Model of Single and Double-Pulley System

large pulley and attach it to the top hook of the lower pulley, as shown in photograph. Retain the weight and arrow in their correct position by invisible brads. Finish as desired.

For the model shown in Fig. 4, the following materials are required:

Base, 6½ by 4 by ¾ in.
Two uprights, 10 by ¾ by ½ in.
Beam, 6¼ by 1 by ½ in.
Single pulley.
Double pulley.
Triple pulley.
Weight (resisting force), base 1¾ in. square, top 1¼ in. square, side 1½ in. high.
Arrow (applied force), 1¼ in. long, ¼ in. thick, ½ in. wide across barbs, shaft ¼ in. square.
Necessary cordage.

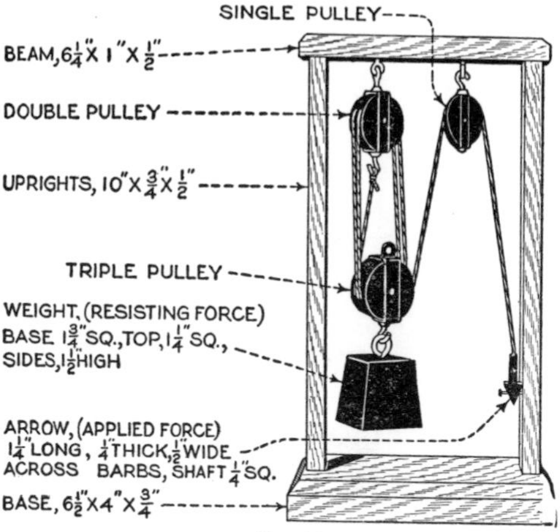

Fig. 4

Construction Details for Model of Double and Triple-Pulley System

Square and face all wooden parts with a finish bevel on the top of the base and beam. Secure the two uprights to the ends of the beam with glue. Attach this frame to the base, securing it with glue and screws from beneath. Attach two screweyes on the center line of the underside of the beam and 1½ in. from each pillar. Hook the single pulley to one screweye and the double pulley to the other. Hook the triple pulley to the screweye used as a handle for the weight. Attach an end of the cord to the lower hook of the double pulley and reeve through corresponding wheels of the double and triple pulleys, carrying the end from the triple-pulley wheel over the single pulley and gluing it in a hole drilled lengthwise in the arrow shaft. Retain the arrow in its proper position with an invisible brad. Finish as desired.

For the model in Fig. 5, the following materials are necessary:

Base, 6 by 4 by ¾ in.
Two uprights, 10 by ¾ by ½ in.
Beam, 5½ by ¾ by ½ in.
Four-sheave pulley.
Three-sheave pulley.
Single pulley.
Weight (resisting force), base 1¾ in. square, top 1¼ in. square, side 1½ in. high.
Arrow (applied force), 1¼ in. long, ¼ in. thick, ½ in. wide across barbs, shaft ¼ in. square.
Necessary cordage.

Square and face all wooden parts with a finish bevel on the top of the base and beam. Insert a screweye in the center of the underside of the beam. Fasten the ends of the beam to the uprights with glue and brads. Secure this frame to the center of the base with screws and glue. Attach the four-sheave pulley to the beam eye. Attach the three-sheave pulley to the screweye used as a handle for the weight.

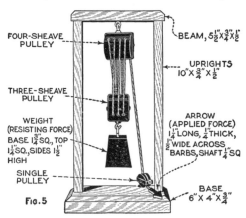

FOUR-SHEAVE PULLEY

BEAM, $5\frac{1}{2}"\times\frac{3}{4}"\times\frac{1}{2}"$

UPRIGHTS $10"\times\frac{3}{4}"\times\frac{1}{2}"$

THREE-SHEAVE PULLEY

WEIGHT (RESISTING FORCE)

ARROW (APPLIED FORCE) $1\frac{1}{4}"$ LONG, $\frac{1}{4}"$ THICK, $\frac{1}{2}"$ WIDE ACROSS BARBS, SHAFT $\frac{1}{4}"$ SQ

BASE $1\frac{3}{4}"$ SQ., TOP $1\frac{1}{4}"$ SQ., SIDES $1\frac{1}{2}"$ HIGH

SINGLE PULLEY

BASE $6"\times 4"\times\frac{3}{4}"$

FIG. 5

Dimensions and Details of Model Showing Combination of Three and Four-Sheave Pulleys

Fasten the end of cord to the upper eye of the three-sheave pulley and reeve alternately through the upper and the lower pulleys, attaching the free end to the arrow by inserting the cord in a hole drilled lengthwise in the shaft. Finish as desired.

In the photograph illustrating this model a direction-changing single pulley is used. This is not necessary for mechanical advantage, being only an illustration of a possible convenience.

(Continued Next Month)

Dirtproof Oilstone Box

In general practice oilstones are usually kept in a plain box with a piece of leather nailed on the cover. When honing, the

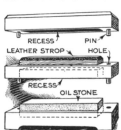

RECESS   PIN

LEATHER STROP   HOLE

RECESS   OIL STONE

cover is laid down wherever most convenient—often in dirt and grit —with the result that some dirt gets on the stone when the cover is put on again. The exposed leather strop is also a place where dirt and grit are liable to collect, and the sharp edge of a tool or knife will quickly be ruined when using a dirty strop. The illustration shows an oilstone box designed to eliminate this trouble. It consists of three parts: a holder for the stone, a

holder for the strop and a cover. The lower section is recessed to hold the stone and the center piece is recessed to fit over it. A leather strop is mounted neatly on a piece of wood of the same size, which is screwed on the middle section and the cover is recessed to fit over this piece loosely. Two $\frac{5}{32}$-in. holes, about $\frac{1}{2}$ in. deep, are drilled in each section as shown, and $\frac{1}{8}$-in. metal pins are provided to fit into these holes.

Auxiliary Finger for Height Gauge

In selecting lines on jigs from which to locate other lines, more or less trouble is encountered by not being able to get an

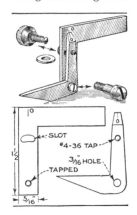

SLOT

#4-36 TAP

$\frac{3}{16}"$ HOLE TAPPED

exact measurement, owing to the stiffness of the height gauge. I therefore made the scriber shown in the illustration, which gives very good results. It is made in two parts, connected by means of a small screw. To set the scriber, the thumbscrew is released so that the pointed end can work freely. The sharp point is inserted into the line and the head of the gauge raised or lowered until the two zero lines meet; the thumbscrew is then tightened, leaving the scriber parallel and the center of the line located correctly. The remaining measurements are taken from the graduations on the height gauge. The drawing gives the dimensions and shows how the tool is assembled.—Fred A. Dufresne, Riverside, Rhode Island.

Turning Piston on Centers

When machining a gasoline-engine piston in a small lathe, which was not equipped with a chuck large enough for this kind of work, the following method was adopted: A piece of scrap iron of irregular shape was placed inside of the piston, and lead was poured in the space between it and the piston wall, to make a solid mass. It was then an easy matter to mount the piston in the lathe between centers in the usual way, and the work of turning it was easily accomplished.—Harold N. Sellan, Peterboro, Can.

Taking Up Play in Crankcase Bearing

When the front crankcase bearing on the frame of a Ford car wears and the motor begins to pound as a result, a quick method of making a repair without using new parts is to cut a piece of thin sheet steel wide enough to fit between the flanges on the bearing spool and long enough to wrap around it one or more times, depending on the amount of wear. The cap is removed and the front end of the motor with the crank is lifted high enough to pass the strip under the bearing spool. The cap is then replaced and the cap screws tightened down. If the cap will not come down on the frame, too much metal has been used and in this case the cap is again removed and part of the strip unwound and cut off. —E. T. Gunderson, Humboldt, Ia.

Novel Drain Installation

With the customary method of fitting a drain flange in the bottom of a water tank it is necessary to take down the whole installation in case the drain tile becomes clogged. This objectionable feature is entirely eliminated by the novel construction shown in the drawing. A recessed cast-iron ring is riveted to the underside of the tank bottom and in this ring studs are provided to hold a brass flange into which the overflow pipe is screwed. A short nipple on the end of this pipe projects into the drain tile leading to the sewer. One can readily see how easy it is to remove the overflow pipe when a thorough cleaning is necessary. Furthermore, the cast-iron ring, being below the tank bottom, allows the tank to be completely drained, which is impossible when it is attached to the upper side.

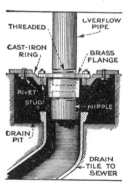

Low Cart for Stenciling Rolls

In a carpet factory, a low cart with a padded seat, ball-bearing casters, and a shelf on one side, is used by the workman who stencils or labels the rolls of carpet. The cart, built especially for the purpose, is just high enough for the worker to sit on comfortably when applying the stencil, the shelf on the side holding the brush, paste, paint, stencils and labels so that they need not be carried from one roll to the next. Obviously, the work can be done

Low Cart Facilitates Work of Stenciling and Labeling Rolls of Carpet

much faster this way than if the worker has to stoop down or get on his knees in front of every roll.

Support for Portable Lamp

The ordinary portable garage lamp is provided with a hook on the end of the wire guard so that it can be hung up conveniently. However, when working underneath a car the lamp can not always be hung up so that the light is thrown on the work and therefore it is usually laid on the floor. A much better method is to provide a simple support of the kind shown for holding the lamp under the work. It is made from a 6-in. length of 1½-in. pipe, slotted as shown to receive the lampcord, and screwed into a floor flange, which, in turn, is securely screwed to a wooden block about 6 in. square. A tin reflector is riveted to the support to shade the light from the worker's eyes.

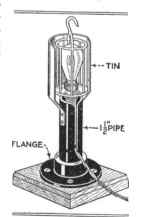

Convenient Farm-Tool Kit

Tools for all ordinary repairs on farm machinery can be conveniently carried in the small kit shown in the photo, according to agricultural experts of a western college of agriculture who designed it. Besides being easily portable—the complete outfit, including all the tools, weighs only about 24 lb.—it has the advantage of being so arranged that the omission of any one tool will be noticed immediately.

The kit can easily be made by anyone handy with tools. The outside dimensions of the box are 17 by 15 by 4½ in. Its two halves are hinged at one side and two hinged hasps are provided on the other for locking. This side also has

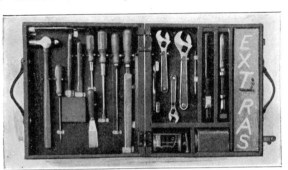

A Neat and Compact Tool Kit for the Farmer; It Weighs Only 24 Pounds Including All Tools

two 7-in. leather handles for carrying, one on each half. The material is ½-in. lumber except for the bottom, in which ¾-in. is used to provide sufficient thickness for the hinges.

The tools are held in place by spring clips, so that any one of them can be removed and replaced without disturbing the others. This arrangement tends to prevent loss of tools.

The hinges, hasps and spring clips are all standard pieces that can be obtained at any hardware store. The guards for the ends of the files, chisels and screwdrivers, and the keepers for the rule, pliers and calipers are easily made of galvanized iron.

A compartment measuring 3½ by 1¾ by 17 in. provides space for extras, such as bolts, nuts, washers and cotter keys. This is closed with a sheet-iron cover, which is divided in the center, hinged at each end and fastened in the middle by a loop and cotter key. This cover is essential in order that none of the contents may be lost when the kit is closed.

The tool equipment consists of 1-lb. ball-peen hammer; 6-in. slender three-cornered file; 8-in. round file; 10-in. mill file; 6-in. screwdriver; 3-in. screwdriver; putty knife; 7 by ⅝-in. chisel; 8 by ⅝-in. punch; 6 by ⅜-in. punch; 8-in. double calipers; 3-ft. four-fold rule; 6-in. slip-joint pliers; 6-in. crescent wrench; 8-in. crescent wrench; 10-in. crescent wrench; 14-in. pipe wrench; 12-in. monkey wrench; 8 oz. oilcan; grease can.

Both oil and grease cans should have screw tops. The opening in the grease can should be large enough to admit the blade of the putty knife, which can be used conveniently for filling grease cups.—M. L. Coultrap, Fresno, Calif.

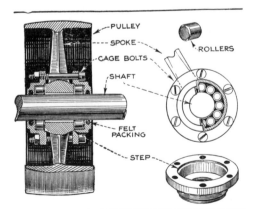

Roller Bearings Fitted to Pulleys Reduce Wear and Friction

Roller Bearings for Loose Pulleys

Pulleys that run loose on a shaft and wear out their bushings quickly due to heavy or tight belts can be fitted with roller bearings to eliminate this trouble; this will also reduce friction. The hub of the pulley is bored out, or in case it contains a bushing, this is knocked out, and the sides of the hub are then turned down to fit the roller cages. These are made of steel or cast iron, turned and drilled as indicated, then slipped over and bolted in place on the hub. Each cage contains its own single row of rollers, and a packing groove is turned in each cage, in which a ring of soft-felt packing is placed; this retains the oil or thin grease that is fed to the cavity in the center of the hub by an oil or grease cup. The outer faces of the cages are machined to bear against the collars used to prevent end motion. The rollers are made of low-carbon tool steel, turned, hardened and drawn to a brown color, then ground to size. Six or eight can be turned in one piece and notched so as to be broken apart easily after grinding. The rollers must have beveled edges as shown in order to run freely in the raceways and should all be of exactly the same diameter and length.—J. V. Romig, Allentown, Pa.

A Bevel-Gear Chuck

Small bevel gears with cast teeth are easily ruined if they are chucked in a regular lathe chuck for boring, or facing, and the time consumed in chucking makes some simpler method highly desirable. Where quantities of such gears are to be machined it will be economy to make the chuck shown in the drawing. A chucking-ring casting of the form and shape illustrated is machined and fitted to the lathe faceplate and

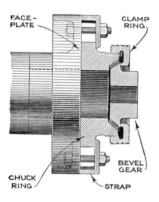

is then bored and tapered to a nice fit for the face of the gears. The beveled face conforms to that of the gears and the internal diameter should permit of sliding the hubs in easily. The outside of the fixture is then threaded and onto this is screwed the threaded clamping ring, the narrow flange of which bears against the back of the gear and holds it firmly in place during the machine operations. For use with small gears, the clamping ring can be pulled up tightly enough by knurling the outer face of the clamping ring, but a spanner must be used for large work.

Lamps Show if Factory Machinery Is Working

In a canning factory having seven food-packing machines the manager has installed a little device near his desk to indicate whether or not all seven are working properly. The device consists of a panel on which seven miniature lamps are mounted, each of which is connected to

one of the machines, so that every time a can passes to the filling machine it causes a lamp to flash. As long as the lamps keep

Flashing Lamps near Manager's Desk Indicate Whether Factory Machinery Is Working Properly

flashing, the manager knows that everything is going well, but if any lamps fail to flash it is a signal to him that he is perhaps needed in the factory to untangle some difficulty. A switch is, of course, provided so that the current can be turned on or off.

Preventing Sticking of Starter Pinion

Occasionally a Bendix-drive gear will stick in mesh and will not release after the engine has been started. In most cases this trouble can be prevented by providing a small stop on the end of the spring as shown in the illustration. The stop is cut out of heavy sheet metal, drilled and bolted to the end of the spring, and bent to conform to the curvature of the flange on the pinion. A small lug must be provided on the head of this stop to fit into the eye of the spring in order to prevent the stop from turning on the screw that holds it. It is then casehardened to keep it from being battered. The stop strikes the weight on the flange of the gear and prevents jamming of the pinion.—Ralph T. Stewart, Statesville, N. C.

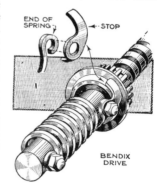

Steel Rack for Lumber Trucks

Trucks used for carrying lumber can be made much more useful by providing a steel rack in front of the radiator, as shown

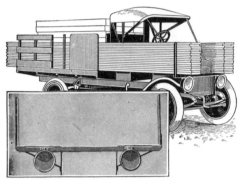

Steel Rack Attached on Front of Motor Truck Permits Carrying Long Lumber

in the drawing. By this means very long planks and timbers can be carried without extending behind the truck farther than a normal load. The rack is made of square iron rod and is bolted directly to the truck frame. If the headlights interfere with the rack, they may be removed and brazed to the rack itself, as shown. This arrangement has been found entirely satisfactory.

Tool for Adjusting Internal Brakes

On many internal brakes there is a small screw inside the drum at the rear of the brake, which cannot be turned with any ordinary screwdriver, as the head of the screw can scarcely be touched with the

finger after the small plate on the drum has been removed. It is therefore usually necessary to remove the wheel and take apart the whole assembly in order to make this single adjustment, and this, of course, is undesirable. However, the brake adjustments can be made quickly and without the necessity of taking the wheel off, by using the simple tool shown in the illustration. It is a hinged, offset screwdriver and has been found entirely satisfactory for use on the Cadillac. It is inserted through the small opening in the drum, so that the lip engages one of the slots in the screw head. Turning the wheel down a trifle while holding the end of the tool, causes the spokes to press against the handle, and this will move

the screw about one-eighth of a turn. Then by striking on the end of the screwdriver with a hammer the screw can be moved another eighth turn, or one-fourth turn in all. As the two slots in the screw head are at right angles, the second slot will now be in position to be engaged by the lip, and the above-described operation is repeated until the screw has been tightened.—J. E. Dekker, Chicago, Ill.

Improving Joint of Double-Beam Compasses

When two beams are used in beam compasses they have a tendency to rock slightly due to the construction of the joint, and this, of course, causes the distance between the points to vary. This trouble can be eliminated by drilling a hole in the end of one beam and turning down the end of the other to fit the hole snugly. This joint will connect the beams solidly and prevent the undesired rocking.

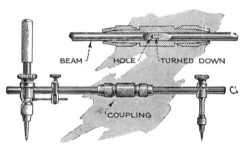

Improved Joint on Beams of Compasses Prevents Rocking

Handy Screwdriver Attachment

For driving or removing heavy screws an attachment for an ordinary monkey wrench, made as shown in the illustration,

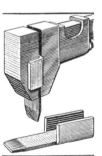

has been found to be of considerable usefulness. It is formed from a piece of tool steel about ⅛ in. thick, cut and bent to the shape shown, with the edge ground down and tempered. The attachment is especially handy for loosening screws that are rusted in place. The leverage obtained is much greater than that of an ordinary screwdriver, and therefore care must be taken not to twist off the head of the screw when trying to loosen it.

ETCHING GLASS

By J. S. Hagans

HYDROFLUORIC acid has the rather unusual property of attacking glass and silicates in general. It is about the only chemical that will attack glass, and beyond this its use is very limited. This feature of hydrofluoric acid makes it of particular value in the decoration and ornamentation of glass without recourse to mechanical processes, such as sandblasting or grinding. The latter processes have the merit of speed and cheapness, but for a number of purposes the acid cannot be displaced, particularly if there is any shading to be done. Another peculiar feature of hydrofluoric acid is that both the acid itself and its fumes attack the glass. Direct contact with the acid leaves the glass clear, while exposure to the fumes leaves a frosted effect, which, however, is not particularly bright. Hydrofluoric acid is not difficult to make, but manufacture is inadvisable because of the risk of burns, and it cannot be overemphasized that this acid is poisonous, and produces bad burns on contact with the skin, wherefore it is recommended that rubber gloves be worn when handling it, and that a breathing mask be worn, or, at least, the work should be done under a laboratory hood that carries off the fumes.

Naturally the acid cannot be kept in glass or earthenware containers, but is supplied in lead bottles. While the acid itself is comparatively cheap, its price is increased somewhat by the cost of the lead containers. Powerful as is its action on glass, hydrofluoric acid cannot cut grease or wax, and for this reason it is possible to use wooden trays and metal dippers for handling the acid, provided they are thickly coated with beeswax; lead trays, of course, are also unaffected by it.

Based upon the above-mentioned properties of the acid, several processes have been worked out for its practical use, chief among them its application to what is generally known as "glass embossing," principally used in the monogramming or decoration of glass, either in relief or intaglio, depending upon the effect it is desired to obtain. Being unaffected by

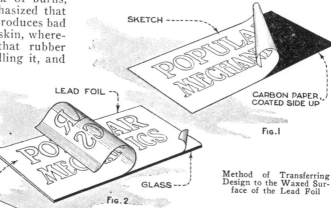

SKETCH

LEAD FOIL

CARBON PAPER, COATED SIDE UP

Fig. 1

SKETCH

GLASS

Fig. 2

Method of Transferring Design to the Waxed Surface of the Lead Foil

CLEAR GLASS

LEAD FOIL

Fig. 3

the fluid and its fumes, beeswax can be used to make an effective "resist"; if the decoration is to stand out above the surface of the glass, it is only necessary to block out the design with wax, and for intaglio work, to use the lead-stencil method described in the article on sandblasting published in the March, 1923, issue, which is preferable. This consists in warming the glass, applying a little beeswax, and then, while the wax is still warm, rubbing a piece of lead foil into absolute mechanical contact. The design is cut out in this. The design may be transferred to the foil by first laying it out on paper, then laying the design on carbon paper, coated side up, as in Fig. 1, and going over it with a hard pencil or stylus. The sketch is then laid on the foil, which has also been covered with beeswax, and rubbed down with the bowl of a spoon or other rounded metallic object; when the sketch is peeled off, as in Fig. 2, the carbon lines will have been transferred to the waxed surface of the foil, which can then be cut out, as shown in Fig. 3. After cutting the stencil, it is advisable, when etching by acid, to wipe off the design with soda water, or in the case of fine work,

Fɪɢ. 4

Producing a Mottled or Pitted Background by Means of Flake Mica or Shot

with castile soap dissolved in gasoline, to remove any wax that does not adhere to the foil.

As mentioned previously, use of the straight acid leaves a clear glass and this process is used when working with "flashed" red or blue glass, in which the color is only on the surface. Using the acid to remove the thin skin of color that may be on either one or both sides of the glass, the effect of clear glass against a strong blue or red background is obtained.

Another particularly good effect is an "antique finish" that gives the glass a mottled appearance, somewhat similar to that of hammered-copper articles. This result is obtained by blocking out the parts it is desired to remain unaffected by the acid either with wax or lead foil and then sprinkling the rest with ground mica, or the artificial "snow" used on Christmas trees, as in Fig. 4. The particles of mica will cause the surface of the glass to be pitted when the acid is applied, an effect that is particularly pleasing for such purposes as leaded-glass windows, panels for

table lamps and similar uses. This effect can be varied by using lead shot or gravel in the same manner, as illustrated in Fig. 5. If shot is used, the effect is considerably more regular; this feature can be utilized to good advantage for some purposes. A similar but better effect is obtainable by using gravel of any desired degree of coarseness in the same manner. There is one objection to the use of gravel, however, and that is its weakening effect on the acid. Ordinarily the acid can be used repeatedly until it loses its strength. However, since practically all gravels contain a considerable proportion of silica, the latter is attacked in the same way that the glass is itself.

Now we come to the use of "white" acid. The plain acid leaves a clear etching, and the frosting obtained by exposure to the fumes is unsatisfactory. However, by the use of the so-called white acid it is entirely possible to get any degree of frosting desired, and to regulate the effect in such a manner that, in the case of monograms and similar work, all the letters can be given a different value. White acid is prepared by mixing full-strength hydrofluoric acid, $\frac{1}{2}$ pt.; carbonate of soda, $\frac{1}{2}$ lb., and water, 1 pt. Only clear crystals of the soda should be used and the white-powder residue should be discarded. The crystals may be crushed to hasten the action. The pure acid, while dissolving the surface, has the effect of leaving it clear, but when modified or neutralized by the action of an alkali, as in the white acid, it produces a dense white frosted surface. By varying the strength of the white acid, that is, by increasing or diminishing the amount of water, and by regulating the time allowed for the etching, almost any variation in shading can be obtained. For example, in etching a monogram on a door panel, it is desired that each of three initials be distinct from the others. This can be done by etching one letter at a time and blocking out the others as the work goes on, as shown in Fig. 6. The full strength of white acid may be used for frosting the first letter. For the second letter, the acid is diluted with water and the time allowed for etching reduced, and so with the third letter. Ornamental de-

Fɪɢ. 5

GLASS EXPOSED

FOIL OR WAX

GLASS EXPOSED

FOIL OR WAX

GLASS EXPOSED

1ST STAGE   2ND STAGE   3RD STAGE

FIG. 6

GLASS EXPOSED

FOIL

SPOUT FORMED TO DRAIN ACID BY BENDING FOIL

FIG. 7

WAX

FIG. 8

EXCESS WAX

SCRAPER

DEPRESSION FILLED WITH WAX

FIG. 9

TISSUE

FIG. 10

Various Steps in the Production of Monograms and Master Plates; the Latter Are Used in Connection with the Sandblast Process for Quantity Work

signs of vines, leaves, and the like, can be produced in this way, but this, of course, is subject to the artistic ability and patience of the worker.

The etching process may be combined with sandblasting in the production of quantity work such as is necessary when making, say, the glasses used for automobile stop signals, where it would be almost impossible to make an individual stencil for each one of an order of several thousand pieces. First, a master plate is made by etching on glass. This plate is used only for transferring the design to the work that is to be sandblasted. The glass is covered with lead foil and the stencil is cut in "negative," that is, the parts that are not later to be affected by the sandblast on the work are left unprotected, and so are eaten out by the action of the acid. Also, the design will have to be reversed on the master plate. The best way to go about the preparation of a master plate, if one has occasion to use it, is to cover the whole of one surface of a piece of plate glass with lead foil, turning up the edges in such a manner that they form a tray into which the acid may be poured, and cut the design through the foil as before. The corners should be daubed with wax to prevent leaking. In this way, when etching has been carried far enough, a part of one side of the foil can be bent down to form a lip, as in Fig. 7, through which the acid is run off into a suitably protected vessel. It might here be added that action of the acid is stopped by applying water to the work, and furthermore, that it will eat the enamel off sinks and similar fixtures as well as the glaze from closet bowls and other earthenware plumbing fixtures.

It is not necessary to carry the etching deeply in making a master or printing plate; 1/16 in. will be found sufficient for most cases. The action of the acid is uniform throughout the work and the depth of etching can be found by the "feel" when the point of a knife is slipped over the edge. Master plates of this kind can be made also from metal in exactly the same way, but substituting nitric acid for the hydrofluoric. Needless to say, the surface of the metal should be perfectly smooth. The master plate having been prepared, it will be necessary to prepare a resist, which consists of a composition of resinous and greasy substances, each of which should be proof against the action of acids. One of the oldest recipes gives bitumen, stearin and turpentine; another gives beeswax, Canada balsam and soap, and a third consists ot beeswax, turpentine, asphaltum, resin and tallow or lard. No proportions are given because it is practically impossible to do so, since every worker has his own pet formula that he guards religiously, just why no one knows. At any rate, this resist should be made about the consistency of rather stiff putty, and as a starting point one might use equal parts of beeswax and soap, adding Canada balsam or turpentine to get the proper consistency. A thorough mixture of the ingredients with the aid of heat is necessary, but the exact nature and proportion of the ingredients can be varied to a considerable extent It is evident, however, that too great a portion of the harder substances, such as wax or asphaltum, will make a "short" compound, which will not adhere sufficiently to both glass or paper, while too much soap, stearin, etc., will have the opposite effect. More grease will be required in cold weather and more resin or similar substance in hot. While a variation in the quantity of turpentine or Canada balsam will be found useful, experiment is the only safe guide.

Assuming that a satisfactory resist has been obtained, a scraper having a perfectly straight and rounded edge is another necessity. A portion of the resist is worked into the depression etched into the master plate and the excess removed with the scraper, as in Figs. 8 and 9. If the scraper edge is perfectly true, the cavity of the design will be filled with the resist, while the excess will have been removed from the surface of the plate. Next a sheet of tissue paper is laid over the design and brought into contact with the wax by patting the back of the paper with a small brush, Fig. 10; a cheap nail brush will answer for this. The paper is then pulled off, and if the resist has been properly compounded, the full design will be found, on the paper. The paper, with its adhering wax, is then laid, with the wax side down, on the plain glass, and patted lightly with the brush as before. When this has been done until the resist is in contact with the glass throughout the design, the back of the paper is dampened with a sponge; then the paper is peeled off, leaving the design in resist on the glass. Of course, a separate piece of paper is necessary for each operation. The process, while requiring this lengthy description, is really quite simple. The resist, as it has been called throughout, forms a mask or stencil that is acted on but slightly by the sandblast and can be removed afterward.

¶A little lead, about 2 per cent, added to molten bronze, will make the casting much easier to cut when machining it.

Centering Work in Lathe

A quick method of centering chucked work, whether it is a rough casting or a machined piece, is as follows: After mounting the work approximately on center, turn the chuck or faceplate by hand and hold a scriber or any convenient tool close enough to the edge to show where the work runs out. In the case of a rough casting, it is often sufficient to put a block of wood or metal on the carriage of the lathe, moving the work until it clears this block about the same distance all the way around. For a machined piece it is best to have a tool with a sharp point to bring it up to the work; a surface gauge resting on the carriage is very convenient and also a scriber held on the toolpost. A strong light on the point is necessary. With this method a careful man can work nearly as accurately as with an indicator.

Convenient Trailer Hitch

Hitching farm machinery or a trailer to the truck, which is frequently done, is an easy matter if a simple hitch of the kind shown in the illustration is attached to the rear axle. It consists of a length of flat-iron stock, 2 or 3 in. wide and ¼ to ⅜ in. thick. The center part is bent to form an eye about 15 in. behind the axle, a rivet being driven through the strap where it

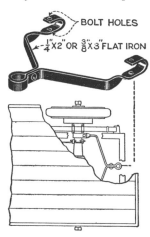

BOLT HOLES

¼"X2" OR ⅜"X3" FLAT IRON

is doubled. The ends are twisted and bent around the axle just inside of the spring seats and bolted securely.

Spectacle Lenses in Camera Hood Aid Photographer

Failing eyesight forces more photographers to retire than old age. This is especially true in case of newspaper photographers and others whose work demands the use of a reflecting camera. Defective eyesight prohibits operating such a camera, and the use of ordinary eyeglasses is impracticable. However, a western newspaper photographer remedied the difficulty by fitting a pair of eyeglasses in the hood of the camera as shown in the draw-

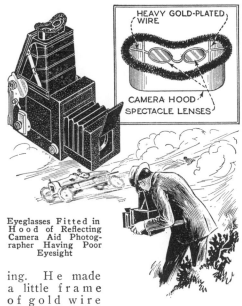

HEAVY GOLD-PLATED WIRE

CAMERA HOOD
SPECTACLE LENSES

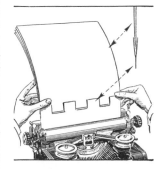

Eyeglasses Fitted in Hood of Reflecting Camera Aid Photographer Having Poor Eyesight

ing. He made a little frame of gold wire obtained at a jeweler's shop to hold the lenses. With this arrangement he can get along without glasses, and is always able to use his camera when going around on his daily assignments.

Crowding the Typewriter

It is usually found difficult to feed any considerable number of sheets and carbons into a typewriter at the same time. This can be done easily, however, by making several cuts in the edge of a sheet of strong paper, and placing the flaps thus formed alternately on either side of the bunch of sheets, then feeding them into the machine as shown in the drawing. In this way the sheets are held tightly and in alinement, and even if it is necessary for any reason to remove them from the machine, and afterward to re insert them, they can be brought to the same position as before.

Folding Shelf for Ladder

Painters, carpenters and others who use ladders frequently and must have some device for holding tools while working, will find the folding shelf shown in the draw-

Useful Folding Ladder Shelf for Painters and Carpenters Is Detachable and Portable

ing of considerable assistance. It consists of a 10 by 11-in. board with strips nailed around the sides to prevent tools and articles from rolling off, and two 14-in. lengths of 2 by ⅞-in. wood, which are hinged to the shelf and bear against the underside of the ladder when the shelf is hooked onto a rung. Two iron crosspieces hold the wooden braces securely, and metal braces hinged in the center keep the shelf in a horizontal position when in use and make the device foldable, as shown.

The upper end of the lower member of each metal brace is cut and bent over at right angles to catch in a slot cut in the upper member, as indicated in the detail; this prevents the braces from doubling up when weight is placed on the shelf.

Frequency of Tillage Operations

The number of times tillage operations are necessary on certain soils depends on the nature of the soil and the kind of weather. Sandy soils must usually be tilled more frequently than clayey soils. Heavy rains pattering down on soils tend to make them more compact, which makes it necessary to loosen them again. During hot weather most soils dry out rapidly and become crusty, which also necessitates tillage operations.

The rapid growth of weeds determines to a great extent how often tillage is necessary. Weeds have been termed "voracious eaters and heavy drinkers," as they rob the crops of considerable food and water. The best remedy is frequent shallow tillage, which should be started before the weeds have made their first appearance, and should be repeated as often as they are about to break ground. By keeping the weeds down in this way it 'is possible to prevent the loss of a great amount of soil water, which would otherwise be taken up by the weeds.—E. R. Haan, Chicago, Ill.

Filing Connecting-Rod Caps

Connecting-rod caps and caps on ball joints can be filed conveniently in the vise when a simple U-shaped holder of the kind shown in the drawing is used. The holder is a length of steel rod of a diameter to correspond to the bolt holes of the cap, and bent to fit in these holes snugly. The handy feature of this holder is that the cap can be removed as often as desired without loosening and tightening the vise.

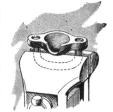

Laying Putty Evenly

When applying putty to windows on large glazing jobs it is desirable to do the work with speed as well as neatness. It is, however, quite difficult to make the putty lie at the same angle and width all over when running over it fast with a putty knife. To overcome this difficulty it has been found very convenient to

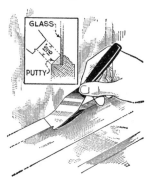

cut a notch in the edge of the knife to ride on the edge of the window frame as shown in the illustration. The putty is first pressed on in the usual way and then smoothed off evenly with the knife.

Washing Tank for Films and Prints

By EDW. H. FLAHARTY

VERY often the photographer, even the professional worker on a small scale, encounters difficulty in finding a suitable method of washing his films, plates and prints in running water without danger of scratching or creasing them.

A washing tank, as shown in the accompanying illustration, has solved the problem for one photographer. This tank can be made of any desired size and capacity to meet individual requirements and particular conditions, although the dimensions given below will be found suitable for most purposes. First a tank is made of gal-

Easily Made Film and Print-Washing Tank for the Photographer; the Outlet Is Arranged So That the Tank May Be Made to Empty and Refill Itself Automatically

vanized sheet iron, measuring about 4 ft. long and 8 in. deep. The corners are soldered to insure their being water-tight. The tank is placed on a board or shelf beside the sink, then a connection is made with the cold-water pipe, preferably between the tap and the end of the pipe to which the tap is connected. This may be done by means of a reducing tee, inserted between the tap and the nipple; the tee connects with a smaller pipe, which in turn is followed by a tap, corresponding in size with the pipe used, and into this tap a pipe is screwed which runs along the entire side and one end of the tank, or it may be made to circle the tank. This pipe has small holes drilled into it a few inches apart, which permit an even spray of water to play over the tank, causing a slight but continual agitation of the water.

The outlet of the tank is arranged so as to give two methods of emptying the tank, and is in the form of a 1-in. pipe connection which drains into the sink. About 1½ in. from the top of the tank a hole is cut and a 1-in. bushing soldered into the hole. A connection, the inlet of which comes at the bottom and on the inside of the tank, is formed by a short piece of pipe leading horizontally from the bushing, then an ell pointing down, to which is connected another piece of pipe. The short piece of pipe leading into the fixed bushing is allowed to remain a little loose so that the piece of pipe which is attached vertically to the ell (and the ell itself) may swing from the vertical to a position nearly horizontal, allowing the tank to be emptied from the bottom or from the top. This sort of connection will prevent an overflow, for after the water has reached a certain height, a siphon is automatically formed and the water drains from the tank into the sink. If the inside pipe is at an angle near the horizontal the tank will contain a large quantity of water all the time, but if the pipe is turned down straight the tank will automatically empty and refill.

To prevent prints or films from adhering to the outlet connection and causing an overflow, a screen of galvanized wire is placed a few inches from the end of the pipe, and fastened in place by small bolts and nuts, or rivets may be used as effectively. A small drain shelf of galvanized sheet iron is placed at the farther end of the tank at an angle of about 30°, directly under a red light used for viewing films and prints in the process of development. While these are being examined the dripping developer falls onto this shelf and drains into the tank. The cost of material for the tank is small, and the tank solves a troublesome film-washing problem.

Buffing Short Screw Heads

It is sometimes almost impossible to hold small articles such as screws in the fingers when polishing them on a cloth buffing wheel, owing to the drag of the

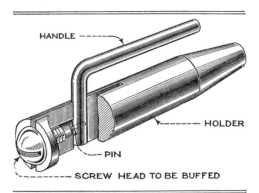

HANDLE

HOLDER

PIN

SCREW HEAD TO BE BUFFED

Holder for Buffing Short Screw Heads that Is Quick-Acting and Holds the Screws Securely

wheel. Unless the work is large enough to enable the operator to secure a good hold it is nearly always advisable to use a holder, especially as the work usually becomes very hot. There are, of course, hundreds of different kinds of holders for this work, but the one shown in the illustration is worth describing, because of its quick-operating feature. The holder itself is made of round steel, tapered at one end to fit into a file handle, and having a hole drilled at the other end a trifle smaller than the shanks of the screws to be buffed. Another hole is drilled through the side at right angles to the first for a handle, which is merely a piece of round steel rod, bent as shown. The holder is then slit open from the end to a distance beyond the handle hole. The short end of the handle is drilled for a small pin, which is rounded at both ends and projects a trifle on both sides. With the tool assembled as shown, the handle is turned at right angles to spread the end so that the screw can be inserted easily, then turned back again so that the screw will be gripped firmly. The spreading is effected by the small pin in the handle. This holder grips a screw so securely that one press into the wheel polishes it. By again turning the handle as explained, the screws are dropped into a box without coming in contact with the fingers at all.

Two Kinks for the Draftsman

Draftsmen frequently find it necessary to scribe an arc of which the center is located outside of the drawing board. This can easily be done by the method shown in the illustration. Two 4-in. boards of a thickness equal to that of the drawing board are cut to suitable lengths, and screwed together from the underside, one being about 4 in. longer than the other. The longer one is clamped to the drawing board by means of a small C-clamp, bringing the upper surface of the shorter one level with the top of the board. The pivot point of the beam compass can then be placed wherever necessary on the extension to scribe the arc. Obviously, the extension can be clamped to the board at any point most convenient for the purpose.

Often a piece of sandpaper is attached to the corner of the drawing board in a handy position for sharpening pencils, but unless the draftsman is very careful, he is likely to get some of the pencil dust on his hands or arms and then accidentally smudge the drawing with it. This can be prevented by providing a simple sheet-metal shield, as shown in the lower detail. The sheet metal is cut and bent to the shape indicated and is tacked or screwed over the sandpaper. The longitudinal flange of the shield is bent inward and in-

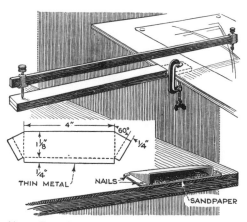

Above, Extension on Drawing Board Aids in Scribing Large Arcs; Below, Pencil-Dust Guard

serted under the sandpaper so that none of the pencil dust can work under it and onto the board.—Warren Scholl, St. Ignace, Mich.

❡ When grinding valves, hang a magnet on the radiator rod so that the valve pins can be stuck on the magnet. This will eliminate the risk of losing them.

Turning Heavy Objects

Heavy objects, such as large pulleys, oil drums and the like, can be readily rolled over the floor but it is quite a difficult task to turn them around. It will be found,

Easy Method of Turning Heavy Pulleys and Drums Around by Rolling Them onto Barrel Stave

however, that if the area of contact is reduced by rolling the object onto a barrel stave, with the concave side up as shown in the drawing, the work of turning it around becomes comparatively easy as there is then only a small part of the stave in contact with the floor and this is in the center.—A. C. Cole, Chicago, Ill.

Novel Exhaust Fan

Unusual in construction, the simple exhaust fan shown in the illustration can be made from a disk of sheet metal, with radial sections cut out on three sides and curved outward as indicated. The disk is cut from $\frac{1}{16}$-in. material and six blades are cut in it, the dotted lines showing where they are bent. A hole is drilled through the center so that it can be slipped on a shaft where it is held securely by means of two nuts and a lock washer. A fan of this kind can be run at high speed without any noise.

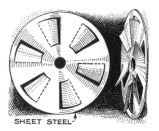

Adjustable Lumber Jack

Piling up lumber is facilitated considerably by the use of a simple jack of the kind shown in the illustration. It is made of hardwood and consists of a base and a

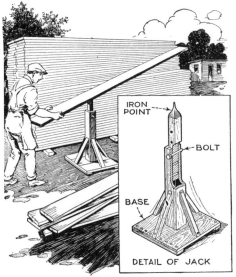

IRON POINT

BOLT

BASE

DETAIL OF JACK

Adjustable Wooden Jack in Lumber Yard Aids Worker in Piling Up Lumber

standard to hold the lift pin. The latter is drilled at several points in a line to take a bolt which passes through the standard as indicated, and is provided with an iron point on the end to prevent the lumber from sliding. In use, the workman lifts a board at one end high enough to get its center on the jack, and he then pushes his end down so that the other end will be raised high and close enough for the man on the stack to take hold of it.—Bunyan Kennedy, McCool, Miss.

Remedy for Puddled Soils

Many soils have a tendency to run together after very heavy rain. This trouble is experienced mostly with silt and clay soils, and is caused by the soil particles being washed close together, making one solid, compact mass. Such a puddled condition forms a very hard crust when the surface dries, and it is only with great difficulty that young plants can force their way through. The circulation of air is also cut off and as a result both crop and soil suffer. The crust also causes increased loss of soil water due to evaporation, as there is a continuous movement of the water to the surface.

Puddling may be prevented to a great extent by increasing the amount of organic matter. This improves the structure of the soil, as it holds the soil particles together in small granules, which will not break up except during the hardest rains. The effect of organic matter on soils is witnessed by examining the soil on which a straw stack or manure heap was formerly located. Careful examination will show that such spots are mellow for a long time afterward, no matter how hard the surrounding soils may be. All soils should have enough organic material in them to prevent running together. Organic matter can be added by applying manures, and by growing suitable crops and plowing them under.—E. R. Haan, Chicago, Ill.

Improvised Countersink

An improvised countersink can readily be made from a hexagon-head machine screw. Each flat on the head is ground or filed down toward the center to the angle desired for the countersink, thus forming tapered cutting edges. It is, of course, advisable to harden the screw.

Holder for Acid Pan

For diluting sulphuric acid and taking care of any spilled acid when filling storage batteries, a most practical method is

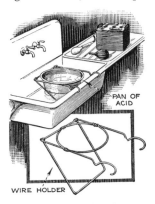

PAN OF ACID

WIRE HOLDER

used by a service-station man. The work is done in an enameled pan which is suspended over the center of a large sink by a simple detachable wire holder. This is made of heavy galvanized wire, and may be made collapsible, for convenient hanging when not in use, by hinging the support that rests against the bottom of the sink to the upper part. To place the pan over the sink, without being in the way of the faucets or blocking the drain, is convenient both for working height and for harmless drainage of any spilled acid, the thorough dilution of the latter being accomplished by opening the faucets. The method is applicable also to use with acid baths for cleaning and pickling small parts.

Production Work on the Drill Press

In the manufacture of a large number of parts that required to be finished on three curved surfaces, ordinary methods were found to be too slow and costly. After giving the matter considerable thought it was decided to try and do the work on a drill press, the table of which was rigged up with a series of blocks between which the pieces would make the proper fit and be held down to the table by means of a circular clamp, The blocks were so spaced that the castings just dropped into place. This arrangement insured all of the work being located centrally. For the radius nearest the center an ordinary small boring bar was used and for cutting the second concave radius the tool shown was used. This had a pilot which centered itself in a hole in the center of the table. The outside radius was machined by a vertical cutter held in a toolholder of the same type.

This arrangement proved to be very efficient, completely machining eight pieces at

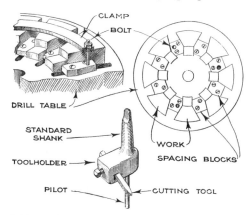

A Method for Turning Radii on a Drill Press, Adapting the Machine to Production Work

a time. The job is one that would ordinarily be done on a lathe or miller, but in the absence of either, it suggests a method for doing other types of work that are generally done on such machines.

¶Copper is annealed by heating to a red heat and plunging into cold water.

Lockers Used in Garages

In Brooklyn, N. Y., a locker system has been put in use in a garage so that customers can leave personal belongings safely while their automobiles are left for

Personal Belongings Put in Lockers in Garage Storeroom While Car Is Left for Repairs or Storage, in Order to Prevent Theft

repairs or storage, without fear of loss or mix-up. The lockers consist of chests, kept in a storeroom at the rear of the garage. Each chest is locked and the key given to the owner of the contents. The cushions of the car are also removed and checked in the storeroom in order to eliminate the possibility of having them soiled while repairs are made. The locker service is free, which is a good advertisement.

Preventing Iron Stains on Buildings

Dark stains on brickwork below the supports of ornamental iron balconies or fire escapes are caused by rain washing away some of the paint on the ironwork and forming rust, which dissolves in the water and is deposited on the wall. On buildings constructed of light-colored brick or stone such stains are especially noticeable. To prevent them a tight-fitting metal collar should be fixed at the lower part of the support, as shown in the illustration. The collar should project about an inch beyond the support and be placed a few inches from the wall. The rain can then run down the support to the collar, but here it drips off away from the building.

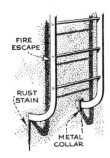

MECHANICAL POWERS

By CARL W. MITMAN

Curator

DIVISIONS OF MINERAL AND
MECHANICAL TECHNOLOGY
UNITED STATES NATIONAL
MUSEUM

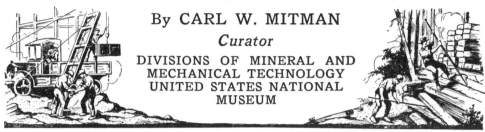

Copyrighted, H. H. Windsor, Jr.

This is the sixth article of a series by Curator Mitman, explaining in simple language what every man who builds or designs a machine must know, and showing in detail just how to build a set of models of the mechanical powers that will exactly duplicate the set in the National Museum at Washington, D. C. The first articles appeared in the March, April, May, June and July issues, and the next will appear in the September number.

Part VI—The Inclined Plane and Wedge

IN addition to the forces that have been discussed thus far and which are applied to a solid body from without, there are forces acting within a body as well. Such forces are known as stresses. The relation between these outer and inner forces is that those acting outside the body tend to deform it, but in so doing create stresses within the body which in themselves resist deformation. The primary stresses thus created are called tension, compression and torsion, or shearing. There are in addition so-called bending stresses, but these are simply combinations of tension and compression. In structures such as buildings, bridges, and the like, individual members of the structures are quite often subject to tension stresses only or compression stresses only, but in machinery and machine parts such simple stresses are rather rare, and instead the stresses are found to be combinations of two or more simple ones of tension and compression. This is especially true of those parts of a machine that are in motion. There is probably nothing more important than to be able to determine the stresses to which each part of a machine will be subjected, so as to give it sufficient strength

to withstand the strain. Calculations can occasionally be made to solve this problem, but there are many instances where calculations cannot be made, or the results are uncertain, so that past successful designs and the results of practical experience ought to be given real consideration. In fact, in many instances one must rely wholly upon practical tests. The designer of machinery must take account of two main items; first, to develop a mechanism that will modify the various contending external forces so that the motions required can be obtained, and second, to proportion the various parts of the machine so that they can withstand the internal stresses set up and be strong enough to do the work intended for them. The first part of this problem is a direct application of the science of mechanics, but the second part involves not only this same knowledge but in addition that generally known as the strength of materials. The two are very closely connected, and the latter is largely used in such cases where it is practically impossible to calculate the size of a machine part because of the peculiar manner in which the forces are applied to it. Then, a definite

test is made to determine the actual strength of the material.

Of the forces acting upon a machine part only the load acting upon or transmitted through the part need ordinarily be taken into account, but there are occasions when the weight of the part must also be considered. In the case of flywheels or parts moving at high velocity, or subjected to changes in velocity, forces other than direct load are encountered that set up combinations of stresses which must be taken into consideration, and, lastly, there must be considered the character of the load. There are three different kinds of load: a steady or dead load; a live load, that is, one constantly in motion, and a

makes a man able to "lift himself up by his boot straps." Its use is as "old as the hills," the most pretentious application, according to a number of authorities, probably being in the construction of the pyramids of Egypt. The average weight of the stone blocks in these pyramids is around 10 tons, and to place them in position,

Model of Inclined Plane, with Illustration Showing How, It Is Supposed, the Ancient Egyptians Used the Plane in the Building of the Pyramids

there were available plenty of desert sand, millions of slaves, and unlimited time for the completion of the job.. It does not require a great stretch of the imagination, therefore, to think that for each course of a pyramid an inclined roadway was first constructed to the proper height, and the blocks dragged or rolled by slaves up the incline and into position.

With the coming of the automobile and the consequent erection of service stations and garages, the simple inclined plane has again found a practical application. At first such buildings were single-storied and covered large areas of ground; later the area was decreased and floors were added, with the installation of elevators; and lastly elevators have been eliminated and replaced by inclined planes, or ramps, between floors, thus making use of the auto-

live load alternating in direction, applied intermittently, applied gradually or applied suddenly. Of course, with manual power as the applied force (equal to about $\frac{1}{8}$ hp.), the matter of strength of materials and internal stresses needs no more than passing attention, but with greater powers this consideration is highly important.

Broadly speaking, the inclined plane

mobile's own power to reach its storage space and saving the cost of elevator installation and operation. Man uses the inclined plane daily, for a stairway is nothing more than an inclined plane the slope of which is notched or stepped.

In mechanics the inclined plane is a hard, smooth surface set obliquely to the resistance. To move a load or weight, the applied force may act either in a direction parallel to the slope, parallel to the base or in any other direction, but in each case the conditions of equilibrium or the principle of work may be derived from those of the simple lever. For example, in the photo of the inclined - plane model, the direction of the applied force is parallel to the slope of the plane, and equilibrium will exist when the applied force is to the resisting force as the height of the plane is to the length of the incline or slope. While the resisting force is raised through a space equal to the vertical height of the plane, the applied force must move through a space equal to its length. In other words, if the slope is 10 ft. long and its height 2 ft., the applied force must move 10 ft. while the resisting force is raised 2 feet.

If, again, the direction of the applied force is parallel to the base of the plane, then equilibrium will exist when the applied force is to the resisting force as the height of the plane is to the base. From these two cases or conditions it follows that the effect of a given applied force is greater as the height of the inclined plane is diminished or its length increased; and that its effect is greatest when its direction is parallel to the slope, for if the applied force acts in any other direction, a part of it is expended either in increasing the pressure of the resisting force against the slope or in lifting it directly.

Instead of lifting a load by moving it along an inclined plane, the same result

Model of Wedge; the Drawing Shows a Common Use of the Wedge, Which Consists of Two Inclined Planes, Base to Base

may be obtained by moving the plane under the load. When so used the inclined plane is called a wedge, which is extensively used in a variety of ways; it is often used, for example, as an aid to hold objects securely, such as a swinging door. A pair of wedges made to slide along their inclined faces forms one of the essential tools of the printer to hold a form of type in position. Since the days of Benjamin Franklin this little tool has been included in the printer's kit and is still indispensable to the trade. Again, some types of the so-called expansion bolt make use of the principle of the wedge, modified, however, away from the conventional form. Furthermore, by joining two inclined planes base to base, there results the familiar wedge used in splitting wood. In the wedge shown in the photograph, force is applied to the back of the wedge and is supposed to move through a space equal to the length of the wedge, while the resisting force (pressure) yields to the extent of the breadth of the wedge.

As a mechanical power the wedge is used only where great force is to be exerted in a limited space. The edges of all cutting tools, as saws, knives, chisels, razors, scissors, etc., and the points of piercing instruments, as awls, nails, pins, needles, etc., are all modified wedges. In general, the softer or more yielding the material to be worked, the more acute the wedgelike tool may be made. For example, chisels intended to cut wood have the edge at an angle of about 30°; for cutting brass from 50 to 60°, and for steel from 60 to 70°. Furthermore, tools that cut by constantly applied pressure may be sharper than those which cut by impact or blows. The theory of the wedge, however, takes no account of friction, which largely modifies the results, so that the relative effect of constant pressure and a blow cannot be defined.

For the model of the inclined plane, the following materials are required:

Base, 7 by 3¾ by ¾ in.
Pillar, 2½ by 1⅛ by ⅞ in.
Pulley, 1-in. diameter, ¼ in. thick, V-groove.
Ramp, 4-in. base, 1½-in height, 3-in. width.
Weight (resisting force), base 1¾ in. square, top 1¼ in. square, side 1½ in. high.
Arrow (applied force), 1¼ in. long, ¼ in. thick, ½ in. wide across barbs; shaft, ¼ in. square.

Square and face the base with a finish bevel on top. On the center line of the base and ¾ in. from the center end, secure the ramp with glue and by screws from beneath. Saw and chisel a groove in the center of the pillar top, ⅞ in. deep and ⅜ in. wide, and round the ends of the lobes or ears thus fashioned. Drill a ⅛-in. hole through the center of the pulley and the ends of the lobes and mount the pulley in the groove on a suitable axle. Attach this assembly to the base on the center line, ⅜ in. from the end, with glue and screws from beneath. Attach the end of a length of lead wire (representing a rope or cord) to the screweye used as a handle for the weight, and to the other end of the wire affix the arrow by inserting the wire in a hole drilled lengthwise in the shaft. Rest the weight on the ramp and the wire in the pulley groove. Finish as desired. The wire may be enameled white to represent a cord more closely.

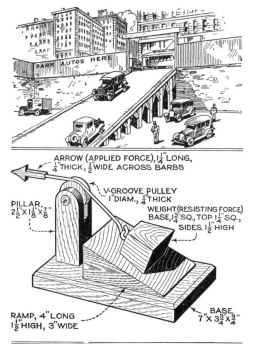

ARROW (APPLIED FORCE), 1¼" LONG, ¼" THICK, ½" WIDE ACROSS BARBS

V-GROOVE PULLEY 1" DIAM., ¼" THICK

PILLAR, 2½" X 1⅛" X ⅞"

WEIGHT (RESISTING FORCE) BASE, 1¾" SQ., TOP 1¼" SQ., SIDES 1½" HIGH

RAMP, 4" LONG 1½" HIGH, 3" WIDE

BASE, 7" X 3¾" X ¾"

Details of Model of Inclined Plane; Above, a Modern Use of the Ramp

For the wedge model, use the following material:

Base, 4½ in. square, ¾ in. high.
Block, 1¾ in. square, 2¾ in. high.
Iron wedge, base 1 by ½ in., side 1½ in. high.

Square and face the base with a finish

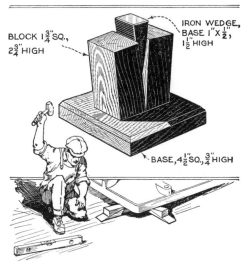

BLOCK 1¾" SQ., 2¾" HIGH

IRON WEDGE, BASE 1" X ½", 1½" HIGH

BASE, 4½" SQ., ¾" HIGH

Wedge-Model Dimensions and Illustration Showing Use of Wedge in Leveling Machinery

bevel on top. Saw a cut lengthwise nearly through the block. Insert the wedge into this cut and force it in for about two-thirds of its length, separating the halves of the block, but taking care not to split it; if necessary, saw the cut in a triangular shape before forcing in the wedge. Square the bottom of the block and secure to the base with glue and screws from beneath. Finish as desired.

(Continued Next Month)

Lubricant for Auto Springs

Oil and graphite applied to the leaves of automobile springs is usually effective for a short time only, but the following mixture has been found to last for an entire season, as the wax contained in it holds the graphite between the leaves and also keeps the grease from forming an emulsion with water: japan wax, 10 parts; flake graphite, 10 parts; cup grease, 5 parts; kerosene, 1 part.

The wax can usually be had at any laundry, but if it cannot be obtained, ordinary paraffin or beeswax will do. The graphite is first mixed with the grease and the wax cut in small pieces and added, the whole being then carefully melted and thoroughly mixed. Remove the mixture from the fire before adding kerosene.

Guard Gates Used as Bridges

Guard gates are used at the Panama canal to accommodate vehicular traffic. When these were first so used it was found that, while the width permitted the

Steel Plate Used at Angle of Guard Gates at Panama Canal to Permit Vehicles to Turn Corner Safely

passage of an automobile, the gates at their meeting point formed too sharp an angle for an auto to turn safely. To overcome this difficulty, removable triangular plates were made to fit into the corner as seen in the photo. When the gates are to be opened, this plate, of course, has to be removed and is then hung on the railing of one of the gate leaves, as indicated by the black arrow.

Valuable Water-Cooling Kink

Customarily the method of cooling water by an ammonia coil is to have the latter located in the water tank as shown in Fig. 1. The objection to this method is that the water may freeze solidly if not kept in continual motion, the result being a burst tank.

Figure 2 shows a method which entirely eliminates this danger. The ammonia coil

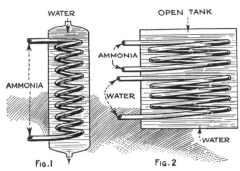

Fig. 1, Customary Method of Coil in Tank; Fig. 2, Better Method Which Prevents Freezing

is placed in a large open tank as indicated, close to the top, and the water runs

through a coil located near the bottom. The tank is filled with water. This water may freeze near the top but will not freeze solidly, and consequently there will be no rupture. As the ammonia coil is located near the top, it cools the surface water and this water then moves toward the bottom. The cold water, which is never below 32° F., surrounds the lower coil and cools the water in it. As water is drawn off intermittently from this coil, new water enters it and the water in the lower part of the tank becomes somewhat warmer than the top layer, causing it to rise again, and thus circulation in the tank is maintained.

Compact Fuse Tester

After using a weatherproof socket with an ordinary 25-watt lamp as a fuse tester, and breaking some lamps as a result, I began to consider the possibility of using a smaller lamp and so protecting it that breakage would be unlikely. The result was the compact tester detailed herewith. I obtained a telephone-switchboard lamp and inclosed it in an empty cartridge fuse of large size, as shown. Holes were

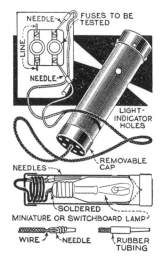

drilled in the sides so that the lighting of the lamp could readily be observed. The brass cap at one end, which in this case happened to be perforated, was made removable by pulling out the small brass rivets which held it in place. A length of common lampcord was soldered to the two base terminals of the lamp and to two darning needles, as shown. The lamp was then pushed into the cartridge and the lampcord threaded through one of the holes in the cap. When not in use, the cord and needles are disposed of inside the cartridge as indicated, permitting the tester to be carried in the pocket. The joints of the wire and the needles were covered with short pieces of small-bore rubber tubing, to provide convenient finger grips, and avoid danger from shocks.—W. W. Parker, Lead, S. Dak.

Keyless Lock for the Tool Cabinet

There are many kinds of combination locks, but few are as simple and effective as the one shown in the illustration. Since I put this on my tool cabinet a number of people have tried to open it without success, some not being able to do so even after the secret was explained to them.

There are no numbers, marks or even turns to count; simply a knob that can be manipulated as readily in the dark as in the light, because operation of the lock depends on the sense of touch. The latch is made of heavy sheet metal, and the drawing shows its construction clearly, so that no detailed description is necessary. The knob has a shank that passes through a hole drilled in the drawer front; this shank may be of any convenient size—an old valve stem, drilled at one end to take a stout wire pin, will serve very well. A coil spring is fitted between the pin and the inside of the cabinet front, to keep the shank pressed back. The shank should be long enough to allow the pin to pass the downward-projecting part of the latch, either in front or behind, without touching. A small nail is driven into the cabinet at the point indicated so that the end of the latch will rest against it.

To operate the lock, the knob is pulled outward and turned until the pin is found, by sense of touch, to rest behind and against the latch; then it is pushed in, thus

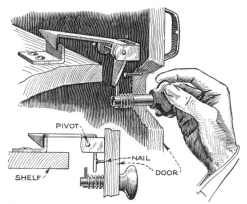

Simple and Fool-Proof Keyless Lock for the Tool Cabinet, Which Cannot Be Opened by Those Not in Secret

raising the latch.—E. Leslie MacFarlane, Nashwaaksis, N. B., Can.

¶A draftsman's pen should not be thrown away when it is worn down and can no longer be used for ruling. It should be put in the shop's first-aid cabinet, as no better tweezers can be obtained.

Refuse Hopper for Fruit Screen

In a section of the country where cranberries are grown extensively, a boat-shaped device with a slatted bottom is used to screen the berries. Much of the chaff, twigs and dirt falls between the slats, but

Hopper Built over Hole in Screen Bed Conveys Unsound Berries into Large Barrel

unsound berries still remain to be separated from the sound ones. It is customary to have a measure standing on the screen into which the refuse is thrown by the pickers. The repeated emptying of the measure causes much loss of time, and therefore one grower built a chute or hopper on the bottom of the screen leading into a barrel, as indicated. Cleats were nailed across the slats at a convenient point underneath; an opening, about 6 in. square, was cut out and the hopper was built up around this opening about 10 in. high. This proved quite a convenience and timesaver, and would no doubt be useful also for screening other small fruits, such as cherries, blueberries, and the like.—L. B. Robbins, Harwich, Mass.

Using Magazine Clips

The large clips used by dealers to display current issues of magazines are equally useful for the same purpose in the home in case the table room is limited. The magazines may be hung from nails driven into the wall, especially in the den or workroom, so that they are readily available. In this way, magazines can also be held open in shops where the pages might be soiled by handling.

Stamping Nameplates

In the manufacture of a number of brass plates on which the lettering had to be stamped neatly and accurately it was a problem just how to stamp the letters so

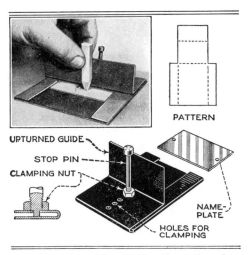

Sheet-Metal Fixture for Holding Brass Nameplates While Lettering Them

that they would be in a straight line. As only the regular steel stamps were available, it was thought best to use some kind of fixture to guide the stamps and hold them squarely in position. The fixture illustrated was the result.

It is made from a piece of sheet iron folded over on two sides as shown, one end being doubled over these folds and then bent up at right angles to form a guide against which the letters are held. A number of holes are drilled in line in the center back of the guide for a stop pin, which consists of a bolt and nut. The pin should be a snug fit in the holes, the screw thread below the nut being ground off to fit the hole and the nut resting on top. The distance between the folded sides of the holder is a sliding fit for the particular plates to be stamped and the plates are pushed against the stop pin. Thus, with the stop pin in the first hole and each stamp held close against the guide the first line is stamped. The holes should be so arranged that the lettering will be properly spaced.

Keeping Paste from Souring

There is no necessity of using sour paste for wall-paper hanging as is often done, for a few drops of formaldehyde will keep it sweet indefinitely. After experimenting with various substances, I found that for-

maldehyde was the most effective. A few drops were added to a cupful of paste, after this had been boiled, and this sample was found still sweet when examined a year later.—A. A. Kelly, Paoli, Pa.

Oiling Valve Stems

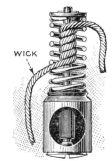

Lubricating valve stems on cars having overhead valves can be accomplished effectively by the method shown in the illustration. An asbestos rope, about 5⁄16 in. in diameter and about 8 in. long, is wrapped a few turns around the stem after the spring has been removed. The ends are folded down along the stem and brought out at the bottom so that the pressure of the coil keeps them from working out of place when the spring is released. The application of a few drops of oil on the wick every week keeps the stem lubricated and prevents dirt from getting in contact with it.

Window Frames for Small Buildings

Framing windows on small buildings, especially those that have only a few studs, is usually quite a problem. A frame put on the outside, however, as shown in the drawing, presents a good appearance

and has been found very satisfactory. It is made of lengths of 2 by 4-in. stock set on edge with the sashes hinged on as indicated. The frame is made long enough for as many sashes as are to be mounted and the latter are separated by 2 by 4-in. pieces. The frame is nailed to the building from the inside. A 1 by 12-in. piece of boxing, nailed at each end, will keep the frame in place until the top and bottom pieces are nailed on. A length of quarter round is nailed along the upper edge of the frame to turn water.

Novel Circular-Glass Cutter

Two 12-in. lengths of 4-in. wood, a short brass rod and an inexpensive glass cutter form a novel tool for cutting glass of cylindrical shape. It has been found very satisfactory by an eastern concern that specializes in manufacturing wicker flower holders, the wicker work inclosing a glass container for the water. These containers are made from round bottles of various sizes and colors, the tops being cut off with the tool shown in the accompanying illustration.

The two lengths of wood are nailed together edgewise at right angles, several holes being drilled in both pieces to receive a brass rod, which serves as a stop during the cutting operation. The cutter is attached to the end of the lower piece by means of a short brass strip and two wood screws. The method of using the device is obvious; the bottle is simply turned by hand until a scratch is made around it, whereupon the top part can easily be knocked off. The sharp edge of the glass

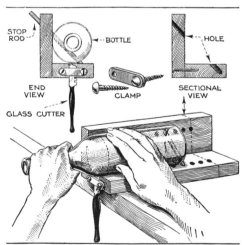

Simple Homemade Circular-Glass Cutter Cuts Bottles Quickly and Accurately

is smoothed on an emery wheel to prevent danger of cutting the hands.—G. A. Luers, Washington, D. C.

Desk and Bookcase Built in Closet

It is often desirable to have a large desk at home for correspondence work, bookkeeping, etc., but on the other hand it may

Left, Part Section, Showing How the Combination Desk and Bookcase Fits into the Closet; Right, Desk in Use

be objectionable on account of the space it occupies, and because the children will put their toys and other articles on it and can not restrain their curiosity as to the contents of the drawers. With this in mind a Washington contractor built a compact desk of large dimensions, the top of which, when not in use, could be pushed entirely out of the way into a locked closet. The closet was fitted with glass doors above and paneled doors below so that it did not detract from the appearance of the room in any way. The general plan of construction is given in the drawing and can, with slight modifications, be adapted to most cases.

The closet consists of two compartments, separated by a horizontal shelf about 1 in. above the top of the desk, which should be about 30 in. high. Under the desk top, which is hinged, is a full-width drawer for the support of which slides are provided, and the space below is divided into shelves and pigeonholes for catalogs, stationery and the like. The drawer may also be partitioned to suit the user's particular needs. Shelves are provided in the upper compartment for books and magazines, and for the typewriter and telephone, if desired.

Making Stranded-Wire Cables

Having had considerable difficulty in obtaining good seven-stranded cable for guy wires, I hit upon the following method of making it myself: I jacked up one of the

Simple Method of Making Neat Stranded Cable from a Number of Galvanized-Iron Wires

rear wheels of my car and fastened one end of a coil of galvanized-iron wire to one of the spokes, brought the wire around a fencepost, directly in line with the wheel, and attached it to the opposite spoke of the wheel, cutting it from the coil at this point. Two other lengths of wire were run in the same way and also a single length from the wheel to the post. I then started the engine and put it in gear, which caused the rear wheel to revolve and twist the wires as desired, making a strong cable. With this method I have made cables 150 ft. long.—L. Cook, Bloomingdale, Mich.

Nonreversible Drain

Water in a reservoir is usually kept below a certain level by providing a drain pipe that carries off the surplus water. Where the drain extends horizontally through the wall and discharges the water into an exterior ditch, it often happens that the water level in the ditch becomes higher than that in the reservoir, due to heavy rainstorms, and water then flows back into the reservoir through the drain. This

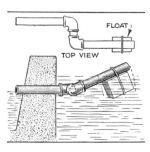

trouble can be prevented by installing a drain of the type shown in the illustration. It consists of two short lengths of pipe, two elbows and a nipple, arranged as shown in the upper detail. The couplings must be loose enough to permit the length of pipe extending into the ditch to move up and down freely. An airtight can is wired to the end of this pipe to keep it above water when the exterior level is higher than that in the reservoir, so that the water from the ditch will not flow back.—Harold E. Benson, Boulder, Colo.

Drilling Glass and Pottery

Drilling holes in glass and pottery is usually done with a highly tempered drill using camphor oil as a lubricant. Another good method—in many cases better—is to grind the holes by means of carborundum stones of proper sizes, set in the drill chuck and revolved at high speed. Holes have been ground through pieces of hard pottery in this way where the drilling method failed.

A Magazine Nut Wrench

Automobile assemblers and others who, from the character of their work, must screw down large numbers of nuts of the same size, will find in the tool illustrated a means of largely reducing the number of movements required. As shown in the drawing, the magazine consists of a hexagonal tube, that can easiest be made by forming a piece of steel tubing over a mandrel of the same size as the nuts to be used, and welding into the upper end a suitable square shank.

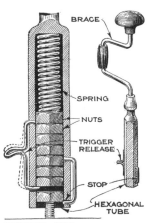

A compression spring inside feeds the nuts forward as fast as they are released by the trigger, which is operated manually, the nut being prevented from falling out by the stop on the opposite side. Both these parts are made from spring-steel wire with their lower points spaced apart just the thickness of one nut.

Worm-Gear Attachment for Sensitive Drill Press

By H. H. PARKER

THE type of small sensitive bench drill shown in the illustration is extensively used for light work in machine shops, factories and garages, as well as similar machines with bevel-gear drive, of slightly greater capacity. The feed is obtained by means of a rack and pinion actuated by a hand lever, and is perfectly satisfactory for small or intermittent work, but for drilling ⅜ to ½-in. holes in hard steel, with the machine working for long periods of time, the pressure required on the hand lever is rather tiring upon the operator, and a worm gear with handwheel feed, as applied to a large drill press, would be of decided advantage. The drawings show how such a feed arrangement can be applied to the bench drill without any considerable alteration of the machine, and without detracting from its appearance or preventing use of the hand lever; the patterns required are simple and most of the

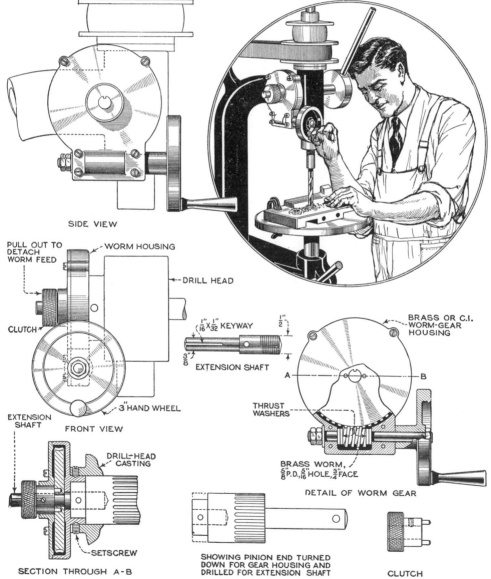

SIDE VIEW

PULL OUT TO DETACH WORM FEED

WORM HOUSING

DRILL HEAD

CLUTCH

$\frac{1''}{16} \times \frac{1''}{32}$ KEYWAY

$\frac{1''}{2}$

$\frac{3''}{8}$

EXTENSION SHAFT

A ——— B

BRASS OR C.I. WORM-GEAR HOUSING

THRUST WASHERS

3" HAND WHEEL

EXTENSION SHAFT

FRONT VIEW

BRASS WORM, $\frac{5''}{8}$ P.D., $\frac{5''}{16}$ HOLE, $\frac{3''}{4}$ FACE

DETAIL OF WORM GEAR

DRILL-HEAD CASTING

SETSCREW

SECTION THROUGH A-B

SHOWING PINION END TURNED DOWN FOR GEAR HOUSING AND DRILLED FOR EXTENSION SHAFT

CLUTCH

Fitting a Handwheel Feed to a Sensitive Bench Drill Press; an Attachment of This Kind Permits Heavy Work to Be Done over a Long Period without Fatigue

machine work can be performed in the lathe. While the drawings are approximately to scale, the exact dimensions will depend upon the type of drill press and the size of the worm wheel and worm. The latter may be obtained, finished, from any manufacturer of cut gearing; they are usually of brass in the small sizes. A diametral pitch of 16 is about right with a worm wheel of 3 to 4-in. diameter. Most of the bench drill presses are built with a feed pinion turned from solid stock, with a shaft at one end to take the feed-lever boss. The other end is left the full size of the gear blank and rotates in a bearing bored out of the drill-head casting. By turning this end down for about $\frac{1}{2}$ in., reducing the diameter by $\frac{3}{8}$ or $\frac{1}{2}$ in., an annular space will be formed in the pinion-bearing housing, with the pinion shaft in place, into which the boss of the worm-wheel housing can be pushed and locked in place by means of setscrews. The pinion shaft will now rotate in the worm-wheel housing as a bearing, while a stub, or extension, shaft must be screwed into the pinion shaft to take the worm wheel.

A cast-iron or brass casting is made for the worm-wheel housing; either in one piece with a cover as in the drawing, the worm shaft being put through a drilled hole, or made in halves like a blower case. In the drawing a worm wheel without a hub is shown; as this is loose on the shaft, the cover is made with a boss that bears against the web of the wheel, to steady it, a similar shallow boss being provided on the inside of the housing casting. The cover is held by three or more setscrews.

A $\frac{1}{2}$-in. extension shaft is driven, or screwed, part way into the solid end of the pinion shaft, pinned in place and then turned down to take the worm gear, which is not fastened to it. Means must, of course, be provided for clutching and de-clutching the worm wheel when the worm feed is to be used instead of the hand lever, and vice versa. The clutch is made from a steel bar, which slides on the shaft extension and engages the worm wheel by means of two $\frac{1}{8}$-in. steel pins that fit into holes drilled in the web of the wheel. A keyway is cut on the outer end of the shaft, and a setscrew, with its end filed to fit the keyway, set into the sliding clutch to make it rotate with the shaft. The filed end must, of course, be a sliding fit in the keyway. When the hand lever is to be used, the knurled end of the clutch is pulled out, which will disengage the worm wheel from the shaft.

Fitting the worm shaft is the only operation requiring special care; the hole for this must be accurately drilled and reamed in relation to the worm-wheel shaft. The worm (unless solid with the shaft, in which case a divided housing, or a large-diameter entrance hole is needed) is pinned, or preferably sweated, to its shaft, and thrust washers, or small ball thrusts, fitted at each end. The handwheel is 3 to 4 in. in diameter, pinned or keyed and held with an end nut; a pair of locknuts are screwed to the other end of the shaft. The arrangement of the housing and type of the clutch may, of course, be changed to suit the individual ideas of the builder, but the type shown is easy to make.

Gripping Square-Head Screws

Pliers, tongs and other similar tools are often used for dipping small fixtures in cleaning solutions, but it often happens that the only part of the fixture that can be gripped conveniently is a projecting square-head screw, and holding this with the tongs or pliers often results in dropping the fixture to the bottom of the tank. An excellent holder for this purpose is shown in the illustration. A round-steel washer is squared out in the center to fit the screw head, and two holes are drilled through it on opposite sides, and in line with the corners of the square. A piece of drill rod is then bent, as shown, to fit these two holes, and with the ends bent backward to fit closely in the corners of the square. The tool is made to grip the screw by first pushing the handle forward until the ends clear the square hole so that

ROUND PIECE   HANDLE

SQUARE HOLE TO FIT SCREW HEAD

SCREW CLAMPED IN TOOL

SQ. HOLE

SCREW HEAD

FRONT VIEW

DETAIL OF OPERATION

Nonslipping Holder for Square-Head Screws

the latter can be passed over the screw head. When clear over, the tool is given an eighth of a turn and the handle pulled backward to lock the ends against the screw head. A little study of the drawing will soon show that the tool is nonslipping and that it is impossible for it to come off while the fixture is being swirled around in the tank. To remove the tool the operations are, of course, reversed.

Prolonging Life of Scraper

After a season of use, the edge of a scraper is usually worn out. It can readily be repaired, however, so that it will be

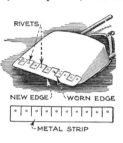

nearly as good as new by riveting a 6-in. strip of steel to the edge, as shown in the illustration. The strip should be as long as the scraper is wide and is slitted so that the resulting "tongues" can be fitted alternately to the top and bottom of the scraper. The strip is then riveted to the scraper, as indicated, and the rivets countersunk on the underside. This will make a strong edge that will not bend easily.—Stanley McCosh, Novi, Mich.

Making Collars in One Operation

The arrangement of tools shown in the illustration has been found very handy in making collars and washers on screw machines directly from tubing without a second operation for burring or countersinking as is

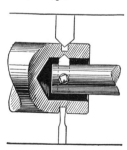

usually necessary. The collars are cut off with the parting tool, which is mounted on the front cross slide, and the outer edge is chamfered with a chamfering tool on the rear cross slide. The inside edges are chamfered with a tool held on a bar carried in the turret. The latter tool is fed in to the proper depth as controlled by the turret stop, and then into the work to such a depth that after the parting tool has gone through, a chamfer will be left on the inside edge.

Control for Roof Trapdoor

Trapdoors are usually rather difficult to open and for this reason the simple and easily operated control shown in the drawing should meet with instant favor. It

Bracket Lever and Iron Rod Used to Control Roof Trapdoor from Below

eliminates the necessity of climbing up on a ladder. A bracket lever is bolted to the underside of the door so that it extends beyond the hinged edge, as shown, and a ¼-in. iron rod is attached to the end of the lever. A quick pull on the rod causes the trapdoor to swing to the position indicated by the dotted lines in the detail, a stop being provided to hold it there.

Wire Bracket Holds Valve Springs

Holding up valve springs is one of the difficulties met with when regrinding valves and removing carbon. Various kinds of holders are on the market, but one that is of simple con-

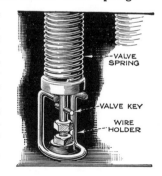

struction and performs the work as well as the best, is shown here. It consists of a length of heavy wire, at least ³⁄₁₆ in. in diameter, bent to the shape indicated. After the valve spring has been raised, the holder is placed under it and will then hold the spring securely, without slipping.

Guide for Special Work in Braiding Machine

In making lamp cords for Christmas trees, two single wires are run together through a braiding machine, taps being

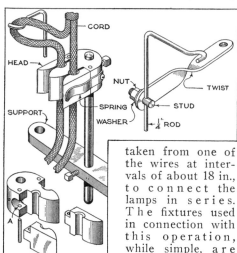

taken from one of the wires at intervals of about 18 in., to connect the lamps in series. The fixtures used in connection with this operation, while simple, are interesting, and the same principles may be adapted to much other work.

The drawing shows the attachment that replaces the regular guide. It is made of machine steel, casehardened. The center part of the head is milled out as shown in the lower detail, the slots at A being machined with an end mill. The two swinging pieces have lugs that fit into slots A, and are fastened to the center part by steel pins. Flat springs bearing against the sidepieces keep a tension on the wire as it is drawn through the guide. The holes for the wire are drilled and countersunk, half in the center and half in the sidepieces, and. the head is held by a ⅜-in. rod, passing through a flat-steel bracket bolted to the base of the machine. To insure all the taps being of equal length the fixture shown at the right was made. This consists simply of a ¼-in. rod, bent as shown and passing through a hole in a stud that binds the rod against a cold-rolled steel bracket. Adjustment of the distance between the rod and guide is effected by swinging the rod.

One insulated wire of each pair is drawn out to the hook, pulled tight, and the machine started, braiding on past the tap. As the braided cord travels up over the tension drum, another ¼-in. rod, fastened to the machine frame, and bent to touch the drum, shows the operator where to stop the machine and form the next loop.

Centering Short Shafts

In the production of a large number of short shafts the work of centering them was quickly and conveniently accomplished with the use of the fixture shown in the illustration. It consists of a cast-iron base, drilled to receive a vertical rod and having a setscrew to hold the latter in position. A similar piece, or head, of cast iron, drilled to a sliding fit on the rod, is also provided. It is held in alinement directly over the base by a key seated in the head and running in a keyway in the side of the rod. Both base and head are countersunk to receive the shafts and a punch is provided in the head, in the center of the countersink, as shown. In use, the shaft is placed in the lower countersink and the head lowered so that the shaft is held as shown. The punch is then tapped, with

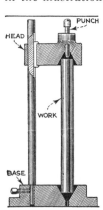

the hammer, and the process repeated for the other end of the shaft.—J. H. Rodgers, Toronto, Can.

Connecting the Universal Joint

The removal of the rear-axle assembly on the Ford car necessitates the disconnecting of the universal joint, and it is quite a difficult job to reconnect the joint by hand. However, with a lever fastened

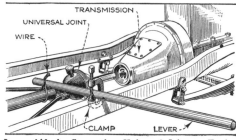

Lever Aids in Connecting Universal Joint to Engine When Rear End Is Replaced

to the joint by wire or rope and pivoted on the frame by means of a C-clamp as shown, the operation becomes quite easy. The arrangement gives a combined lift and thrust. The universal joint is packed with heavy cup grease, which will steady the end. An open-end wrench is used to bring the shaft end in alinement with the socket.

Oiling Typewriter Bars

When overhauling typewriters the bars must be oiled a little before they are replaced. This is usually done by squirting a few drops of oil on the bars or by rubbing them with an oil-soaked rag, but these methods are slow, and therefore a repairman devised the oiling pad shown in the drawing. The pad consists of a piece of thick felt, fitting inside the tin cover of a typewriter-ribbon box, the edges of which are bent over and flattened down to hold the felt in place. Enough oil is applied to the felt so that a slight pressure will bring it to the surface. Each side of a bar is pressed against the felt with the result that it is moistened with just sufficient oil.

TIN COVER OF TYPEWRITER – RIBBON BOX

FELT SATURATED WITH OIL

BENT-OVER SIDES

Neat Safety Paint Pot

The paint pot shown in the drawing is designed for inside work, to prevent spilling of the paint if accidentally tipped over, and also to provide a guard against which the brush can be wiped, in order to keep the outside of the pot clean. For these reasons the pot should be shallow and of fairly large diameter, and the guard as wide as possible, while permitting the brush to enter freely through the center opening. The safety cover

or guard is made of tin and shaped as shown in the detail. It is held on the pot by means of two bayonet slots in the turned-down edge which engage the ends of the bail. Only as much paint should be put into the pot as will be confined in the space under the cover if the pot is accidentally tipped over.

Handy Glass Carrier

Large panes of glass, which are ordinarily difficult to carry due to their bulkiness, can be carried conveniently by means of the holder shown in the illustration. It

HANDLE DETAIL

WEDGE

Convenient Holder for Carrying Large Panes of Glass

is made in any desired size from lengths of 1 by 2-in. wood. The lower rail on which the glass rests is screwed to two strips which are attached to the handle. A taper groove is cut lengthwise in the lower rail to receive the glass and a felt-covered wedge is provided to fit in this groove, against the glass, to hold it in place.—J. R. Minter, Chester, Pa.

Novel Arrangement of Cash Register

Cash registers in most stores are set to face the space inside of the counter, which is often inconvenient as it necessitates passing around the

counter to "ring up a sale." However, by mounting the cash register on a small turntable on the counter, clerks on either side can use it by turning it around.

¶Brass is annealed by heating to a cherry red and then allowing it to cool slowly.

Depth Gauge for Drilled Holes

Measuring the depth of drilled holes is a somewhat uncertain operation, as the bottom is conical and dimensions are invariably given to the top of the cone. Most

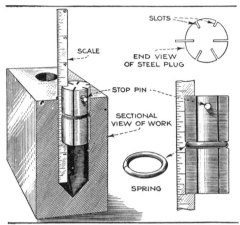

Accurate Plug Depth Gauge for Measuring Drilled Holes

measuring devices used for this work tend to slip down into the conical end, and

therefore one cannot be sure whether the holes have been correctly gauged or not. On the production of a machine part furnished with several holes of slightly different diameters, one shop uses the gauge shown in the photo.

It consists of a round-steel plug with slots sawed in it lengthwise, the depth of these slots varying to suit the different hole diameters so that when the scale is inserted in the slot the plug and scale will fit the hole exactly, as shown. A groove is cut around the plug in the center and a single coil of spring wire slipped in it to hold the scale lightly in any of the slots. At a definite distance from the top a pin is driven through the plug to prevent it from falling into the hole. In use, the scale is slipped in the slot marked to suit the hole to be measured and the plug inserted into the hole until the pin rests on the top. The scale is then pushed down until it strikes the bottom and the reading of the scale taken from the top of the plug. Thus if the face of the pin is ½ in. below the top of the plug, the correct measurement will be ½ in. less than the depth to the top of the plug. With slots sawed in the plug to suit the different holes it fits snugly in each case, and the measurements are accurate.

Steel Fence Posts

Good fences add to the appearance and value of a farm, and save the farmer many losses of live stock and crops. In recent years steel-post fences have gained popularity because they are rot-proof, lightning-proof, weather-resisting and durable in every way. Although they cost a little more than wooden ones their use is economical because they will outlast the latter many times. There are, in fact, records of steel posts set up 35 years ago that are still in good condition, while the average wood post lasts only six to ten years.

The durability of a steel-post fence, like any other, depends on the manner of installation. End and corner posts must be securely anchored in concrete to keep the wires tight and assure resistance to violent shocks. One method of doing this is shown in the illustration. The posts referred to are set vertically in slabs of 18 by 18 by 42-in. concrete, this being done, of course, while the concrete is soft. The steel braces bolted to the vertical posts are anchored in smaller slabs, 18 by 18 by 20 in. in dimensions.

One of the best features of steel-post fences is that there is little or no danger from lightning by which farmers annually lose millions of dollars, as, for instance, when cattle are driven against the fence by a storm and killed by a discharge of lightning conducted along the wire. This

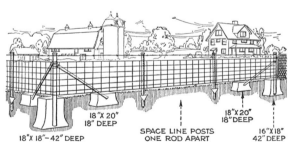

18"X 20" 18" DEEP   18"X20" 18" DEEP

18"X 18"–42" DEEP   SPACE LINE POSTS ONE ROD APART   16"X18" 42" DEEP

Proper Method of Setting Steel End and Corner Posts in Concrete Foundations

will not happen when steel posts are used, as they generally will ground such discharges. Another advantage of steel posts is the speed with which they can be set. One wagonload of posts is enough for a 40-acre field, and a man and boy can drive the lot into the ground in a day, while four men at least would be required to do the same work with wooden posts.

Shop Notes

Homemade Portable Floor-Sanding Machine

By J. S. OPFERMAN

MANY painters and carpenters do not use a floor-sanding machine often enough to justify the expense of purchasing one, but as they need one occasionally, a homemade machine of the kind shown in the illustration will be found quite convenient. It can be improvised from an electric drill and some gas pipe, with little work

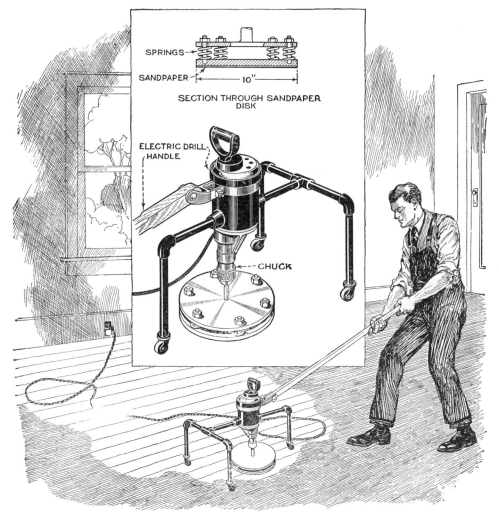

SPRINGS

SANDPAPER |←— 10" —→|

SECTION THROUGH SANDPAPER DISK

ELECTRIC DRILL HANDLE

CHUCK

Portable Floor-Sanding Machine, Consisting of a Small Electric Drill and a Pipe Framework Mounted on Casters, Enables Carpenters and Painters to Sand Floors Quickly and Satisfactorily

and expense, provided, of course, the drill must not be purchased specially for this purpose. The outfit is so constructed that the drill can be detached from the gas-pipe framework and the handle in a moment. The sander can be used wherever electric current of the kind for which the drill is made, is available.

Most drills are fitted with two handles, which are screwed into tapped bosses on the sides. These handles are removed, and two 1-ft. lengths of pipe, of the same diameter and threaded to fit the bosses, are substituted. Other short lengths of pipe and fittings are then assembled to complete a three-legged framework, holding the drill as shown in the illustration. The legs should be about 8 in. high and are fitted with ordinary furniture casters to permit the outfit to be pushed over the floor. The pieces composing the frame should be of such a length that the edge of the sanding disk will project past a line drawn from the rear casters to the front one, so that the floor can be sanded close to the wall.

The sanding disk and shank are either in one piece, being turned down from a piece of flat steel, or the shank may be welded to the disk after both have been turned separately. The best diameter for the disk is about 10 in. and its thickness about ¼ in. The shank must, of course, be turned down to fit the chuck of the drill, in which it is held while in use. Six holes are drilled through the disk at equidistant points around the edge, as indicated, so that another disk of the same material, and turned to the same size, can be attached by means of studs threaded into holes corresponding to those in the first disk. The studs must be long enough to permit small coil springs to be held on them between the two disks and to allow nuts to be turned on the ends to hold the assembly together. The function of the coil springs is to give a certain degree of flexibility so that the whole surface of the lower disk will always lie flat on the floor and the pressure can be varied. Sandpaper is cut in 10-in. disks and glued to the bottom disk with elastic, non-hardening belt cement, which allows the paper to be pulled off easily when worn down. A handle of sufficient length, for pushing the machine, is clamped to the body of the drill as shown in the detail. When sanding close to the wall, the clamp can be loosened, the handle swung to one side, and clamped tight again.

Turning a Corner on a Conveyor

In the plant of the Purcell Butter company, at Elgin, Ill., a simple method of transferring packages from one conveyor to another running at right angles is em-

A Simple Method of Making Packages Turn a Corner on a Conveyor

ployed. At the junction of the two conveyors, a thick wooden disk or roller, fitted on a vertical shaft, is mounted. The packages are placed on the first conveyor in such a manner that, when they reach the junc-

tion, the inner end of each package will press against the roller guide. This retards the motion of this end, while permitting the outer end to swing around, and thus the packages are turned at right angles to the line of travel and guided onto the second conveyor.—Orin C. Crooker, Wheaton, Ill.

Keeping the Pop in Popcorn

When popcorn is first harvested it is too wet to pop well, but under proper storage conditions it can be brought to good popping condition in a relatively short time. With artificial storage the drying-out process may be accelerated, but there is always danger of getting the corn too dry, which is just as bad as having it too wet. The safest way is to store the popcorn in a place where the outside air will have free access to it, but where the corn will be protected from the rain and snow. New popcorn stored in this way will be in excellent popping condition by Christmas. Popcorn kept in a living room will soon become too dry for popping. In most cases where popcorn fails to pop well, the trouble is caused by the corn being too dry rather than too wet. For popcorn to pop at its best, it should contain from 13 to 14 per cent moisture; but corn stored in a dry room will drop as low as 8 per cent during the winter months.

When corn fails to pop as well as it should, the following procedure will be found quite helpful: Two pounds of popcorn are put in a 2-qt. fruit jar and from two to five tablespoonfuls of water added, depending on how much the corn has dried out as shown by the way it pops. Very dry popcorn will not give over a third of the normal yield of popped corn and should receive the maximum amount of water. After adding the water, the lid should be screwed on the jar tightly, using a rubber ring. The corn should then be thoroughly shaken and allowed to stand for two days. This method has been found very satisfactory with popcorn that was excessively dry.

Concrete Hog Wallow

Hogs must have their mudholes. But the ordinary hog wallow in the barnyard soon becomes a filthy, reeking place, as a great quantity of straw, dirt and slops is continually dragged into it, which cannot be cleaned out. It is much better, therefore, to make a concrete wallow as shown in the photograph, which will permit the installation of a drain, down which the

Concrete Hog Wallow from Which Mud Can Be Easily Removed at Regular Intervals

mud can be washed at regular intervals. This will aid in making conditions more sanitary and help to combat disease.— J. C. Allen, West Lafayette, Ind.

Protecting Roads from Drifting Sand with Poles

Automobile roads built through country where the soil is light and sandy present many problems, both in construction and

Preventing Sand Drifts on Hard Roads by Means of Poles Laid on the Banks

maintenance. Not the least of these is that of preventing sand from drifting onto the road, especially where grading has been done and a cut bank left along the side of the road. A simple method of overcoming this difficulty has been successfully used by road engineers in several places in Michigan.

Long, slender poles, laid on the bank, fairly close together and at right angles to the road, as shown in the photograph, prevent the wind from eroding the surface of the soft bank and sweeping the sand along to form drifts in the road. The poles are usually dead and worthless timber, so that the cost is practically nothing. In the course of time, the banks become sodded with natural growths of wild grasses, so that the poles need never be renewed. This method has been found to be the cheapest and most satisfactory that has been tried.

Bushing for Accelerator Rod

Some foot accelerators used on Ford cars have a rod passing through the floorboard. The rod is liable to wear the hole larger, causing the rod to move out of its place and rattle. To remedy the trouble, a common tire-valve nut with a threaded sleeve can be turned down into the hole and fastened in place with a few small nails. The rod is then passed through the nut and connected. Such a nut has been in use on one machine for four years.

Adjusting the Binder Hitch for Small Tractor

Many small tractors will easily pull a grain binder, but as they are built with the

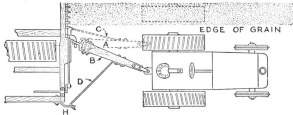

Arranging a Binder Hitch So That It Can Be Used with a Small Tractor, Enables the Farmer to Harvest More Effectively

idea of corn cultivation, they are found too wide to use with the binder when the regular tongue system of the latter is used. The wheel on the grain side crowds the crop down before the cutting bar can reach a full swath. Binder hitches are made, but for these small, wide-set wheel tractors they are of little use in correcting this trouble. The illustration shows how we overcome this difficulty.

On our binder, as on most, the brace rod that holds the stub tongue in line with the binder is on the side of the tongue next to the cutting bar, bolted to the tongue, and hooked into an eye on the binder frame at the end of t h e b a r. This is shown in the drawing by the dotted lines. The brace rod C was removed when the binder was in position for a full swath, and the tongue pushed over until it met the drawbar of the tractor when the latter was in position to travel along the side of the standing grain. A short piece of flat iron, H, was then fitted to the binder frame next to the bundle carrier, in such a manner that it would not interfere with the crank driving the sickle. To this bracket a brace rod, D, was fitted, the other end running to the tongue, and fastened w i t h the same bolts as those used for t h e shorter brace originally used. A better bracing is provided for the tongue with this arrangement when turning corners, and there is no danger of kinking the brace, as it is in tension.

With one of these small but fast tractors a 40-acre field can be cut in a long working day, while with the same binder, used with horses, not more than 15 or 20 acres could be harvested.—G. G. Mc-Vicker, North Bend, Neb.

Novel Milk-Delivery Cart

The dairyman operating on a small scale will find a cart of the type shown in the

Special Delivery Wagon That Will Prove of Value to the Dairyman

photograph of great value in peddling his wares.

The one shown is used by a man who sells his milk to the people of a small prairie town. A special box body is built on a light buggy frame and divided into compartments for the various sizes of bottles. It has room for forty quarts of milk besides several pint bottles of cream. On the back there is a small platform on which the dairyman stands when driving the horse.

¶Tin or copper can be soldered in a heavy wind, or where ordinary flux has a tendency to slide off, by using a flux consisting of resin dissolved in gasoline. The resin is first melted and enough gasoline is added to make a thick sirup. This is applied to the tin.

Novel Boat Hoist Made of Concrete

Many repairs on motorboats can be done without hauling the boat entirely ashore. Frequently it suffices to lift the bow or stern only out of the water as, for instance, in case of propeller repairs. Steel-girder hoists are sometimes used to lift the boat out of the water, but unless kept painted, the steel rusts rapidly. For this reason a concrete hoist is much more satisfactory. A hoist of this kind is shown in the photograph. It consists of two horseshoe-shaped members and a block and tackle is fastened under the center of each arch, a strong steel hook being set in the concrete, while it is poured, to hold the block and tackle. The lower part of each block carries a steel spreader from which the boat is suspended by chain slings when lifted. To afford easy access to the top part of the arches, steps, which are formed from lengths of ¾-in. iron rod, are set in the concrete as shown in the insert, and the whole rests on concrete platforms, a few feet above water level, so that every part of the boat is within reach. A hoist of this kind has been in use for nearly ten years.—C. A. Oldroyd, Barrow-in-Furness, England.

Useful Concrete Hoist, of Novel Design and Permanent Construction, for Lifting Small Boats Out of the Water

Carrying Case for Dynamite Fuses

Dynamite fuses are not regularly equipped with detonating caps, but when block shots must be fired, it is necessary to

Carrying Case for Dynamite Fuses Prevents Accidental Explosion of Detonating Caps

have a large number of fuses already fitted with caps. As these are carried to the blasting place, there is more or less danger of having them go off accidentally and injuring the workman who carries them. To eliminate this risk a quarry foreman provided a safety-first carrying bag, which is similar to an ordinary golf bag, but longer. A large number of fuses equipped with detonating caps can be carried in it without any danger of getting tangled or striking against the rocks.

Another safety measure that works well in practice, where the fuses are cut progressively shorter so that the first fuse lighted will fire its shot at the same time as the last one, is to provide an additional fuse, which is cut shorter so that it will explode just one minute sooner than the first fuse. This additional fuse is lighted at the same time as the first one and is thrown down on the quarry floor. When this detonates it is a warning that the real shots will explode within the next minute.—Thomas J. Paxton, Chicago, Ill.

Plunger Aids in Laying Tile

In a large building in Washington, D. C., foot traffic is so great that it is necessary frequently to replace tiles broken by constant wear and tear. After the old tile has been completely removed and the hole prepared with cement, the new tile is picked up by means of an ordinary force cup or plunger of the kind used for cleaning stopped drains. It is surprising how easily the tile can be placed in its proper position in this way.—Reuben Stafford, Jr., Washington, D. C.

Cases for Small Tools

Handy cases for holding hacksaw blades, drills, files and other small tools that may be lost or damaged when lying around loose, can be

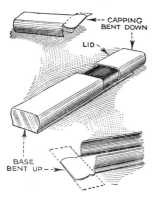

made from metal molding, such as is used for interior wiring. This molding comes in two parts, the base and the capping that slips over the base. To make a tool case from this material, take a piece of the base of sufficient length and close one end as shown in the lower detail. The capping is cut in two pieces and the shorter one is closed at one end in the same manner as the base. The longer part of the capping is sweated to the base, while the other piece forms a sliding lid.—Thos. W. Benson, Philadelphia, Pa.

Measuring an Odd-Fluted Reamer

The large number of odd-fluted taps and reamers now on the market calls for some means of easy measurement as, obviously, these cannot be

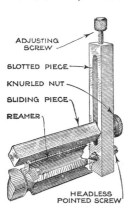

measured in the same way as the tools having an even number of flutes. The measurement of the odd-fluted tools is generally done by some more or less roundabout method, as by first reaming or tapping a hole and then measuring this to get the size. A useful tool can easily be made that will avoid uncertainty and delay, and, besides, will prove of great convenience in measuring the diameter of odd-toothed gears, although the latter require to be plugged for a center. The main part of the tool is made from ⅜ by ½-in. stock slotted and tapped for an adjusting screw at the top and for a headless pointed screw near the bottom. Next, a piece of ¼-in. drill rod is turned down on one end to fit the slot, and threaded for a knurled nut. This sliding piece is then filed or machined to the diamond-shaped cross section shown and the turned portion that enters the slot should be large enough to allow it to be flattened on opposite sides so that the sliding piece will remain in the position shown. The headless screw is ground to a conical point and this completes the gauge.

When measuring a tap or reamer, adjust the headless screw until it fits the center snugly when the tool is flat against the end. Then by means of the upper adjusting screw bring down the sliding piece until it just touches the nearest tooth and then tighten the knurled nut. Now swing the whole tool around on the center until it is exactly opposite a tooth on the reamer and measure over the whole in the ordinary manner with a micrometer. Subtract the thickness of the sliding piece (.25 in.), which leaves the diameter of the tool.

Photographing Tracings

About the simplest job done in a professional photography shop is the copying of black and white drawings, but the job is

more difficult if the drawing happens to be on gray tracing cloth. The best way of making a good black-on-white copy in such a case is to stretch the tracing cloth against a window, and then photograph it. If the shutter of the camera is set at F. 16, only a one-second exposure is required and the result will be entirely satisfactory.—J. G. Pratt, Washington, D. C.

Taking Up Play in Bushings

When a bushing has worn until there is an excessive amount of play in it, and a new one is not at hand, it may be repaired in the following manner: Carefully caliper the shaft and the bushing to determine the amount of wear, then slit the bushing lengthwise, making the width of the slit three times the amount of the play, as previously determined. The bushing is then carefully hammered all around until the lips of the slit come together, and a piece of thin metal bent around the outside to serve as a liner or shim. The thickness of this liner will be equal to half the amount of play in the bushing. The latter is then pressed home, with the liner around it. It is not advisable to drive the bushing in with a hammer; it should be pressed in with an arbor press, or, lacking this, under the drill-press spindle, or even in a vise, if this can be done. If the inside of the bushing seat is well greased, no trouble will be experienced in pressing it and the liner in together.—Felix Helsmoortel, Saugerties, N. Y.

Using Two-Wheel Hand Truck for Bulky Loads

The small two-wheel hand truck can be used to advantage for handling bulky loads, such as desks, cases, machines and a variety of other equipment, by arranging a wide plank on it as shown.

The plank, which should be 4 or 5 ft. long, is placed under the crossbar at the handles and over the lift bar forward of the wheels. The load to be moved is tilted and the truck moved under the center, so that it is balanced over the wheels. It is then possible to move the load or turn it about easily.

This kink has proved of value in a large office building, making it possible to rear-

HEAVY PLANK

Utilizing the Two-Wheel Truck for Moving Cabinets and Other Heavy Equipment

range equipment without scarring hardwood floors as would be the case if the desks, etc., were pushed about on the bare floor. A further advantage of this method is that the hand truck can readily be pulled up steps, while with a four-wheel truck an elevator is necessary.

Markers for Road Culverts

Many accidents are caused each year by automobiles running into ditches at the ends of small culverts on country roads.

Painted Markers Set at Ends of Road Culverts Protect Passing Motorists from Accidents

The culverts are usually from 16 to 20 ft. long and the ends are difficult to see, especially when the roadside is overgrown with grass and weeds. When two autos pass each other at these points, there is scarcely enough room and an accident is often the result. The danger can be eliminated by providing 7-ft. fenceposts as markers at the ends of the culverts. The drivers will not run into these very readily because they can easily be seen, especially if painted red and white.—Geo. G. McVicker, North Bend, Neb.

Spark-Plug Cleaner

Stranded copper wire makes a spark-plug cleaner that can be used without taking the plug apart and is harmless to the porcelain. It will not clean the insulator as well as when the plug is taken apart and polished with steel wool, but will serve in an emergency. The best results are obtained when a length of lamp-cord is doubled over and both ends used. The insulation of the wire should not be removed for more than $\frac{1}{2}$ in. as it stiffens the end of the wire if left on.

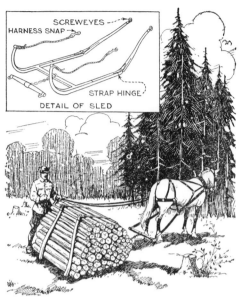

A Novel and Effective Sled for Transporting Cordwood

Novel Cordwood Sled

When cutting and trimming a scattering grove of second-growth timber, which was made into cordwood on the ground, a Wisconsin farmer was considerably inconvenienced by the necessity of carrying the pieces to be piled to a place where they would be out of the way during the curing period. Loading and unloading with a team and wagon consumed too much time, and the sled illustrated was finally constructed for the purpose.

A pair of discarded buggy shafts were cut and hinged at the points indicated, and a large screweye or a ring and staple attached to the end of each. To the bow ends two lengths of ½-in. rope were fastened, and provided with harness snaps; with a singletree chained to the crosspiece, as shown, the sled was complete.

In use one horse is hitched to the sled, and, after the wood is piled upon it, the ends of the shafts are raised until the snaps can be hooked into the rings.

Laying Out Work for Kerfing

Many woodworkers are puzzled when they have a piece to kerf for bending, as to the proper distance to space the kerfs. This is a simple matter, however; to determine the distance from kerf to kerf, take the piece to be bent, mark off from one end a distance equal to the radius of the required arc, and at this point saw one kerf to the desired depth. Then hold the piece firmly down on the bench, or other straight sur-

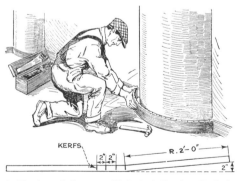

A Simple and Accurate Method of Spacing Kerfs in Work to Be Bent

face, and lift the end until the edges of the kerf pinch together. Whatever height the end must be raised is the required distance to which the kerfs must be spaced.

The illustration shows how simple this

method is. For convenience we have taken a radius of 2 ft. The kerf is made with a 10-point saw to the ordinary depth, which is about three-fourths of the thickness of the material. On lifting the end we find that it must be raised 2 in. before the edges of the kerf come together; this, then, is the distance from kerf to kerf. When the piece is bent to the circle it will be found that each kerf pinches equally, and that the bend is uniform.

It should be remembered that the depth of the kerfs makes considerable difference in the distance between cuts. The deeper the cuts, the shorter the distance between them. The kind of saw used also makes a difference, as a fine saw brings the kerfs closer together, a coarse one making the distance longer.—H. H. Siegele, Emporia, Kansas.

Emergency Substitute for Broken Gland

When the gland on a 10-ton refrigerating machine broke it was found that there was no spare part among the plant supplies. An ordinary 2-in. pipe flange was obtained and a slot, large enough to fit over the piston rod, cut from the edge to the center. The flange bolt holes were then drilled out to fit over the studs and the improvised gland put in place. The time required for the slotting and reaming operations was only 20 minutes, and the flange gave just as good service as the regular gland.—J. J. Noble, Toronto, Ont.

MECHANICAL POWERS

By CARL W. MITMAN
Curator

DIVISIONS OF MINERAL AND
MECHANICAL TECHNOLOGY
UNITED STATES NATIONAL
MUSEUM

Copyright, H. H. Windsor, Jr.

This is the seventh article of a series by Curator Mitman, explaining in simple language what every man who builds or designs a machine must know, and showing in detail just how to build a set of models of the mechanical powers that will exactly duplicate the set in the National Museum at Washington, D. C. The preceding articles appeared in the March, April, May, June, July and August issues.

Part VII—Forces; the Screw

ALL of the forces dealt with in mechanics are definite quantities, and to determine them with precision, three things must be considered for each one: First, the point of application; second, the direction, and third, the magnitude, or the energy with which the force acts. Lines are generally used to represent forces; one end of a line representing the point of application of the force; the direction of the line indicating the direction of the force, and the length of the line its magnitude. By this assumption, a force

This Illustration Shows How the Screw Is Used in Putting a New Front in a Building; Jack Screws Are Fitted in the Bottom of the Vertical Posts to Support the Upper Stories

is defined in each of its three elements and is thus brought within the limits of mathematical analysis. Whatever may be the number and direction of the forces acting upon one point, they can impart motion or pressure in only one direction. It is assumed, therefore, that there is a single force that can produce the same action as the whole group of forces, and which may replace them. This individual force is called the resultant, and the forces of which it is the equivalent are termed the components. Both the components and resultant may be interchanged without changing the condition of the body acted upon or the mechanical effect of the forces themselves. A force is, therefore, mechanically equivalent to the sum of its components and, conversely, any number of forces are mechanically equivalent to their resultant. Since forces are known only by their effect in producing motion or pressure, any forces that produce equal motions or pressures are equal.

When several forces act upon a body they may be arranged in three ways according to their direction: All in one direction; in exactly opposite directions, and at some angle. In the first case, the resultant is the sum of all the forces and the direc-

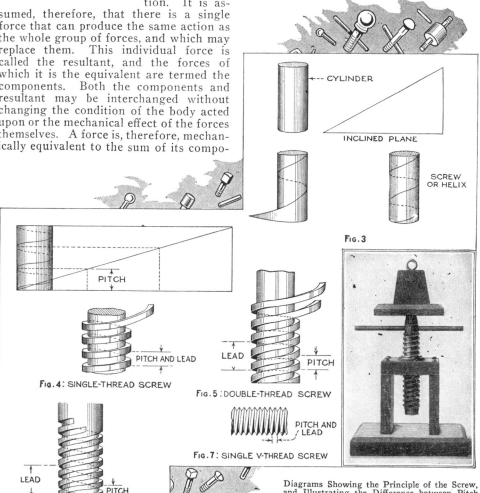

Fig. 1

Fig. 2

CYLINDER

INCLINED PLANE

SCREW OR HELIX

Fig. 3

PITCH

Fig. 4: SINGLE-THREAD SCREW

PITCH AND LEAD

LEAD

PITCH

Fig. 5: DOUBLE-THREAD SCREW

PITCH AND LEAD

Fig. 7: SINGLE V-THREAD SCREW

LEAD

PITCH

TRIPLE-THREAD SCREW
Fig. 6

Diagrams Showing the Principle of the Screw, and Illustrating the Difference between Pitch and Lead in Single and Multiple-Thread Screws; Right, Model of Screw

tion is not changed; in the second, the resultant is the difference of the forces and takes the direction of the greater, and in the third case, the resultant is found by applying the law of what is called the parallelogram of forces. Thus, in Fig. 1, if two forces applied at the point A are represented in direction and magnitude by the lines AB and AC (adjacent sides of the parallelogram ABCD) their resultant will be represented in magnitude and direction by the diagonal AD; or, in Fig. 2, if two forces A and B do not have the same point of application but it is evident that their directions intersect, the forces may be imagined as applied at the point of intersection and the resultant of the two forces may be found by constructing the parallelogram of forces, as shown, the lines being set off from the intersecting point in proportion to the magnitude as before. In mechanics the finding of the resultant of two or more forces is often desirable, and, in addition, the finding of the components of a single force is equally desirable. The solution of the former problem, as shown above, is called the composition of forces and that of the latter the resolution of forces, which is carried out in a similar manner to the composition except that the work is done in the reverse order.

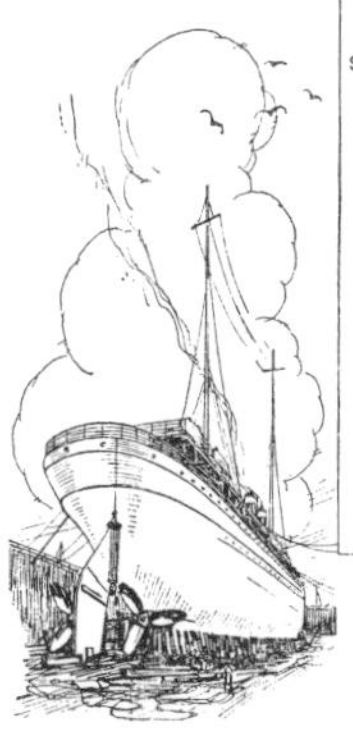

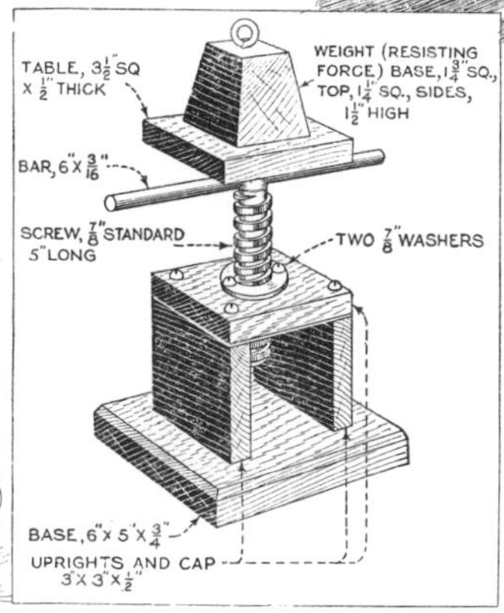

The screw bears the same relation to the inclined plane that a spiral staircase does to a straight one. Theoretically it is a cylinder surrounded by a spiral ridge or groove, every part of which forms an equal angle with the axis of the cylinder so that if the spiral could be unwound on a plane surface it would be an inclined plane. This is illustrated in Fig. 3.

There are a number of varieties of screw-thread forms, and also a variety of types. A single-thread screw is represented in Fig. 4, taking a screw with a square thread as an example. This may be considered, for our purpose, as consisting of a square bar wound in a helix or screw around a cylinder, and will illustrate, with Figs. 5 to 7, the difference between pitch and lead in a screw.

The pitch of a screw is the distance between the top of one thread and the top of the next, or, in the case of the square thread, from one edge of the thread to the corresponding edge of the next; and this

holds true regardless of the type of screw, or whether it has a single or a multiple thread. The lead of the screw, however, is the distance that the screw will advance through the nut when turned through one complete revolution, and this varies with single and multiple threads.

In Fig. 4, the pitch and lead are the same, that is, the screw will advance in one revolution, a distance equal to the pitch. Fig. 5 represents a double-thread or, as it is sometimes called, a "two-start" screw; this has, so to speak, two square bars wrapped around the cylinder, each starting 180° apart. In this case, while the pitch is still the distance from one thread edge to the next, the lead is double this distance, for the screw will advance, in one revolution, a distance equal to twice the pitch. Similarly with Fig. 6, which shows a triple thread or "three-start" screw, where the ends of the threads are 120° apart, the lead is three times the pitch. This applies to all forms of screw threads.

Fitting the thread of the cylinder into a spiral groove cut in the interior of a block and attaching a lever to the head of the cylinder result in a combination of parts technically known as the screw and recognized as one of the mechanical powers. A conventionalized form of such a machine is shown in the first photo, reproduced from a model. The screw is used in a variety of ways to do work, the most common and yet opposite applications probably being the lifting jack (Fig. 8) and the screw press. The jack operated by hand levers can be designed to lift loads up to about 20 tons or exert a pressure in the form of a press of almost that same amount. There are screw presses

Detail drawing labels:

TABLE, 3½" SQ. x ½" THICK

WEIGHT (RESISTING FORCE) BASE, 1⅜" SQ., TOP, 1¼" SQ., SIDES, 1½" HIGH

BAR, 6" x 3/16"

SCREW, ⅞" STANDARD 5" LONG

TWO ⅞" WASHERS

BASE, 6" x 5" x ¾"

UPRIGHTS AND CAP 3" x 3" x ½"

Detail Drawing for Constructing the Model of the Simple Screw with Illustrations Showing How It Is Used

FIG. 8

for clothes, oil and fruit; there are screw-arbor presses in the machine shop and hay balers and waste-paper balers which use the screw to pack the bale. The wood screws and clamps used especially in the carpentry trade do their work through the agency of the screw. The screw propeller on watercraft is so named because its action is that of a screw which utilizes the water as a nut and so pushes the boat forward. In calculations involving the screw and lever, as in the jack in Fig. 8, equilibrium will take place when the applied force is to the resisting force as the lead is to the circumference described by the lever arm. During each revolution the applied force describes a large circle but the end of the screw advances only the distance between two threads; in other words, in this, as in all cases of the use of machines, what is gained in power is lost in speed. From this statement, it is evident that its mechanical efficiency is augmented either by increasing the length of the lever or by decreasing the lead. For instance, if the lead of a screw is ½ in. and the lever arm describes a circle of 5 ft. (equal to 120 half inches) circumference, an applied force of 1 lb. will balance a resisting force of 120 lb.; while with a lead of ¼ in., 1 lb. will balance 240 lb. In other words, the efficiency is doubled. It follows, too, that fine screw threads are more powerful than coarse ones. Continuing in this fashion, theoretically, the mechanical advantage of the screw can be made as large as we please simply by decreasing sufficiently the lead. In practice, however, this is impossible, for, if the lead is decreased too much, the threads themselves will not be suffi-

WEIGHT (RESISTING FORCE) BASE, 1¾" SQ., TOP, 1¼" SQ., SIDES, 1½" HIGH

UPRIGHTS, 5½" X 1½" X ½"

BEAM, 2⅝" X 1¼" X ½"

TABLE, 3¾" X 1¼" X ½"

BASE, 4½" X 2 X ¾"

Constructional Details of the Model of the Differential Screw; Above, an Arbor and Gear Press Utilizing the Screw

ciently strong to bear the strain put upon them.

To overcome this difficulty, John Hunter, the celebrated English surgeon (1728 - 1793), invented the differential screw. This consists of two screws, the threads of which are of different pitch and mounted upon the same shaft, one unwinding as the other winds. The effective lift or pressure obtained is equal to the difference of the leads of the two threads, and by making this difference very small great power may be obtained without the weakness due to a very finely threaded single screw. The second photo, reproduced from a model, incorporates Dr. Hunter's principle. The larger single-thread screw turns in a fixed beam. The inside of this screw is hollow and is tapped to admit the smaller screw, which also has a single thread. This screw is free to move up and down, carrying with it a sliding table, but is restrained from rotating by the table. It also has more threads to the inch than the larger screw. When the larger screw makes one clockwise revolution, it moves upward a distance equal to the pitch, but at the same time the smaller screw goes into the large screw a distance equal to its pitch; hence the smaller screw with its sliding table and also the load move upward a distance equal to the difference between these two distances. As in the cases of the Chinese or differential windlass and the differential pulley, the speed of operation of the differential screw is slow, but the mechanical advantage is enormous.

Figure 9 shows a slightly different application of this principle, and represents diagrammatically a part of a machine on which a very fine adjustment is required. Screw C, with a coarse pitch, works in the fixed bracket A, while D, which is a part of C, and has a fine pitch, works in the loose, sliding part B. When C is turned the sliding part B moves a distance equal to the difference between the pitches of the screws.

Another common application of the differential screw, in a different form, is in taking up wear on the feed screws of planer toolboxes. Here the feed screw passes through a circular nut, which is finely threaded on the outside, the inside being threaded for the screw. This nut screws into a recess drilled in the toolbox casting, which is also threaded for the screw. Now, by screwing down on the nut, any backlash that has developed between the screw and the thread in the toolbox may be taken up very easily. The take-up nut is usually fitted with a locknut. A differential arrangement is sometimes used on a lathe tool slide, in which case the fine thread is used

Model of the Differential Screw: Above, One Application of This Mechanism

for feeding and the coarse for rapid withdrawal of the tool.

For making the simple-screw model the following material is required:

Base, 6 by 5 by ¾ in.
Two uprights and one cap, 3 by 3 by ½ in.
Table, 3½ in. square by ½ in.
Screw, ⅞ in. standard, 5 in. long, with nut.
Two ⅞-in. washers.
Bar, 6 in. long by 3-16-in. diameter.
Weight (resisting force), base 1¾ in. square, top 1¼ in. square, side 1½ in. high.

Square and face all wooden parts with a finish bevel on top of the base and table. Turn off the threads of the screw for 1 in. of its length at one end, rounding the extremity. Three-fourths inch from the end, drill a ⁷⁄₃₂-in. hole through the diameter and insert the rod therein. Locate the center of the cap and about this point chisel out the outline of the screw nut. Insert the nut in the space and retain it in position by bolting the washers on each face; thus, the walls of the cap prevent rotation of the nut and the faces of the washers prevent end movement. Form a bridge by screwing the cap to the top of the two uprights. Center this assembly on the base, securing it with screws and glue. Drill a No. 18 hole ½ in. lengthwise of the screw, in the rounded end. Drill a No. 29 hole in the center of the table and insert therein a 8-32 machine screw, 1 in. long, securing it with a nut. Place the extension of this machine screw in the end of

the large screw and insert this assembly into the nut, revolving same into suitable position by means of the rod. Rest the weight on the table. Finish as desired.

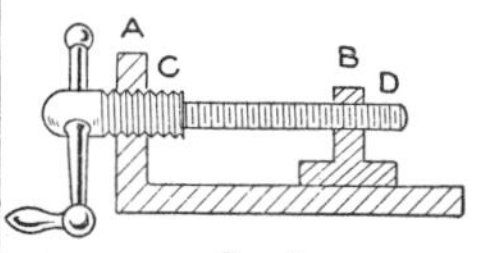

For the model of the differential screw use the following material:

Base, 4½ by 2 by ¾ in.
Two uprights, 5½ by 1½ by ½ in.
Beam, 2⅝ by 1¼ by ½ in.
Table, 3¾ by 1¼ by ½ in.
½-in. bolt and nut, 3 in. long.
2-in. flat-head machine screw, 16-18.
Brass rod, 3-16. diameter, 2½ in. long.
Wood screws; four round-head, No. 6, 1 in.; four flat-head, No. 6, 1½ in.
Weight (resisting force), base 1¾ in. square, top 1¼ in. square, side 1½ in. high.

Square and face the wooden parts with a finish bevel on the top of the base and on the edges and one end of the uprights. Drill two ½-in. holes in the side of the uprights, with centers ¾ in. and 2½ in., respectively, from opposite ends. Saw out the material between these holes, leaving long round-end slots, 2¾ in. long. On a line across the uprights, 2 in. from the flat end, center two ⅛-in. holes ⅝ in. apart. In the center of the beam, chisel a hole to accommodate the ½-in. nut. Saw out shoulders in each corner of the table blank, leaving ½-in. central tenons. Drill and countersink a No. 6 hole in the center of this table and screw therein the 16-18 machine screw, sinking the head. Turn or saw off the head of the ½-in. bolt and drill a hole laterally through the shank to accommodate the ³⁄₁₆-in. brass rod. In the other end of this bolt drill longitudinally a No. 6 hole, 1 in. deep and tap 16-18. Screw the ½-in. bolt the full length of its threads into the nut in the beam. Screw the table screw into the hole in the opposite end of the bolt. Secure this differential assembly to the two uprights by round-head wood screws passing through the two ⅛-in. holes in the uprights and into the beam, allowing the tenons to be guided by the upright slots. Center this assembly upon the base, securing with glue and screws from beneath. Place the weight on the table. Finish as desired.

¶A mechanic who lost the nut from a hand emery grinder when on a job away from the shop, made a new one by bending a piece of tin into a square, about ¾ in. across, laying this on the spindle and casting it full of babbitt.

Coping Serves Double Purpose

Stucco houses of Spanish type are becoming quite popular in many places. They are made without eaves, to imitate the adobe houses of early days. The top of the walls is usually made flat and a considerable amount of soot and dirt gathers on it, especially in cities. With every rain this dirt is washed off and runs down the walls, leaving ugly stains on them which

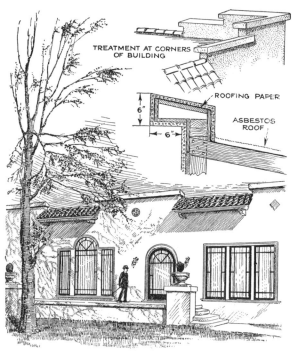

TREATMENT AT CORNERS OF BUILDING

ROOFING PAPER

ASBESTOS ROOF

Wide Coping Slanting toward the Inside Prevents Rain and Dirt from Running Down the Outside Wall

greatly detract from the neat appearance of the building. This can be prevented by slanting the top of the coping toward the roof so that the water will run that way. A coping, 12 in. wide, slanting toward the inside with a 6-in. overhang and broken at regular intervals with tiled eaves as shown in the drawing, also gives a distinctive touch to the design of the building. The roof drains toward the center and then to one side, where the water is carried away by a single pipe.—A. May Holaday, San Jose, Calif.

Using Blue-Stained Lumber

While blue stain in lumber is not an early stage of decay, but merely an indication of the presence in the sapwood of a fungus which does not materially affect the strength of the wood for ordinary commercial purposes, no absolutely effective method of preventing it other than kiln drying has been found. Kiln tests have shown that a temperature of 140° F. for a period of six hours is sufficient to kill the blue-stain fungus in the center of test pieces up to 4 by 4 in. square. No chemical dip for green lumber has been found that is remedial, in periods of continued rain, during the warm months. Until a suitable method of prevention is found applicable in cases where kiln drying is not feasible, intelligent utilization of the discolored stock remains the only means of discounting the damage done by the blue-stain fungus, when the methods now available have failed to keep it out. Resurfacing does not help when the fungus has made substantial penetration.

As blemish in any degree destroys the beauty of the grain of the wood, bright stain-free stock is highly desirable for a large variety of uses requiring a natural finish. But for many purposes where the wood is to be covered up or painted, and where the use of sapwood is permissible, there is no reason for discriminating against blue-stained material, provided no wood-destroying fungi are associated with the stain.

As the conditions that favor the development of the blue stains in sapwood also offer the opportunity for infection with the wood-destroying fungi, the holder of such material should assure himself that no indications of these harmful fungi are present before recommending the use of badly blued stock.

Blue stain is freely accepted in rough lumber, lath, scantling, plank, and some of the larger sizes of dimension stock. More could well be used in the manufacture of sash, doors, millwork, and other products when the wood is to be painted or the discoloration otherwise hidden from view.

Greater confidence in decay-free blued stock can be built up if the dealer will make clear to the customer the fact that blue stain does not seriously affect the strength of wood, and will suggest specific uses. Efforts in this direction will be greatly reinforced when blue-stained lumber comes into wider use and justifies the claims made for it.—U. S. Forest Products Laboratory, Madison, Wis.

HOMEMADE CIRCULAR SAWS

ONE of the handiest tools around the farm is a circular saw; uses will be found for this tool almost daily. Even the amateur woodworker can well spare the time to make a circular saw when the time and labor saved on subsequent work are taken into consideration. The saws described in this article can all be made by any man handy with tools, and will prove desirable additions to any workshop.

The power saw shown in Figs. 1 to 8 was built by a California carpenter. The power plant is one taken from an old automobile; the belt, lacing, 1-in. mandrel and 12-in. cut-off and rip saws were purchased from a mail-order house at a cost of $12.50, and the cost of the bolts totaled $2.00. Fir, 2 by 4 in. and 2 by 3 in., was used for the frame. The drawings give the actual dimensions of the original saw, but these, of course, can be readily modified to suit any

the 2 by 4-in. stock, 4 ft. 11 in. long, assembled with three cross sills, 18½ in. long, the cross sills being gained into the long ones. The height of the saw frame is 26 in., and it will be noted from the drawings that the two mandrel rails, as well as the third rail at the outside, are gained into the end rails, and that the legs are bolted in two directions through the inside corners with ⅜-in. carriage bolts, 6 and 8 in. in length. To stiffen the mandrel rails, two 2 by 3-in. crosspieces are bolted edgewise on the underside with the same bolts that hold the bearings in place. The legs are braced by nailing 1 by 4-in. strips inside them, as indicated.

The detail of the saw table shows a form of construction productive of rigidity, while enabling the underside of the oak-flooring surface to lie close to the saw washers, thus providing for a maximum

Above, Engine End of Saw Frame; Center, Saw Mounted on Skids for Farm Use; Right, Closeup of Table Guides and Gasoline Tank on Frame

type or size of engine and mandrel. The base of the frame consists of two sills of

rise of the saw blade

27"

38"

27"

HAND-
WHEEL

1¼"

1"X4"

14"

3"X4"

3"X3"

12"

16" AUTO FLYWHEEL

FIG. 9

FLYWHEEL

CRANK

CRANK ROD

PEDAL

HINGES

TREADLE

FIG. 10

FIG. 11

Figs. 9 to 11, Working Drawings for Building a Foot-Power Circular Saw, with Detail of Mounting of the Treadle and a View of the Saw in Use; Fig. 12, Saw Mounted on the Front End of a Ford Automobile for Contractor's Use

FIG. 12

above the table. The oak flooring is run crosswise of the wide span between the rails, with the four end boards running full width, while the remaining space is filled with boards running lengthwise. The boards are toenailed with six-penny box nails and nailed through the surface with six-penny finishing nails, the heads being set in and the surface scraped flat and sanded smooth. A saw slit is cut as indicated, and widened for 6 in. along the center for dado-head clearance. To provide for accurate placing of the table, three pieces of 1 by 4-

against the 1 by 6-in. pieces of the dado table when the rider is put in position for use. Since these pieces act as stops against which pieces for cross dadoing are held, they are cut accurately square.

In use, the table is slipped over the vertical guides of the saw frame and tacked in place with small nails to prevent shifting. The rider is then placed between the guides, which have previously been waxed to reduce friction, and the stock to be dadoed is held firmly against the near stop while the rider is slid forward against the dado saw. For long

Details of the Construction of the Power Saw; Figs. 1 to 5 Show the Construction of the Frame and Table; Figs. 6 and 7 the Dado Table and Its Rider, and Fig. 8 the Method of Building Up the Flywheel

in. stock, 7 in. long, are nailed vertically on the outside of the end rails of the mandrel frame, as shown in one of the photographs, and extend above the rails 3¼ in. These bear accurately against the table rails and prevent sliding of any kind. For use with a dado head, the special table shown in Fig. 6 is used. It consists of two pieces of 1 by 6-in. fir, 2 ft. 8½ in. long, nailed to crossrails of 2 by 3-in. stock, leaving the distance between the 1 by 6-in. pieces exactly 15 in. These pieces form guides for the rider, Fig. 7, in which two slides of 1 by 3-in. material are held parallel, 15 in. apart (outside edges), by crosspieces 20 in. long. The projecting 2½-in. lugs at each end of the crosspieces bear

work, it is useful to tack a strip of wood over the tops of the cross strips, so that a wedge or chisel can be driven between it and the work. Where it is desirable to dado at an angle, a suitable wedge-shaped piece is held between the stop and the work.

In mounting the engine, the automobile was stripped and the frame cut through behind the engine, and the assembly, complete with the radiator, mounted crosswise on the saw frame. The flywheel was thickened with two layers of wood, in the manner indicated, to form a drive pulley, which was belted to the mandrel. A gallon oilcan, with a feed pipe soldered to the lower end and held against the saw frame with strips of thin iron, serves as a gasoline tank, and a stout cord brought under the table, through a sash pulley, and attached to a T-hinge on the base, as a foot accelerator.

It will be noted that no special provision is made for varying the height of the table. Since most dadoes in carpentry are only ⅜ in. deep, the dado rider is equipped with shims of suitable thickness under the cross strips to hold the stock at the right height, and as for tilting, the same effect is obtained by the use of guide strips tacked to the top of the table. The fence consists of a length of 2 by 3-in. stuff, nailed to the bar of a wooden clamp, which is screwed tight across the table wherever needed.

In measuring the belt, the length should be taken when stretched around both pulleys and 2 in. cut off before lacing. Friction tape wrapped around the mandrel pulley prevents slipping, but if the belt persists in coming off, two wooden strips can be nailed to the frame, above and below the belt, and connected with a third strip across the outer edges of the belt, and this will effectually prevent the loss of a belt that is properly fitted.

To make the saw still more useful to the farmer, a heavy sled or skid, made of 4 by 4-in. stock, can be fitted under the saw frame. The saw can then be drawn by a couple of horses or the tractor to the wood lot, or elsewhere it is required.

The saw shown in Figs. 9 to 11 is more suitable for the amateur woodworker than the one just described, and while it is operated by foot power, is every bit as practical for the small shop as the other one.

The legs of the frame in this case are made of 3 by 4-in. stock, and the cross-pieces or shaft-bearing rails of 3 by 3-in. stuff. The rails may be gained into the legs as before, but a simpler construction is to fasten them, as shown in the drawing, with lag screws. The bearings for the crankshaft and mandrel, the mandrel, belt and hinges can all be obtained from mail-order houses. The crankshaft and flywheel can be picked up at any auto junk yard, and the crankshaft can be used in some cases just as it is, without sawing it off to length, and using only one crank. The table top should be made of oak, 1¼ in. thick—flooring boards will serve—and the hinged top of the same material. The auxiliary top is hinged to one end of the table proper, or rather to the top 1 by 4-in. cross brace at one end, and the other end of the table is fitted with two pieces of ⅜ by 2-in. iron or cold-rolled steel, drilled and countersunk for heavy screws and

slotted for the ⅜-in. clamp screws. The clamp screws pass through the cross brace from the back, and are fitted with large handwheel nuts and washers. A table-raising screw is fitted to this end of the table also.

A foot lever is hinged to the center cross brace at the opposite end of the table, and connection made to the crank by means of a short connecting rod, as shown. The details of this rod are left to the maker, as the one on the original machine was made of scrap parts, and probably could not be duplicated; however, this is a part that is readily made. Care should be taken that the crankshaft is placed at such a distance from the pivot that the travel of the outer end of the foot lever will not be too great for convenience in operating it. The lever is made of 1 by 4-in. material.

Figure 12 shows a saw rigged up on the front of a Ford car by a contractor, for use on work away from the shop. The frame was attached to the axle and the crank handle removed, so that a sleeve could be fitted in its place. The inner end of the sleeve is slotted to engage the pins on the forward end of the crankshaft in the same manner as the crank handle, and a shaft carrying a pulley welded into the front of the sleeve. The front end of the shaft is carried in a bearing on the frame, and the pulley drives the saw mandrel in the usual way. Constructional details are not given for this saw, as the method of connecting the frame to the car differs with the automobile used, and also the method of driving the pulley shaft, but with the illustration given no great difficulty will be met.

Replacing Broken Wood Inlays

Broken wood inlays can be neatly repaired as follows: Dissolve in ether a piece of gum arabic large enough to replace the missing piece, making a solution about the consistency of soft putty. Add some finely powdered wood of the same kind, color and shade as the missing piece. This powder can be made by simply filing a piece of wood. When the mixture matches the wood, it is worked into the depression left by the missing piece, so that every corner is filled, and tamped down tightly, but allowing the patch to project a little above the surface. The tamping can be done by pressing in the mixture evenly with a spatula or, in case a large quantity is used, with a putty knife. After the mixture has dried thoroughly, it is sandpapered down and polished.— Matt C. Roemer, Appleton, Wis.

Emulsion for Spraying Fruit Trees

An emulsion of kerosene and water is effective for killing all leaf-eating or sap-sucking insects on fruit trees. One pound of wheat flour is mixed in 1 qt. of kerosene and then about 15 qt. of water are added. This mixture will remain emulsified for some time, but it is best to use it immediately.— J. W. Walker, Wellington, New Zealand.

A Stanchionless Dairy Barn

There is a dairy barn near Omaha, Neb., which houses 76 cows without having a single stanchion, as shown in the photo. The owner claims that this arrangement gives the cows more freedom and costs much less than stanchions. The interior of the barn has a row of 6 by 6-in. posts on each side of the feed alley to support the roof. Near the bottom of each post an iron rod, bent to the shape shown, is provided to hold a chain, which is run along the posts the whole length of the barn and is securely fastened at both ends. A rope with a harness snap is put around the neck of each cow and then snapped to the chain. As the bars on the posts are 14 in. long, the chain can be moved vertically this distance, while lateral movement is limited by the length of the rope, so that the cows cannot crowd each other. Another advantage of the

Stanchionless Dairy Barn Houses a Large Number of Cows and Can Be Cleaned Easily

freedom from stanchions is that the barn can be cleaned much more easily, a decided advantage in the average dairy.— Dale R. Van Horn, Walton, Neb.

A Novelty in Cellar Excavation

Basements for large buildings are usually dug with steam shovels, or some similar type of excavating machine. In such cases, an inclined roadway is left in some

A Novelty in Small Cellar Excavation; the Shovel Was Jacked Up and Removed from the Hole on Rollers

part of the basement over which the machine pulls or pushes itself out of the basement when the job is finished. The roadway is then removed by men and teams. The complete excavation of all material in a comparatively small cellar by a steam shovel, and the subsequent removal of the shovel by raising it on jack screws and moving it out on rollers, is a distinctly novel performance.

The accompanying photo shows a 21-ton ¾-yd. shovel being removed in this manner, after having completed the excavating of a cellar, 12 ft. deep, in the congested district of Dayton, Ohio. The use of teams and wagons was impracticable on account of the small area of the excavation and the cramped quarters in which it was located. It required one day to dig the cellar, and one day to remove the shovel. —Ivan E. Houk, Dayton, Ohio.

¶In making a mechanical drawing, the French curve was found too short. A length of ⅛-in. wire solder bent to the desired curvature was found to be an excellent substitute.

Novel Roof Economizes Lumber

Temporary buildings can be roofed much more quickly and with less lumber if the roofing boards are laid across the rafters diagonally, as shown in the illustration. Each board overlaps the one below it in order to shed rain, making the roof practically waterproof. Roofs made in this way have been found quite satisfactory.—Bunyan Kennedy, McCool, Miss.

Stand for Tube Polishing

Anyone who has had the job of polishing brass tubes as commonly used for rail fittings will appreciate the method shown in the drawing, as it relieves the operator of most of the exertion required. By using this method large lots of tubes have been polished without undue fatigue, whereas it is a very tiring task when each tube must be held in the hands and pressed against the wheel by the operator. When using the method illustrated, the tubing is slipped through holes drilled in a wooden stand, made up of hardwood planks, the base being about 6 ft. long and fitted with two adjusting screws at one end.

Two shorter sidepieces are bolted to a center piece, and this is in turn bolted to the base near one side, just tightly enough to allow it to be swung on the bolt without difficulty. Both sidepieces are drilled through near the top to take the tubes to be polished and the stand is set up under the buffing wheel. The operator inserts the tube through both holes in the fixture and stands on the base while revolving the tube and pushing it along. To prevent a hollow being worn in the center of the wheel, the tube is worked back and forth sideways now and then. It is for this purpose that the bolt connecting the sidepieces to the plank on the floor is put off center, so that a slight side movement of the tube sweeps the latter across the face of the wheel. As the wheel wears down, the two screws in the end of the plank are turned to raise the stand, in order to attain the right pressure on the wheel.—Harry Moore, Montreal, Can.

A Comfortable Machine Handle

In many instances the handles supplied on machines are not suitable for the conditions under which the machine is used. Handles for raising tables, for example, are usually made in such a way that they barely clear the edge of the table, and the operator's fingers are liable to be pinched. If the handles are bent outward to give good clearance they interfere with the free movement of the workman unless they are taken off the machine after use, which is also inconvenient. To overcome this trouble the handle shown in the illustration was devised and found entirely satisfactory, as it has the advantages of providing abundant

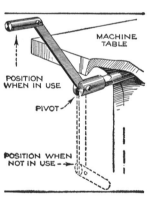

clearance and being completely out of the way when not in use. The sleeve fitting the rod on the table screw is slotted on the end opposite the square to take a flat extension, which carries a round handle riveted tightly at an angle at the other end. The extension piece turns easily on a pin driven through the sleeve and is rounded at this end to permit it to drop down as shown. The slot in the sleeve is cut at about a 45° angle to the axis so that, when the handle is pressed up against the bottom of the slot while turning, it clears the table easily. The raising or lowering of the table is always finished with the handle up, and, when released, it drops completely out of the way.

Shop Notes

A Price-Ticket Printer for Stores

By EDWIN M. LOVE

BUSY grocerymen and other storekeepers who have many price cards to make can save considerable time by using the simple printing machine shown in the illustration. Few tools are needed in its construction and the lumber used can be

obtained from packing or similar boxes. The base is made of 1-in. material and measures 9¼ in. by 16¼ in. A notch, 1½ in. deep and 3½ in. long, is cut in the center of one end to receive the large end of the pillar, which is glued and nailed in place, and a ⅜-in. strip, 1½ in. wide, is mitered around the outside to hide the end wood and to resist warping; beginning 2½ in. from the back, ¼-in. holes, spaced 1 in. apart, are drilled in a row on each side of

A Simple Homemade Device for Printing Price Tickets That Saves Considerable Time for the Busy Storekeeper; the Lumber Can Be Obtained from Packing Boxes

1

the base to receive the stops or pins that guide the card while it is being printed.

In making the pillar, yoke and disk support, care should be taken to make the joints fit accurately so that the pillar and support piece incline toward each other at an angle of 60°.
When the glue is dry, each joint is drilled and a ⅜-in. dowel driven into place.

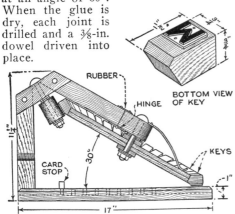

Side Elevation of the Ticket Printer, Showing the Arrangement of the Parts, Also Detail of Key

The inking roller is built up of a roll of thin felt or cloth, 1½ in. in diameter and 2 in. in length, wound on a piece of ⁵⁄₁₆-in. brass tubing, such as a length of umbrella handle, the open ends being closed by washers soldered on. These washers take the thrust and reduce the end friction on the carriage bolt that passes through the roller, and fastens it to the yoke.

The type disk is ¾ in. thick, built up of two pieces of ⅜-in. pine, 12 in. in diameter, glued together with the grain running at right angles to prevent warping. Through the center a ½-in. hole is drilled and the bearing is lengthened by gluing a 1½-in. wooden washer, ½ in. thick, on each side of the disk. The 40 type keys are spaced at regular intervals about the circumference, and are fastened by glue and nails. Shallow ⅜-in. holes, drilled opposite the center of each key and 5 in. from the center of the disk, form stop seats for the small curved end of the stop spring, which is screwed to the upper side of the disk support, and keeps the disk from turning while the key is making its impression upon the card. To insure contact between the inking roller and the keys as they pass, a small roller may be fitted in a convenient position on the underside of the disk support so as to bear against the top of the disk as close to the inking roller as possible.

For type, ¾-in. rubber stamps, all capitals, are used, or if desired, the letters may be cut from linoleum. If rubber stamps are used the keys should be recessed to receive them, although by cutting off the rubber backs the letters can easily be glued and tacked in place. The letters are arranged alphabetically around the disk, following with the numerals from 2 to 0, the dollar sign, fraction bar, cents sign, period and the "&" sign.

The disk support is cut and hinged as shown, the two parts being kept in contact by a heavy rubber band or piece of inner tube, tacked under tension on the upper side. When the letter to be printed has been passed over the inking roller and brought into position by the spring stop, it is then depressed to make contact with the card to be printed; the distance between key and card should not exceed ⅛ in. The printer should be kept covered when not in use to prevent the accumulation of dust on the inking roller.

Attaching Brake Lining

Rivets are usually used for attaching brake bands to their shoes but it takes considerable time to drill, countersink and place the rivets. In the construction of a small hoist where a brake was used considerable wear was anticipated and in order to avoid the work of riveting the bands on frequently, the method of fastening the lining shown in the drawing, was used. T-shaped bolts were passed through holes punched at each end of the lining and the lining was then pulled down into grooves cut in the ends of the shoes. Obviously, by this method very little time was lost in changing a lining.

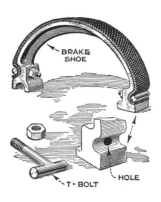

Cleaning Steel of Burnt Oil

The oil, coming in contact with steel in hardening, will burn in places, and is hard to remove. The cleaning can be accomplished by immersing the hardened steel in gasoline, and, when exposed to the air, it will dry immediately. This will leave parts to be polished without the marks of burnt oil.

Waterproofing Blueprints

To overcome the annoyance of having blueprints spotted by rain or moisture, the following simple plan is useful: Melt two or three cakes of refined paraffin, then immerse a number of absorbent cloths in the wax. Withdraw the cloths and allow them to drain. To treat a print, lay one of the cloths on a dry, smooth surface, place the print on top of it, then another cloth on top of the print, and iron the top cloth with a moderately hot flatiron. The paper immediately absorbs paraffin until saturated and becomes translucent and waterproof. This method is better than dipping the prints into the paraffin, which leaves too heavy a coating.

Determining Grade Lines

The device shown in the photo is used to determine grade lines when locating a terrace on washed land, or land that has a tendency to wash. One leg is made adjustable so that it may be lengthened or shortened to give the definite grade desired. For instance, if the front leg is ½ in. shorter than the rear leg on the level, which is 16⅔ ft. long, the grade established will be 3 in. to each 100 ft. rise. In use, the rear leg is placed at the lowest point determined, the front end swung back and forth until a point is found where the level shows center and a stake driven to mark the point. The level is then moved forward again so that the rear leg is placed

Quick Method of Determining Grade Lines for Terracing Land and Laying Ti e Drains

at the point just staked. This device will save much time and trouble in working out grade lines for terracing land, and also for working out the grades for laying tile drainage. A carpenter's level is used with the device.—J. C. Allen, Lafayette, Ind.

Sand-Drying Stove for Contractor

On a job where thoroughly dried sand was needed in large quantities, a contractor built the simple drying stove, shown in the drawing. It consists of two

Simply Made Stove Used by Contractor for Drying Large Quantities of Sand

truncated cones made of heavy sheet metal, mounted one on the other. The lower one has a collar at the top, for the attachment of a length of stovepipe, and a fire door near the bottom. To the upper cone are welded four curved feet so that it will rest steadily on the lower one, leaving a space of 1 in. or more between them. Sand is shoveled into the hopper formed by the upper cone, and as soon as it becomes dry it sifts through the space between the cones to the ground. An occasional tap against the hopper may be necessary to keep the drier going without waste of fuel. The stovepipe can be taken off so that the stove takes little space on a truck.—G. E. Hendrickson, Argyle, Wis.

Soldering Small Parts

A solder for small parts can be made by cutting tin foil to the shape of the surface to be soldered and moistening it on both sides with sal ammoniac. The parts to be soldered are cleaned carefully and the foil is placed between them. They are then heated until the tin foil melts. This gives a good, neat job and can be done without difficulty.—Frank N. Coakley, Buffalo, N. Y.

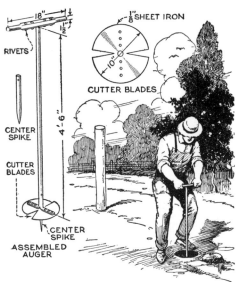

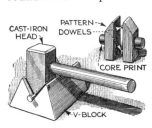

Durable Homemade Post-Hole Auger Is Inexpensive

A Serviceable Post-Hole Auger

A serviceable post-hole auger, which is just as good as the manufactured article, can readily be made by anyone. It consists of a 4½-ft. length of 1¼-in. pipe. Both ends are slotted with a hacksaw for about 6 in. and bent over and flattened, as shown, so that a handle and a blade can be attached. The handle is made of an 18-in. length of hardwood, about 1½ in. thick, and is securely riveted to the bent ends of the pipe. A 10-in. steel disk, about ⅛ in. thick, is riveted to the other end, as shown. The blade is cut radially and the edges thus formed are bent to "bite" the soil. A spike, sharpened to a point, is driven into the lower end under the blade and is held in this position by means of a rivet. An auger of this kind has been giving satisfactory service for almost two years and the initial cost of the material was only 5 cents, as most of it was found about the workshop. —G. A. Luers, Washington, D. C.

Nail-Straightening Device

Anyone who has had experience in straightening old nails in large quantities will appreciate the device shown in the drawing. At least, the owner of a building, which was torn down to be erected elsewhere, found it very useful, when he found himself in possession of several kegs of quite usable nails, all of which were more or less bent. After a bit of experimenting he cast a V-block of iron and made a hammer with a heavy head to fit the block. The block was made from a single-piece pattern, the groove being cut to an angle of 45°. The hammer was made from a two-piece pattern, as shown at the upper right. The core prints were about 1³⁄₁₆ in. long and as large as the required hole, where they joined the pattern, but tapered slightly toward the ends. The halves of the pattern were doweled together.

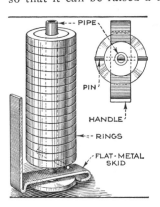

In use, the nails are placed in the vee and are given one or more blows with the hammer. Sometimes it proved necessary to roll a nail over and give it another blow and a few of them had to be held by the head with a pair of pliers in order to straighten short bends close to the head, but in most cases one operation sufficed. Sloping heads can be straightened by placing the hammer flush with the edge of the anvil and striking the head of the nail hard with another hammer.

Sliding Round-Work Holder

Work holders of the kind shown in the illustration are very convenient for holding disks, gear blanks, wheels, etc., but are difficult to move around the shop when loaded. This trouble can easily be overcome by fitting a skid under the holder so that it can be raised a trifle above the floor and the skid then pushed around wherever desired. The skid is made of flat steel, bent as shown and drilled and tapped so that it can be screwed onto the pipe standard, which is threaded for this purpose. A hole is drilled through the pipe to take a short round bar used for turning the pipe and thereby raising the holder from the floor. Then by pushing on the handle the skid can be slid over the floor with little effort.

Brake-Spring Replacing Tool

One of the most difficult jobs in over-hauling the rear-wheel assembly of an automobile is the replacing of the coil spring in an internal brake. These springs are heavy and strong, so that they can be depended upon to draw the brakes together as soon as they are released, and consequently it is not easy to hook the springs in place by hand. A tool, for this purpose, easily made by any garage mechanic, is shown in the illustration.

It consists of a ¼-in. steel rod with a thread cut at one end and a flat filed on the threaded section to one-third of its diameter. Two head-pieces are made of ⅛-in. sheet metal, cut and bent to the shape shown, and screwed to blocks of ¾-in. square steel. The upper one is drilled to fit loosely on the flattened part of the rod, the screws bearing against the flat to prevent the block from turning around. A nut is run on the rod first and the block then slipped on, so that by turning the nut the block can be forced along the threads. The lower block is riveted securely to the unthreaded end of the rod. In use, the tips of the head-pieces, which are notched or hooked slightly, are slipped into the ends of the spring and the nut then turned up, which

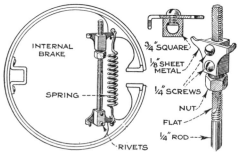

Tool for Expanding Coil Springs When Attaching Them to Internal Brakes

forces the spring open until it can be snapped in place on the lugs.

Distributing Liquid Manure over Fields

Liquid manure is usually applied to the fields by means of a tank wagon, but the

Distributing Liquid Manure over a Field by Means of an Electric Motor and Rotary Pump; Insert, View of the Distributing Pipe

method used at Robert's Sanitary Dairy Farm in Nebraska is entirely different; it saves a great deal of time and has proved satisfactory for four years.

The barn accommodates about 75 head of cattle. Being up-to-date, it has concrete floor and gutters covered with iron gratings. Once a day the floor is flushed, and the rush of water through the gutters carries with it all the waste matter into a concrete reservoir, where it is stored. A 15-hp. electric motor attached to a rotary pump is located above the reservoir and pumps the liquid up to the crest of a hill through a 6-in. pipe. This pipe is run underground until the crest is reached, and is then elevated and supported on poles. The overground part runs the length of the field and is perforated with two rows of holes drilled at a 45° angle to the ground, so that the liquid is sprayed on both sides of the hill. Any subsequent rain will carry the fertilizer downhill and the whole field will benefit from it.

Running Separator with Water Power

Most farms have an elevated water tank into which water is pumped by a windmill. As the water is cheap, it can be used for running machinery as well as watering stock and irrigating the land. A simple application of this idea is shown in the drawing and photograph; the water being used in this case to run a cream separator. A small wooden water wheel of the undershot type is set up near the tank and the discharge pipe arranged to direct the water against the blades, a shut-off valve being, of course, provided in the line to control the flow. The speed of the wheel can also be regulated with the valve by opening it more or less to vary the amount of water flowing out.—Mrs. M. W. Annis, Shafter, Calif.

California Rancher Uses Water from Storage Tank to Run Cream Separator; Arrow in Photo Points to Valve

Gear-Tooth Template for Drafting

There is nothing that shows up so badly on an otherwise good drawing as poorly drawn gear teeth and while many draftsmen will be satisfied with showing three or four well-drawn teeth, leaving the rest of the circle blank, it is often advisable, if not necessary, to show all the teeth for a perfect understanding of the drawing. Perfect work is made possible by the use of a template made from thin celluloid which is cut out to shape as shown, with the profile of the tooth worked to shape with a sharp knife. These templates should be made to cover the range of gear teeth common to the work in hand and a good set will include all pitches from 3 to 12. To form the tooth correctly, the black chart forms and shapes found in mechanical handbooks are used as a pattern. In order to draw a perfectly sized tooth, allowance must be made for the width of the pencil so that the template is smaller than the charted form by the width of the pencil line. A valuable aid is the small pencil hole on the base or root diameter of the tooth which enables one to easily draw the line connecting the teeth on their bases. The template is centered and held in position by a thumbtack so that both hands are left free for manipulating the device. While a single template will function for gears of minimum diameter to those of 8 in. or more in diameter, larger ones can be made. A center line scratched or drawn down the center will show the correct position for all centers. Ratchet, sprocket and many other shaped projections often used in drafting can be produced by the same method. These templates should be marked with their corresponding sizes and pitches.

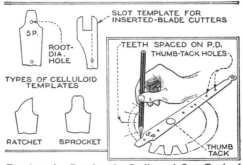

Templates for Drawing the Outlines of Gear Teeth of Different Forms and Other Machine Details

A BENCH FILING MACHINE
by
J. V. Romig

ONE of the handiest and most useful of small machine tools for the experimental or small shop is the bench filing machine. It may be used to finish dies, forming tools and gauges, and for filing the angular clearance in blanking dies is invaluable, as it insures that the clearance will be uniform all around the die. Another advantage of the filing machine as compared with hand filing is that straight or flat surfaces are filed with much less difficulty because the file is mechanically guided and moves in a straight line, thus producing much more accurate work than is possible by hand. When equipped with a sawing attachment the machine may be used for sawing out the cores of dies and similar work, thus reducing the time necessary for this operation.

A very neat and serviceable machine may be built by the small-shop owner by using structural-steel shapes for the frame and other principal parts, thereby avoiding the necessity for castings, and reducing machine work to a minimum. The machine shown in the drawing has a 1¼-in. stroke and takes files up to ⅜ in. square, although the regular ¼-in. machine files are recommended.

The frame of the machine is made from a short section of 6 or 8-in. I-beam, the latter making the easier job as the web may be cut through below the flange, while with the 6-in. stock the flange must be cut on both sides. A hand hacksaw and a good coarse file are the only tools needed to shape the frame. A depression is filed in the top of the web to form two lugs as shown, and these are filed parallel to the bottom web, which forms the base. A ½ by 1-in. slot is drilled and filed for the table bolt, a 1⅛-in. hole drilled and reamed in the web, holes drilled in the base for lagscrews or bolts, and the frame is finished.

The table is made from a piece of 6-in. channel iron, the flanges of which are tapered as shown. A piece of ½ by 1-in. steel is fitted between the flanges at the high end and fastened in place either by ¼-in. flat-head screws or by welding. This piece forms the rear of the table, and is slotted vertically for the ½-in. bolt that clamps the table to the frame. The sides, front and top of the table should be machined dead true, preferably on a surface grinder, if one is available. When in the level position the top of the table rests on the two lugs on the top of the frame.

The crank mechanism is of the Scotch-yoke type, is easy to make and operates satisfactorily. A bearing, made from a piece of steel 3 in. in diameter, is turned to the shape indicated and fitted with two bronze bushings. The front bushing, which is the longer of the two, projects ⅟₁₆ in. beyond the front of the frame when the bearing is in place. The bearing is fastened to the frame with four ¼-in. capscrews, as shown in the assembly drawings. The crankshaft may either be turned from a solid piece, or built up, as desired. The crank throw is 1¼ in., the shaft proper being ⅝ in. in diameter and the crankpin ⁷⁄₁₆ in. in diameter. An oil passage is drilled to lead from the oil cavity in the bearing to the upper side of the pin; this permits the oil not only to lubricate the crankpin but also the yoke itself through tiny oil holes drilled in the yoke bearing or crankpin block. This bearing is flanged, and is made by sweating two pieces of bronze together and boring the crankpin hole central with the split, after which the block is shaped to size. When finished, the halves are separated and the joint smoothed with a fine file and emery cloth.

The slide is made from a piece of cold-rolled steel, 4 by 2½ by ¼ in. in dimensions; it is lightened by cutting away parts of the center, as shown. The sides and faces of the slide should be made as straight and true as possible, testing with the micrometer and straightedge to insure this. The surfaces of the yoke slot also must be square, straight and flat, and should be polished perfectly smooth and made a good fit over the yoke block.

The file holder is fastened to the slide with four 3/16-in. screws and should be lined up square with the sides of the slide. It is made of steel, shaped as in the drawing, and it should be kept as light as possible, consistent with strength. Four 1/4-in. setscrews are used to hold the files; these should always be tightened with a special socket wrench, made for the purpose. To eliminate machine work, the guides for the slide are built up on the front face of the frame from lengths of flat brass. Two pieces, 3/4 by 1/2 in. in size,

are used at the back, two pieces, 1/4 by 1/2 in., in the center, and two pieces, 1/8 by 5/8 in., on the outside. All are held to the frame by stove or other small bolts, and the holes in the center pieces are slotted so as to permit adjustment to fit the sides of the slide and also for taking up wear, the back pieces being drilled and tapped for adjusting screws. Oil holes are drilled in the guides leading to the inner surfaces, and these should be oiled every time the machine is used—several times if the machine is used for a long run.

The saw and file frame is made of 1/4 by 5/8-in. flat steel, bent at a right angle at the bottom corner. A steel foot is shaped as shown and riveted to the bottom of the frame; this foot fits the side of the file

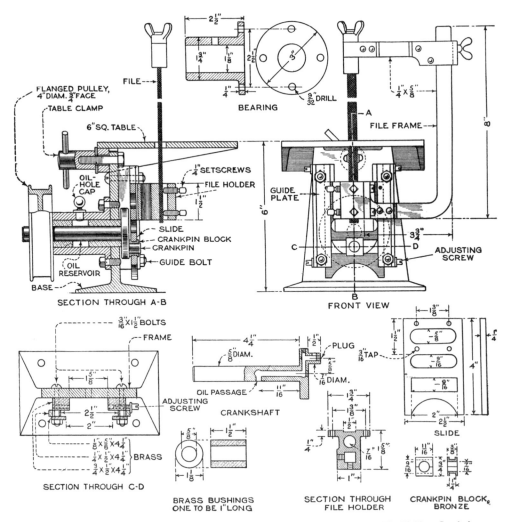

Assembly Views of the Machine, with Details of the Crankshaft, Bearings, Slide, File Holder, Crankpin or Yoke Block and Yoke Guides; Note How the Latter Are Adjusted

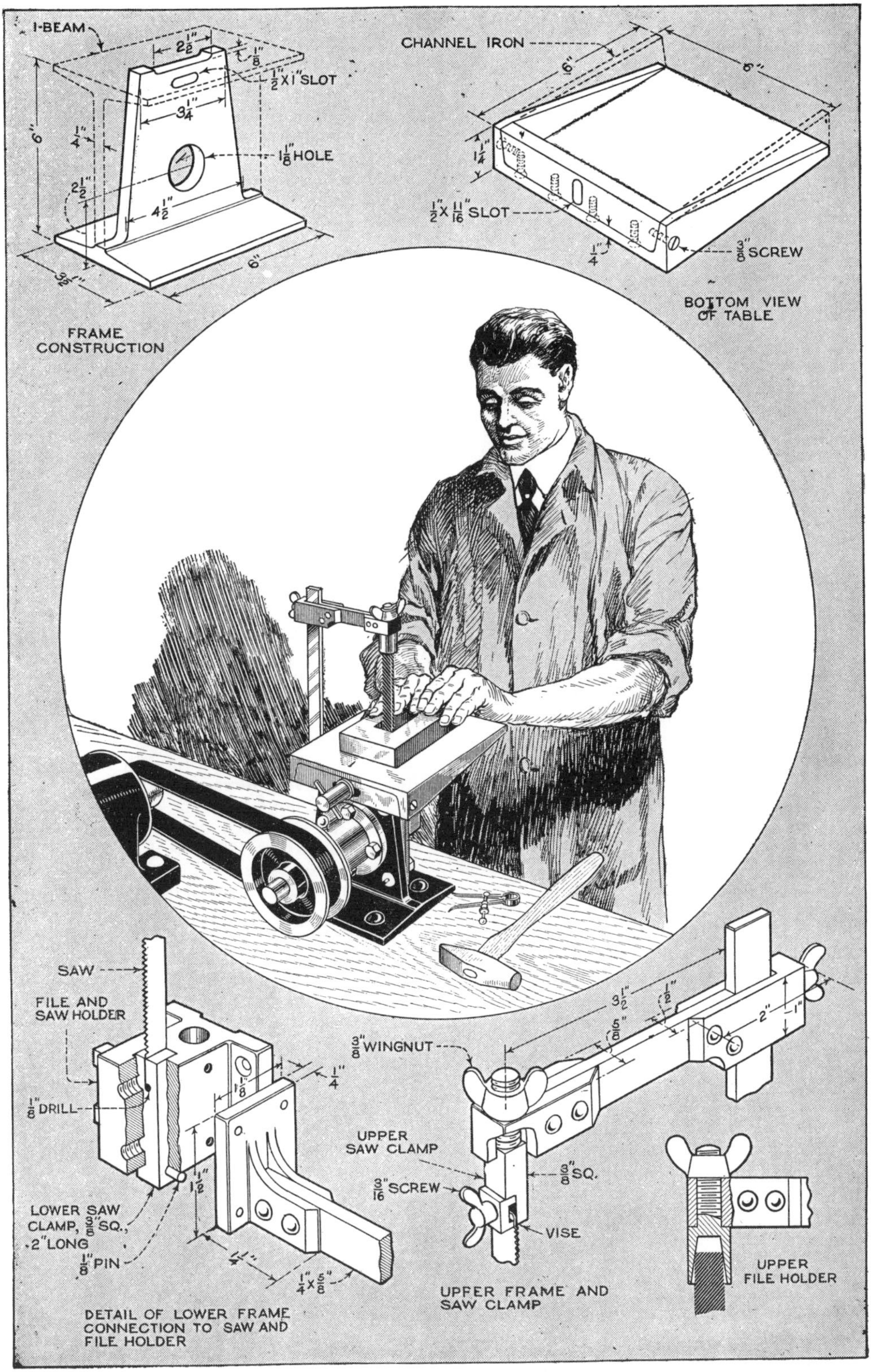
I-BEAM
$2\frac{1}{2}$"
$\frac{1}{8}$"
$\frac{1}{2}$"X1" SLOT
$3\frac{1}{4}$"
6"
$\frac{1}{4}$"
$1\frac{1}{8}$" HOLE
$2\frac{1}{2}$"
$4\frac{1}{2}$"
6"
FRAME CONSTRUCTION
CHANNEL IRON
6"
6"
$1\frac{1}{4}$"
$\frac{1}{2}$"X $1\frac{1}{16}$" SLOT
$\frac{1}{4}$"
$\frac{3}{8}$" SCREW
BOTTOM VIEW OF TABLE
SAW
FILE AND SAW HOLDER
$\frac{1}{8}$" DRILL
$1\frac{1}{8}$"
$\frac{1}{4}$"
$1\frac{1}{2}$"
LOWER SAW CLAMP, $\frac{3}{8}$" SQ., 2" LONG
$\frac{1}{8}$" PIN
$\frac{1}{4}$"X$\frac{5}{8}$"
DETAIL OF LOWER FRAME CONNECTION TO SAW AND FILE HOLDER
$\frac{3}{8}$" WINGNUT
$3\frac{1}{2}$"
$\frac{1}{2}$"
$\frac{5}{8}$"
2"
1"
UPPER SAW CLAMP
$\frac{3}{16}$" SCREW
$\frac{3}{8}$" SQ.
VISE
UPPER FRAME AND SAW CLAMP
UPPER FILE HOLDER

Details of the Frame, Table, File and Saw Holder, Upper Saw Frame, Lower Saw Frame and File Clamp; Center, a Perspective View of the Finished Filing Machine Finishing the Sides of a Die

holder and is fastened to it with four ³⁄₁₆-in. screws. The top part of the frame is built up to the dimensions given, and slides on the upper part of the vertical member. A thumbscrew locks it at any desired height. The upper end of the saw is clamped in a tiny vise made of square stock, and the shank of the vise fits the square hole in the frame top. The corners of the shank are threaded, and a ½-in. wingnut is used to strain the blade. The lower saw clamp is a piece of square ⅜-in. steel drilled and slitted as shown, and is fitted with a pin that bears against the lower end of the holder. The blade is clamped by tightening either of the upper setscrews in the holder. Saws can be used in any position by arranging the clamps to suit, although a blade is best supported when the teeth face away from the back of the frame.

While a file can be used without any support at the upper end, the addition of a simple file clamp makes it possible to cut faster and truer. As shown in the detail, this clamp is simply a piece of square stock with a taper hole which fits down over the file, either flat, square or round, and braces it against side strains.

The machine should be fitted with a pulley and belted to run at between 250 and 350 r.p.m. The drive can be direct from a slow-speed motor or through a countershaft. The machine should be bolted solidly on a substantial bench, in position to receive the best light.

Files and saws for the machine can be bought from any supply house; saw blades can be bought for either wood or metal, and the kind wanted should always be specified. A new file should be broken in with very little pressure on the teeth at first, gradually increasing the pressure as the teeth wear even. Too much pressure on the teeth of a new file will strip off the points and ruin the file.

An Improved Spring Toolholder

A spring toolholder for the lathe, of the kind shown in the illustration, has been found very successful in a large machine shop for cutting slots and radii, cutting off and threading. The most important features in this design are the guide key in the bottom and the spring bushing that permits the amount of spring to be ad-

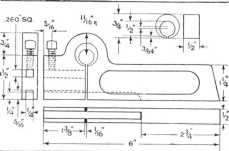

Spring Toolholder for Cutting Slots and Radii, Cutting Off and Threading

justed for different jobs. The key is a press fit in the shank of the holder and a snug sliding fit in the part holding the tool. The slot in the spring part was cut quite deep, to allow it to spring down without striking the top of the key. The spring bushing was made of ¾-in. drill rod, drilled eccentrically and sawed through on the thin side. After the bushing was hardened, it opened enough to make a tight press fit in the ¾-in. hole drilled for it in the holder. For light work the bushing is left out and for medium work it is inserted with its slot in line with the slot in the holder. For heavy work, such as cutting wide grooves, the bushing is turned around so that the slot is at the top, which makes the holder rather stiff. The holder was made of cold-drawn steel, annealed and pack-hardened, and it was then polished on the buffing wheel. An ordinary square-head setscrew is used to hold the tool. Dimensions that were found most suitable are given in the illustration.

Some of the men in my shop made their toolholders more fancy than the one described above. After pack-hardening them they ground them all over and then color-hardened them with cyanide, which made a nice job. They also made fancy screws to hold the tool, and ground a radius on all the corners but the bottom ones. In all cases the sides of the shank were recessed, using a cutter of 1-in. radius; this made the toolholders lighter and added to their good appearance.—C. R. Haynes, Endicott, N. Y.

❡Sometimes a mired car can be pulled out by means of a rope, tied to a tree or fencepost along the road and to a spoke of one of the drivewheels so that when the wheel turns the rope is wound on the hub, causing the car to move ahead slowly.

Tractor, Steel Cable and Scraper Used to Load Dirt on Trucks, a Method Found Much Quicker and More Convenient Than Doing the Work by Hand

Novel Method of Loading Dirt on Trucks

When grading and leveling a city lot in Alhambra, Calif., about 300 cu. yd. of dirt had to be hauled off the property. This represented several days of labor if it had to be shoveled on trucks by hand. A little thought on the part of the contractor developed the simple method of doing this with a tractor and a scraper shown in the illustration. The tractor was hitched to the scraper with a length of steel cable and the latter was run over the truck so that the scraper could be pulled up a skid to the top of the truck and the contents then dumped. The skid was made of four lengths of 2 by 4-in. wood, decked over with 1-in. boards. Horses were used to do the ground leveling. The animals pulled the scrapers to the incline where the steel cable was hitched on, and one man did all the dumping. A considerable saving of time was made in this way.

Protecting Lanterns during Building Operations

Building operations in every large city often necessitate the blocking of the sidewalks with the box-like structures inclosing the work. At night these inclosures must be marked by lanterns for the protection of pedestrians. The arrangement shown in the drawing not only permits the proper placing of the red lanterns but also protects them against accidental overturning or theft. A small opening is cut in the corner of the inclosure and covered with wire screen; the lantern is placed immediately behind the opening on a small shelf nailed to the braces.—R. F. Lufkin, Medford, Mass.

Removing Lugs from Storage Batteries

Garage men and car owners frequently have difficulty in removing the cable lugs from storage batteries when they have to be taken out for recharging. No matter how carefully the lugs have been attached to the battery terminals, corrosion will take place, and this usually makes it necessary to use a pair of pliers, which often results in bruised knuckles or pinched fingers. To prevent this trouble a 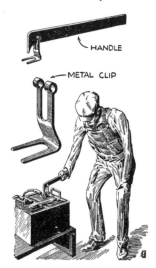 Wisconsin battery-repair man constructed the tool shown in the illustration. It consists of a discarded flat file, with one end heated and shaped to a point, as indicated in the upper detail. It is used as a handle and a metal clip, shown in the center detail, is hinged on near the pointed end. In use, the handle is held horizontally with the pointed end on the battery post, and the jaws of the clip are pushed under the lug so that when the tool is raised the lug is readily pulled off.—G. E. Hendrickson, Argyle, Wis.

❡Iron tanks can be protected against corrosion by painting the exposed surface with a thin mixture of "neat" Portland cement, applied with a paintbrush.

Clogs for Asphalt Workers

Many pairs of shoes can be saved by asphalt-paving workers by using wooden clogs of the kind shown in the drawing.

Wooden Clogs for Asphalt Workers Protect Shoes and Feet from Burns

They are made from 2 by 4-in. material, sawed to suitable lengths and roughly shaped to resemble shoe soles, pieces of auto tire being tacked on, as shown, to keep them on the feet. They are worn while spreading the hot asphalt, which quickly ruins the soles of the shoes and also burns the feet.—W. L. Salvage, Beaumont, Calif.

Making Plate-Steel Levers

The plate-steel lever shown in the drawing will prove of interest to mechanics in shops where the facilities for forging are limited or lacking entirely. It was made to replace a lever for the brake connections of an automobile, the original one having broken in a manner that made repair impossible. A strip of steel plate was cut to the proper length and doubled over at the ends and center, as shown, to form counterparts of

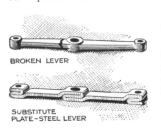

BROKEN LEVER

SUBSTITUTE
PLATE-STEEL LEVER

the bosses on the original lever. The pivot and clevis-pin holes were then drilled, when the only work remaining was to file the sides of the bosses to fit into the forks. This lever was just as strong as the one it replaced, and as a lever of this type is easily made, the kink will prove a time and money saver in other instances.

Setting a Lathe Steady Rest

To set a lathe steady rest proceed as follows: Chuck a piece of scrap stock and turn down the projecting end to the exact diameter of the work and a little longer than the width of the steady-rest jaws. Now clamp the rest in place and adjust the jaws in the usual manner to the turned part of the piece in the chuck. One jaw of the rest may now be loosened and the rest moved to any part of the ways. The work is then chucked and trued at the chuck by chalking or indicating, and the free end supported in the steady rest, where it will be in perfect adjustment.

Fastening Screens and Storm Windows

There are several methods of fastening window screens, but one that has been found very simple and entirely satisfactory is shown in the drawing. All that is necessary is to drill four holes in the window

NAIL

SPRING
WINDOW BOLT

casing at the points indicated and provide two nails and two spring window bolts in the frame of the screen in corresponding positions, as shown. In placing a screen in the window casing, the two nails projecting from the upper edge are inserted in the holes drilled to receive them and then the window bolts are snapped into place. Screens held in this way are tight and cannot fall out, and there are no metal parts that remain on the window casing when the screens are removed for the winter. The same method can, of course, be used with storm windows.

Sawing Circular Segments

In sawing circular segments on the band-saw, it is usually necessary to mark out each segment on the wood and then follow up by cutting along the outline marked. This requires much time and also several men, if the pieces to be cut are of thick and heavy timber, such as those required in shipyard work.

To enable the work to be cut more accurately, eliminate all unnecessary marking, and also to permit one man to do the same amount of work that formerly required four or more, one shop made the fixture shown in the drawing. Two rollers were mounted on the saw table, projecting about $\frac{1}{8}$ in. above the top; the rollers were mounted at an angle found by experiment to be correct for the radius to be cut. At the front of the table a guide piece, made of wood of the same thickness as the stock to be cut, was clamped. The inner edge of the guide was cut on a radius the same as the work, and was just far enough from the saw blade to make the finished pieces the proper thickness. The sawing operation then consisted simply of feeding the stock into the saw, while pressing it against the guide. This not only proved to be a labor saver, but aided in turning out a more uniform product.

Time and Labor-Saving Fixture for Cutting Segments on the Bandsaw

Filing Piston Rings

It is sometimes necessary to file down the edges of rings for auto-engine pistons so that they will enter the grooves. To remove an even amount of material all around the edges is quite a task, so one mechanic devised the fixture shown in the drawing to facilitate the operation. A flat block forms the base of the fixture, and a steel plate, with a hole bored through it of such a diameter that it will hold the rings when compressed, and slightly thinner than the ring to be filed, is fitted to the base with dowel pins. Steel plate comes in standard sizes corresponding to the proper width of the rings, so it should not be necessary to grind it thinner, except where the groove in the pistons is undersize. The fixture is not held in the vise, but the base is center-drilled at directly opposite points, and the fixture swung between the centers of the lathe, or between two centers fixed to the bench. The work thus adjusts itself to the file, and the ring is easily made uniform in thickness throughout its circumference.—G. A. Luers, Washington, D. C.

Non-Slipping Hammer Handle

Usually the slipping of a hammer handle in greasy hands is partly remedied by wrapping friction tape around the handle, but this soon becomes oil-soaked and ineffective. A better method of preventing this is to cut a number of grooves around the handle as shown in the illustration. These should be about $\frac{3}{16}$ in. wide and $\frac{1}{16}$ in. deep, and spaced about $\frac{3}{4}$ in. apart. They can easily be made with a file, burned in with a hot wire or cut on the edge of an emery wheel.—Francis M. Weston, Jr., Pensacola, Fla.

Wheeled Platform for Plasterers

An eastern contractor finds that a platform on wheels is much better for plasterers than the usual kind, as it takes so

Plasterers' Platform Mounted on Wheels Is Readily Pushed Along without Getting Off

much time to move the latter around, whereas the wheeled platform, shown in the photo, can be moved along by pushing against the ceiling. If the floor is uneven, the wheels can be blocked up to prevent them from turning. Obviously, the time saved by using such a platform soon pays for the cost of making it.—A. S. Bowes, Chicago, Ill.

Transporting Long Poles by Rail

When constructing a power line recently, German engineers found it necessary to transport huge concrete poles, 130 ft. long, a considerable distance by rail.

This involved the problem of turning several sharp curves, which could not be done if the poles were loaded on the cars in the usual way. The method of mounting them to eliminate this difficulty is shown in the illustration. Three poles were carried on two flat cars, by separating the cars a distance of about 80 ft. The ends of the poles were clamped down securely on pivoted cradles, centrally located on the car floors. In this way all the curves were made without breaking the poles.

Getting the Most Out of the Lathe

It is accepted as an axiom that the most useful all-around tool for the garage and jobbing shop is the engine lathe, but it is doubtful if all the small-shop users of lathes really get the utmost from them. The usefulness of the lathe is increased immeasurably by the addition of a few attachments, and the cost of these is made up in a short time by the time and labor saved by their use. Homemade attachments also are used to increase production on the lathe, or to adapt it to work that otherwise must be done on a miller or drill press.

The illustrations on the following pages are intended to show what can be done on the engine lathe by the addition of such attachments, toolholders and fixtures, and thus to help our readers obtain the most in service from their lathes. These, of course, are only a few of the possibilities of the lathe, and if our readers know of any unusual jobs that are being done in this way and will send us photos showing the operation, we will be glad to accept them and to pass the information on to others through the medium of these pages.

¶A good black varnish for finishing metal parts on machinery can be made by mixing the following ingredients: Benzine, 10 parts; pulverized asphalt, 3 parts; pure India rubber, 6 parts. Enough lampblack is added to the mixture to give the desired consistency.

CONCRETE POLES, 130 FT. LONG

RAILWAY FLAT CAR   PIVOTED CRADLE

Method of Transporting Concrete Poles, 130 Feet Long, to Prevent Them from Being Broken When Turning Curves

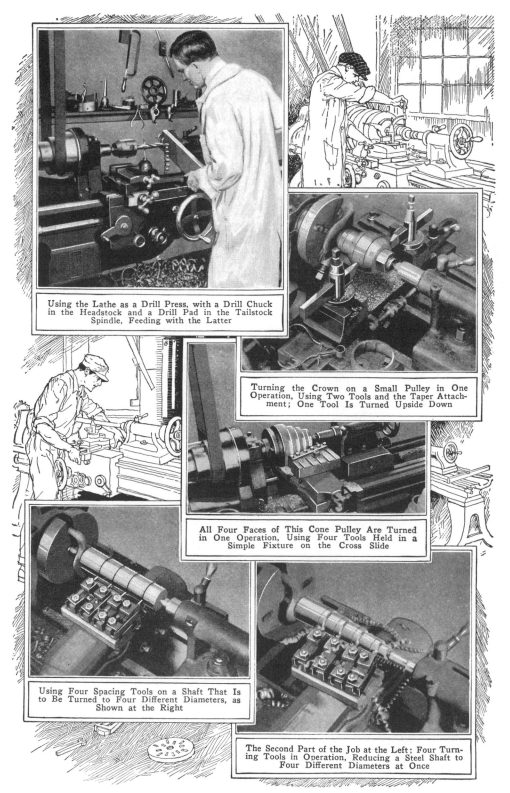

Using the Lathe as a Drill Press, with a Drill Chuck in the Headstock and a Drill Pad in the Tailstock Spindle, Feeding with the Latter

Turning the Crown on a Small Pulley in One Operation, Using Two Tools and the Taper Attachment; One Tool Is Turned Upside Down

All Four Faces of This Cone Pulley Are Turned in One Operation, Using Four Tools Held in a Simple Fixture on the Cross Slide

Using Four Spacing Tools on a Shaft That Is to Be Turned to Four Different Diameters, as Shown at the Right

The Second Part of the Job at the Left; Four Turning Tools in Operation, Reducing a Steel Shaft to Four Different Diameters at Once

Photos. Courtesy So. Bend Lathe Wks

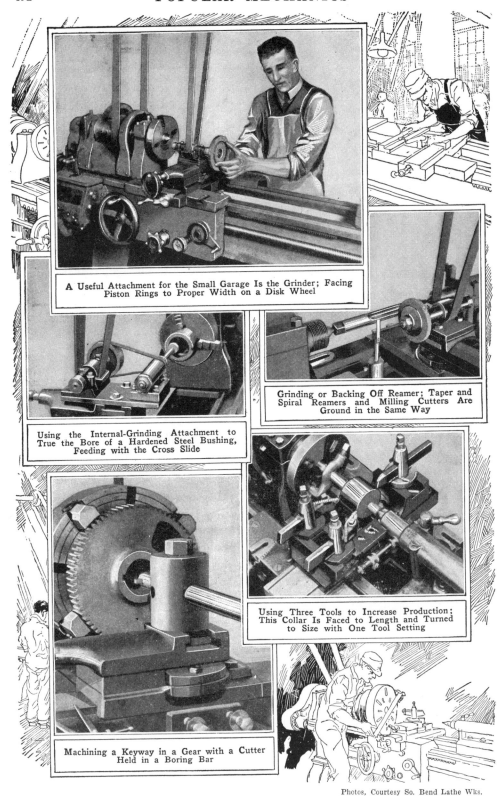

A Useful Attachment for the Small Garage Is the Grinder; Facing Piston Rings to Proper Width on a Disk Wheel

Using the Internal-Grinding Attachment to True the Bore of a Hardened Steel Bushing, Feeding with the Cross Slide

Grinding or Backing Off Reamer; Taper and Spiral Reamers and Milling Cutters Are Ground in the Same Way

Using Three Tools to Increase Production; This Collar Is Faced to Length and Turned to Size with One Tool Setting

Machining a Keyway in a Gear with a Cutter Held in a Boring Bar

Photos, Courtesy So. Bend Lathe Wks.

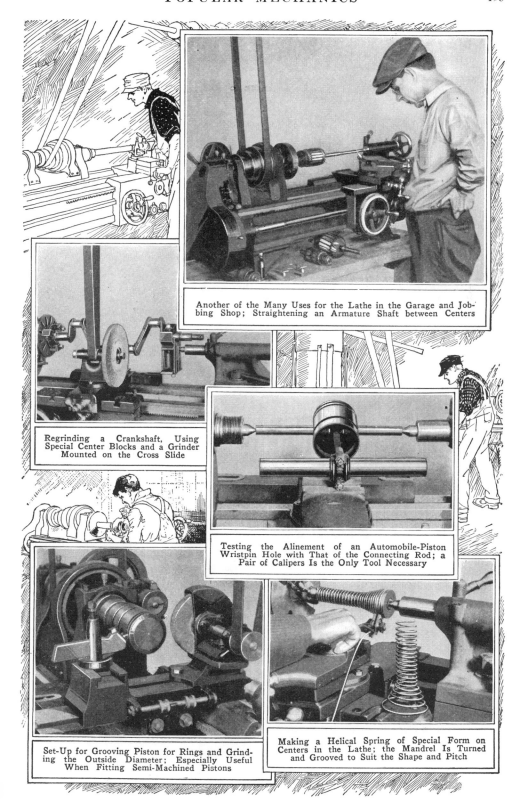

Another of the Many Uses for the Lathe in the Garage and Jobbing Shop; Straightening an Armature Shaft between Centers

Regrinding a Crankshaft, Using Special Center Blocks and a Grinder Mounted on the Cross Slide

Testing the Alinement of an Automobile-Piston Wristpin Hole with That of the Connecting Rod; a Pair of Calipers Is the Only Tool Necessary

Set-Up for Grooving Piston for Rings and Grinding the Outside Diameter; Especially Useful When Fitting Semi-Machined Pistons

Making a Helical Spring of Special Form on Centers in the Lathe; the Mandrel Is Turned and Grooved to Suit the Shape and Pitch

Swinging Tray Aids Draftsman

The accompanying drawing shows how one ingenious draftsman solved the problem of keeping his tools instantly accessible, yet out of the way, by means of an

The Draftsman with This Swinging Tray on His Table Need Not Hunt for His Tools

adjustable swinging tray that holds his supplies. The tray is mounted on the end of a swinging arm, as shown, so that it can be pushed aside or pulled close when additional tools are needed.

The swinging arm is made in two pieces, connected by a pin joint, and is attached to a ¾-in. steel shaft mounted in two small brackets which are fastened to the end of the table as shown. The tray can be raised or lowered by adjusting the collar on the shaft just above the upper bracket. If desired, it may be fitted with compartments for ink bottles, pens, pencils, scales, etc. The outfit is inexpensive; any blacksmith can supply the metal parts for a small sum, and the tray can be made in spare moments. The time and cost involved are well spent, considering the increased convenience gained. — Ivan R. Houk, Denver, Colo.

Distributing Wear in Starter Ring Gears

Flywheels of automobile engines invariably stop in certain definite positions when the engine stops. Four-cylinder engines come to rest in one of two positions, while six-cylinder engines stop in one of three positions. This brings the ring gear on the flywheel opposite the starting-motor pinion in some one of these positions every time the engine is shut off, and the engagement of the starter pinion with the gear, and the consequent wear, is confined to two or three points on the gear.

To distribute the wear, particularly when the edges of the teeth begin to chip, it is advisable when overhauling the car to turn the ring gear of the four-cylinder engine a quarter turn, and that of the six-cylinder engine one-sixth of a revolution. New and unworn teeth are thus brought opposite the pinion, and fracture of the teeth is not so likely to occur. Of course, this only applies to ring gears that are screwed to the flywheel.

A starter that sticks due to the fracture of one or two teeth on the gear can usually be cured by this simple expedient.

Shaft-Centering Tool

The shaft-centering device described in this article will prove a money saver in any shop where a large number of small shafts must first be centered to prepare them for a turning operation. While it is customary to do this work in a small speed lathe, greater accuracy and higher production are possible with this tool. The shank and shell of the device are made of machine steel. The shank is turned to No. 3 Morse taper as this will fit the drill-press spindle as well as most lathe spindles. After drilling and reaming a 7⁄16-in. hole through its center, as shown, the outer diameter is threaded, 16 to the inch, and screwed into the outer shell. The bottom part of the shell is machined with a flange to limit the

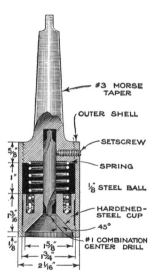

movement of the hardened-steel centering cup. A groove is machined in the back of the centering cup, before hardening, for ⅛-in. steel balls. The steel balls in the groove are covered by a small, thin race, which is grooved on both sides, to conform to the contour of the balls on the underside and to form a spring seat on the upper. In assembling the tool, a stiff steel spring is inserted just before the shank is screwed into the sleeve. Then, a hole is drilled and tapped for the center-drill setscrew.

In use, the centering appliance is brought against the end of the stock, and the cup, touching it first, stops rotating. The spring then compresses with the pressure on the drill and its thrust is taken by the ball bearings. Further movement against the stock brings the drill against the work and the center hole is drilled. As the whole device is inclosed no chips can enter and interfere with the operation of the tool.

Planing Window Frames

For fitting windows and doors, etc., the device shown in the illustration will be found very handy.

It consists of a long board of any suitable size at hand, a short piece of wood nailed to this at an angle of about 45°, a vertical brace for the angular piece, and a block nailed to the base at the bottom of the brace. The upper end of the angular piece or stop is notched deeply to take the ends of the windows or doors, and the block is notched in the same manner; the method of setting up the work to be planed is apparent from the illustration.

A Simple Jack Which Will Hold Doors and Windows That Must Be Planed to Fit

The device will be found convenient not only for doors and windows, but for other similar work too large for the vise, and it can easily be carried from room to room. —J. E. McLaughlin, Chicago, Ill.

Barrel for Feeding Slops

Feeding slops, which are mixed together in a barrel, is quite a tedious task, as the stuff has to be dipped out of the barrel and fed to the hogs by the bucketful. A much

Pivoted Slop Barrel on Farm Facilitates Task of Feeding Hogs

easier method of emptying the barrel is shown in the drawing. The barrel is pivoted between two posts, securely set into the ground. This is done by bolting or screwing around the barrel a heavy iron band, in which two short sections of shafting are mounted to serve as pivots. A metal spout is nailed to the edge of the barrel at the mouth to facilitate pouring the slop. A wooden chute, slanting toward the feed trough, is extended from the barrel, and the slop is poured into this.—R. E. Deering, Clements, Kans.

Preventing Sticky Counters

Under certain atmospheric conditions the glass or marble slabs on counters in banks and offices becomes moist and sticky to such an extent that customers have considerable difficulty in picking up checks, bills and other papers. In one bank the paying teller eliminated this trouble in a simple way. A can of cheap talcum powder was kept at hand for just such conditions, and a little of it was sprinkled on the counter as occasion arose. Thus papers and bills slid easily on the surface and could be picked up without difficulty.

Useful Corn-Crib Door Hood

By LOUIS SCHNEIDER

ONLY a few of the thousands of corn cribs in use are equipped with any arrangement to allow free, quick and easy removal of the contents. Most cribs are of the horizontally boarded type, with spaces between the boards to permit free circulation of air. If the owner of such a crib will install the door and hood arrangement shown in the illustration, every trace of his feeding and crib-cleaning troubles will be over.

The door, as usual, is placed between

This Simply Made Hood for the Corn Crib Enables the Corn to Be Shoveled Out with a Minimum of Trouble, Yet Is Easily Removed When Necessary

two studs. It should not be less than 6 ft. in height, so that entrance and exit will be easy when the hood is removed. Nail the door cleats in place before doing anything else, taking care not to get the outside one so close to its stud that the door will not open freely. Then saw through, close to the stud, two boards at

the points where the hinges are to be placed; attach the hinges, saw the remainder of the boards free, and the door is complete.

The hood is made of such a length that its ends will extend about 16 in. on each side of the door. Its eave, or lower edge, should be about 2 ft. away from the inner edge of the studding. Only two frame pieces are required, to which the ends and the top boards are nailed. Let the top boards be of ample strength, as there is quite a bit of pressure on them when a high crib is full. The construction of the hood is clearly shown in the lower detail of the drawing. The upper ends of the frame pieces are fitted on their lower sides with flat-steel hooks of such form and so spaced that they may be thrust between two siding boards and engaged with the top of the lower ones. It is possible that a trifle more space may be required to pass the hooks than the spacing of the siding affords. In this case, cut away the upper boards slightly, as shown on the left of the door in the drawing. The hooks should be hung on a board at such a height that when the hood is in place its lower edge will be about 18 or 20 in. from the floor.

The end boards or wings of the hood

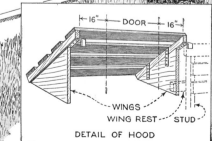

|←16"→|— DOOR —|←16"→|

WINGS
WING REST --- STUD
DETAIL OF HOOD

are of such a length that they bear against the wing rest, shown in the detail and in the cut-away section at the left; the rest consists of a length of 2 by 4-in. stuff nailed to the two studs next to each side of the door. This construction is used to avoid having the hood wings rest against the siding, for if this were done, the pressure of the corn on the hood would push out the siding boards against which the lower edge of the wings rested.

At the top of the outside door a header must be inserted to fill the space between the studs. To close the space between the top of the door and the top of the hood, provide a second door and hang it loosely on nails in the proper position so that when the crib is filled, the pressure of the corn will hold it in place.

When the level of the corn has fallen to the point where it is desirable to walk into the full-height door, remove both loose door and hood and hang them to one side, when the crib may be entered freely. It may be seen that this construction allows a free flow of corn from every part of the crib, as there are no posts to retard it. Scooping also is rendered very easy.

It would be well to armor the upper edge of the board with which the hooks engage with a length of light angle iron, to give them extra strength to carry the load. The construction shown can also be adapted to granaries used for small grain. These must be built stronger and grain-tight, and the method of hooking the hood to the side must be altered also.

Stropping Safety-Razor Blades

One of the simplest and best methods of keeping safety blades in good condition is to strop them often on the palm of the hand, before and after shaving. Hold the blade between the thumb and finger of the right hand and strop it on the inner edge of the palm of the left hand.

Unloading Automobiles

Automobiles are loaded onto and unloaded from the steamers of a San Francisco navigation company by means of

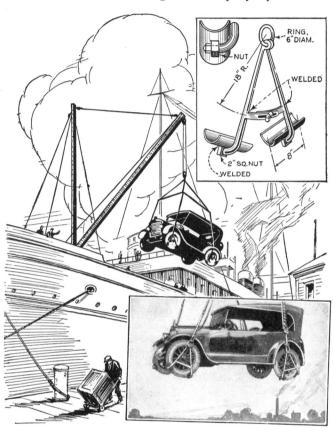

Simplified Method of Holding Disk-Wheeled Autos Securely While Hoisting Them with Crane

large cranes. Recently, with the increasing number of cars equipped with disk wheels, considerable difficulty was experienced in handling them until fixtures of the kind shown in the photograph were made. The ordinary sling with spreaders is used, but instead of tying the four ropes to the wheels, they are attached to triangular fixtures adapted to receive the tires of the wheels, as indicated. The construction of the fixtures is clearly shown in the detail; each consists of a 6-in. ring to which two 18-in. lengths of 1-in. rod are attached. These rods have arms welded on at right angles, which are clamped together with a heavy bolt and nut to hold the rods apart at a convenient angle. The lower ends of the rods are bent as shown and have curved plates of heavy sheet iron welded on.

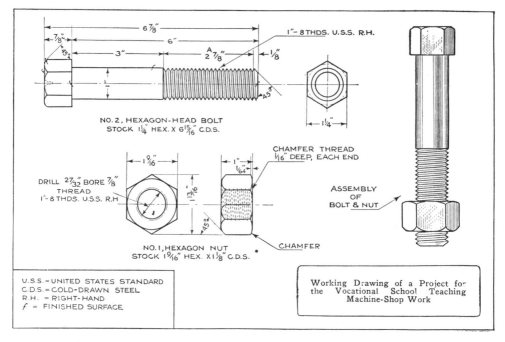

NO. 2, HEXAGON-HEAD BOLT
STOCK 1¼" HEX. X 6¹⁵⁄₁₆" C.D.S.

1"- 8 THDS. U.S.S. R.H.

CHAMFER THREAD
¹⁄₁₆" DEEP, EACH END

ASSEMBLY
OF
BOLT & NUT

DRILL 27⁄32 BORE 7⁄8"
THREAD
1"- 8 THDS. U.S.S. R.H

NO. I, HEXAGON NUT
STOCK 1⁹⁄₁₆" HEX. X 1⅛" C.D.S.

CHAMFER

U.S.S. = UNITED STATES STANDARD
C.D.S. = COLD-DRAWN STEEL
R.H. = RIGHT-HAND
ƒ = FINISHED SURFACE

Working Drawing of a Project for
the Vocational School Teaching
Machine-Shop Work

A Project for Vocational Schools

The illustration accompanying this article shows an excellent project for vocational-training schools giving a machine-shop course. This is presented in cooperation with one of the largest machine-tool manufacturers in the country, who will be more than pleased to help any machine-shop instructor in his problems.

The operations necessary for the completion of the nut, which should be drawn up in the form of a job sheet for the pupils, are as follows:

1. Select stock as per drawing
2. Place stock in 3-jaw universal chuck with ¼ in. extending; adjust so stock runs true
3. Arrange belt for proper spindle speed
4. Set lathe tool for facing
5. Face end
6. Center with centering tool held in toolpost
7. Rough-drill hole through stock as per drawing, with drill held in drill chuck in tailstock spindle
8. Set tool for boring
9. Bore hole to size
10. Arrange lathe for cutting thread
11. Set tool for thread cutting
12. Cut thread, leaving .005-in. stock for tap to remove
13. Finish thread to size with tap, guiding tap with tailstock center
14. Chamfer end of thread as per drawing
15. Chamfer outside corners
16. Turn stock end for end in chuck, truing as before
17. Face end
18. Chamfer end of thread
19. Chamfer outside corners

The following operations, which should also be incorporated in a job sheet, are for the bolt:

1. Select stock as per drawing
2. Lay off and center both ends
3. Attach clamp lathe dog and place stock on centers in lathe
4. Arrange belt for proper spindle speed
5. Set lathe tool for facing
6. Face end
7. Turn stock end for end between centers
8. Face end
9. Rough-turn round section
10. Finish-turn round section
11. Face shoulder at end of round section
12. Turn threaded section (A) .010 in. undersize for threading
13. Turn stock end for end on centers
14. Chamfer corners
15. Turn end for end on centers
16. Arrange gears for cutting thread
17. Set tool for thread cutting
18. Cut thread, fitting it to nut
19. Chamfer end of threaded section

It is hoped that this project will prove of value to the vocational instructor. Blueprints of this drawing, 12 by 18 in. in size, will be furnished free to readers on request.

Rust-Preventing Oil for Gun Barrels

Gun barrels and other metal articles can be prevented from rusting by an oil consisting of equal parts of sperm oil and high-test grain alcohol. This mixture should be kept in a tightly corked bottle. It is shaken well before using and is rubbed on the surface with a cloth. Any moisture on the article to which the mixture is applied will be absorbed by the alcohol, and this will evaporate quickly, leaving a film of oil to protect the metal.
—Frank N. Coakley, Buffalo, N. Y.

Shop Notes

Mixing Machine for Small Bakery

By GEO. W. VAUGHTERS

THE illustrations accompanying this article show a homemade cake and dough-mixing machine that cost me less than $10, counting the cost of all the new material used. This included two 3½-in. tees, 4½ ft. of 3½-in. pipe, 8 ft. ¼ by 2-in. flat iron, two lengths of 1-in. steel rod, and two pieces of 1-in. pipe, 8-in. long. The remainder of the material was taken from the junk pile. The base of the machine is an old coffee-mill base; into this is screwed the 3½-in. pipe upright, and on top of this a tee. A short length of pipe connects this tee with another one, as shown in the drawing. The horizontal shaft, that runs inside the tees, and the short pipe were taken from an old auto transmission, using the direct-drive gears as a clutch. A slot is cut in the top of the tee on the top of the column, to allow the end of the bent rod that acts as a clutch handle or shifter to enter and engage with a groove cut around one side of the clutch. This part of the clutch slides on a square shaft, to which an additional 8-in. length is welded, to allow the driving pulleys to be attached to it. The transmission case had round sleeves screwed into it to contain the shaft roller bearings, and these just fitted inside the pipe. By drilling and tapping the tees, I was able to

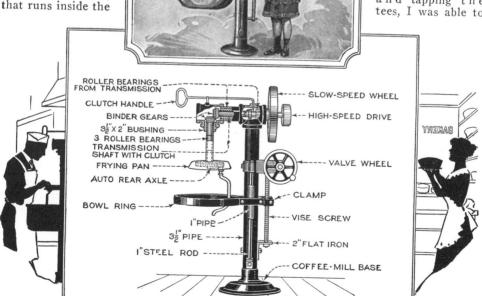

ROLLER BEARINGS FROM TRANSMISSION
CLUTCH HANDLE
BINDER GEARS
3½" X 2" BUSHING
3 ROLLER BEARINGS TRANSMISSION
SHAFT WITH CLUTCH
FRYING PAN
AUTO REAR AXLE
BOWL RING
1" PIPE
3½" PIPE
1" STEEL ROD

SLOW-SPEED WHEEL
HIGH-SPEED DRIVE
VALVE WHEEL
CLAMP
VISE SCREW
2" FLAT IRON
COFFEE-MILL BASE

A Mixing Machine for the Small Bakery That Cost Less than $10, and Mixes Dough, Mashes Potatoes and the Like, Much Quicker than the Operations Can Be Done by Hand

use setscrews to adjust the bearings. On the outer end of the shaft a binder bevel gear is keyed, engaging with a similar

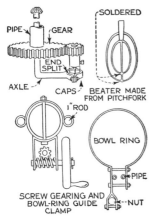

gear keyed to the end of an old Ford axle shaft. This shaft was bent 4 in. from the opposite end, the bent end slit lengthwise, and the two ears thus formed bent back at right angles to the shaft. The ears were then drilled, and two old connecting-rod caps bolted in place as shown in the detail, to form a bearing for a 2½-in. gear or pinion taken from the transmission. This pinion has a long hub that runs in the bearing, and is drilled and tapped below the latter for a setscrew to hold the beater.

Into the outer tee a 3½ by 2-in. bushing is screwed, and a length of 2-in. pipe is screwed into this. On the end of the pipe an 8-in. gear, also from the transmission, is screwed, and this meshes with the 2½-in. gear, which travels around it. Roller bearings are fitted inside the 2-in. pipe for the axle. A hole is cut in an old frying pan to fit over the 2-in. pipe, and the pan is bolted to the 8-in. gear to serve as a guard.

The gearing for raising and lowering the bowl is mostly scrap, with the exception of the bowl ring, which is made of the ¼ by 2-in. iron. This is fitted with two pieces of 1-in. pipe, which slide on the two 1-in. rods fastened to the column; the wheel is one taken from an old valve. The method of making and mounting the bowl ring and gearing is quite apparent from the drawing.

The beater rod shown in the large drawing is made of ⅝-in. round-steel rod, and is used for stiff dough. This can be removed and a beater made from a five-tine fork substituted for it; the latter is used for soft dough, batter, and for mashing potatoes. The drive is arranged so that when the belt is on the large pulley, the beater travels around the bowl 16 times a minute, and when on the smaller one 60 times a minute.

This machine will mash 1½ bu. of potatoes in a few minutes, and will mix 40 qt. of cake dough in a surprisingly short time.

Portable Ladder Scaffold

Cleaning and repairing skylights, hanging fixtures, painting and papering ceilings and other work that requires scaffolding, can often be done easily on an improvised ladder scaffold of the type shown in the illustration. It consists of two ladders,

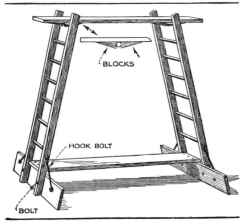

Portable Ladder Scaffold that Has Been Found Very Convenient for Reaching High Ceilings

four planks, and a few bolts and bolt hooks, to hold the ladders and planks together securely, and can be set up much more quickly than a scaffold made entirely of planks. Besides this, it is easily portable.

To the legs of each ladder a plank is bolted so that the edge rests on the floor as shown, holes being drilled through the legs and planks to receive the bolts. The hook bolts are used as braces to provide additional stability. A crosspiece is securely nailed to the top of the planks in order to keep the ladders from slipping apart, and another crosspiece, with cleats nailed on one side to receive the top rung of each ladder as shown in the detail, holds the tops of the ladders apart. The height of the ladders may, of course, vary and the length of the planks should be proportional.—G. A. Luers, Washington, D. C.

Lathe-Center Lubricant

White lead and sperm oil, mixed together with just enough graphite to give it a dark color, makes a good lubricant for lathe centers. This grease can be kept in a tin box and oil added when necessary, to keep it from becoming too thick.

Acetylene-Flame Shield

Much use is now being made of the acetylene torch for tool hardening and in this connection the shield shown in the illustration will be found handy. When heating up the ends of short, round pieces it is necessary to keep the work turning around so that the heat will be applied evenly. To do this by means of tongs held in the hand is a difficult matter, but with the aid of a shield to protect the hands from the heat, the work can easily be done. The shield is made from a short length of 6-in. iron pipe with the bottom end closed with a piece of sheet metal, and a piece of the side cut out, as shown in the back view. A number of holes of various diameters are drilled in a diagonal line through the side of the pipe, as shown, and the same thing done to the piece cut out, with the difference, however, that the holes in this piece slant in the opposite direction.

In use, the loose or sawed-out portion is placed inside of the main piece, as shown, resting on the plugged end. It will be seen that if two holes are brought in line to take a certain size of work all the other holes are out of line and therefore closed. To accommodate various sizes in this way the inside piece is turned around until both holes of the particular size required are

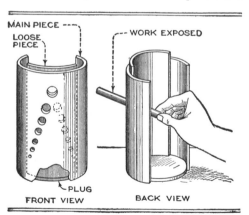

Hardening Small Tools with Acetylene Torch Is Aided by Flame Shield

brought together. The work to be heated is then inserted through these holes and can be turned by means of tongs, or held by hand. The danger of burns from the flame is entirely eliminated with this shield.

¶For tightening bicycle-spoke nipples, use an ordinary screwdriver with a slot in the center and of a width equal to the thickness of the spoke.

Cloud Effects on Drawings

In a studio where quantity of production was a prime factor an unusual method was resorted to for putting cloud effects on drawings. An ordinary sponge was cut

Cloud Effects Put on Drawings with Sponge Speed Up Production in Drafting Room

with a pair of scissors so as to leave several flat spots on the surface. India ink, diluted so that the color was very faint, was then applied to the drawing with a flat side of the sponge. In this way little spots of clouds were printed on the drawing. The sponge was, of course, turned around each time to prevent making each print identical. The objects on the drawing were protected by covering them with a sheet of paper cut to the same shape. Almost any cloud effect can be produced in this way in a very short time.—G. M. Beerbower, Tarrytown, N. Y.

Cementing Leather to Iron

To cement leather to an iron surface, paint the iron with a mixture of white lead and lampblack in oil. Then cover with a cement made of the best glue soaked in water until soft, and dissolved in vinegar. This is thoroughly mixed with one-third of its bulk of white-pine turpentine, and thinned with vinegar until it can be spread with a brush. The cement should be applied to the iron hot and the leather put on and quickly pressed into place; the parts should be held tightly in a clamp while drying.

Farmer's Concrete Mixer

Mixing concrete by hand was too slow and tedious a job for an Indiana farmer, so he made the novel horse-drawn mixer

Metal Cylinder, Drawn by Team of Horses, Used to Mix Concrete

shown in the illustration. It consists of a large metal cylinder the ends of which are closed with 2-in. boards. A shaft of 1½-in. pipe is run through the center and a wooden frame is made, as shown, an ordinary doubletree being attached to it. A small opening is cut at one end to permit shoveling in cement, sand and gravel, in the proper proportions, and adding water, and a door is provided to close the opening. After these ingredients have been put in the door is closed and a team of horses is hitched on to roll the cylinder a few hundred feet, which thoroughly mixes the concrete. The end opposite the opening is driven up on a log or some other slight elevation to cause the mixture to run out as soon as the door is opened. If the concrete is to be used for foundation work, very little extra handling is necessary as the mixer can be driven close enough to run the concrete directly into the forms.—J. C. Allen, West Lafayette, Ind.

Handy Welding-Rod Holder

I do considerable welding along with other work, and was bothered a good deal by having to weld the end of one welding stick onto another in order to avoid waste and to prevent burning my fingers and gloves. In steel welding also the rod had

to be bent to keep the hands away from the heat, so I made the holder shown in the drawing from old material, and it works splendidly.

The material used is one burnt-out 600-volt, 60 to 100-amp. cartridge-type fuse; one piece of ⅜-in. pipe, 1½ in. long; one ⅛-in. coupling; one piece of coil spring, 3 in. long; ⅛-in. pipe, 12 in. long; one piece of cold-rolled steel rod, 15 in. long to fit inside the ⅛-in. pipe; one piece of flat iron, ¼ by ¹⁄₁₆ in., 7 in. long, and scrap material for the trigger. To make the holder proceed as follows: Remove the caps from the fuse and push out the copper contacts from them; then fit the ⅛-in. coupling into one cap, as shown, and weld the cap and coupling together so that the coupling comes flush with the outside of the cap. File the end of the ⅛-in. pipe to an angle of 45°, then drill a hole in the center of the ⅜-in. pipe, fit the end of the ⅛-in. pipe into the hole, and weld. Make a yoke from the ¼ by ¹⁄₁₆-in. stock, as shown, the width being about ¾ in. over the outside, so that it will fit inside the fuse, drilling a hole in the back of the yoke to fit the cold-rolled rod, and a loose-fitting hole on one side for the end of the trigger. A slot is cut opposite this hole, through which the trigger works. Two small pieces of the same stock are welded to the tips of the yoke, to make it a neat fit in the cap in which the coupling was

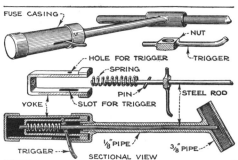

A Welding-Rod Holder Made from Scrap Parts That Will Be of Value in Any Shop

welded. When fitted, the yoke is welded in place.

Cut the cold-rolled rod long enough so that it will touch the front side of the ⅜-in. pipe and pass through the hole in the yoke. Make a trigger, as shown in the detail, by welding two pieces of cold-rolled rod to a nut that will pass over the rod in the cap. The end of the trigger passes through the slot in the yoke, and a similar slot in the cap. The remainder of the assembly is obvious from the drawing.

To operate the holder, pull back the trigger and insert the welding rod in the angular pipe. Releasing the trigger causes the spring to push it forward and with it the steel rod, which locks the welding rod in the holder.—A. S. Jamieson, Springfield, Mass.

Making a Reamer Cut Oversize

When a smooth round hole of small diameter is required, a hand reamer is used to produce it, and many times the reamer is from .001 to .004 in. undersize. The reamer may be made to cut oversize in the following manner: With a scraper made of a medium-size half-round file, burnish the face of each flute, using the oval side of the scraper. This will raise a burr and cause the reamer to make the hole larger by an amount depending upon how hard the faces were burnished. It does not make a permanent edge, but serves very well in an emergency.

Reversing a Single-Valve Engine

To reverse a single-valve engine put the crank on either dead center and scribe a line on the valve stem next to the stuffing box; loosen the eccentric and turn it on the shaft until the mark on the valve stem is again even with the face of the stuffing box. Then tighten the eccentric, and the engine will run in the opposite direction. Care should be taken not to move the stuffing box during the operation and to see that the crank is on the same dead center when tightening the eccentric as at the outset.

Working Paint from Brush

Paint is usually worked out of a brush by rubbing it on a board. The objection to this prac-
tice is that the paint accumulates and gives the board a smooth surface, which is not effective for the purpose. A better method is

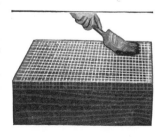

to rub the brush over ½-in. wire mesh, stretched and nailed over the open top of a box. This makes a handy accessory that every painter will appreciate.—J. H. Shadek, Oradell, N. J.

Useful Surveyor's Mark

Every surveyor engaged in running the level on paved streets and highways knows how difficult it sometimes is to establish a satisfactory mark upon which to sight the instrument. This is particularly true in traffic, where vehicles break off stakes

Tin Funnel Makes Handy Mark for Surveyors Doing Street and Road Work

or throw aside stones and other objects set up to be sighted. To them the method devised by Roger Sweier, an engineer with the Los Angeles county-road department, will prove of interest. He experienced endless trouble in maintaining surveying marks until he hit upon the idea shown in the illustration. A large tin funnel was painted white, and after the paint was dry, four black sighting marks were painted on the conical part, as indicated. Into the small end of the funnel he fitted a soft-wood stick, whittled to a needle point. Now, when out surveying for pipe trenches and similar work, he sets the mark down on the pavement wherever desired. It does not blow over in the wind and is seldom disturbed by traffic because of its visibility. Motorists have to strike the funnel squarely to damage it, but they do not do that because the dangerous-looking but harmless wooden spike suggests a puncture, so that, as a rule, they avoid it. The device is light, compact and always ready for use.—J. E. Hoag, Los Angeles, Calif.

¶A good filler for cracks in stoves and furnaces is made by mixing equal parts of salt and wood ashes into a paste.

Novel Window Advertisement

A novel method of attracting attention to a window display was used by a druggist. To all appearances the plate-glass

SIDE VIEW

WOODEN BOX SAWED AT ANGLE

Novel Window-Advertising Scheme Attracts Attention of Curious Crowd and Increases Sales

window had been broken and a wooden box, which apparently just fitted the hole, inserted in it to keep out the cold, while the cracks radiating from the hole had been covered with adhesive tape. All day groups of people gathered in front of the window, and, of course, could not help observing the merchandise in it, so that the druggist's sales increased considerably.

The window was really not broken at all, but the box was cut in two at a slight angle, and the parts glued to the glass, one on the inside and one on the outside. Dark-gray adhesive tape concealed the edges of the box and was pasted on the window, radiating from the box, to convey the impression of cracks in the glass. Tape was, of course, used on both the inside and the outside.

A Homemade Monotone Glass

To the amateur photographer colors seen on the ground glass of a camera are very deceptive and contrast with each other much more than their tones do on the negative. Seemingly charming views, clusters of brightly colored flowers, and the like, often prove disappointing after being developed. To see the true tone values of colored objects, a monotone glass is used, and anyone can easily make one himself. A piece of waste film, preferably cut film, which has been fixed in the hypo bath and thoroughly washed, is soaked in a tray containing enough blue fountain-pen ink to cover the film, which should be submerged long enough to stain the emulsion a deep shade. When this shade is obtained, the film is washed to clear it of surplus ink, and when dry, it is mounted between two pieces of clear glass, which are bound together with adhesive tape. Two small glass plates that have "missed fire" can be dyed blue and bound together in the same way, the emulsion sides being in contact. However, when plates are used, they should not be given such a deep blue tint as when a single film is used, as the depth of the shade when the plates are laid together will be doubled. When the subject of the picture is viewed through the monotone glass, it appears as it will in the print, in black, white and half-tone, so that the effect can be judged much more accurately than when the ground glass only is used.— M. E. Hopkins, Corry, Pa.

¶About as good a belt dressing as can be had is made by mixing melted beeswax and neat's-foot oil in the proportion of ½ lb. of wax to ½ gal. of oil. Melt the wax first, then add the oil slowly, stirring constantly to get it thoroughly mixed.

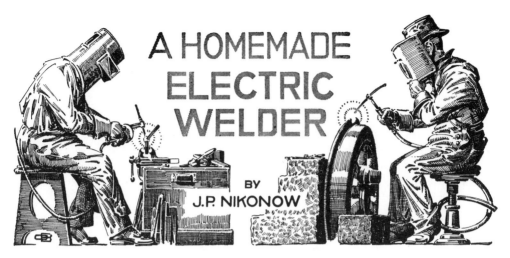

A HOMEMADE ELECTRIC WELDER

BY J.P. NIKONOW

ELECTRIC welding, while it has certain limitations, in many respects is much superior to acetylene welding. We all have heard of the wonderful work of repairing what appeared to be hopelessly damaged engine parts on big German liners. Complete new portions of cylinder walls had to be made in some cases, welded into places and finished smooth inside for the piston. All this work was done with the help of the electric welder.

Of course, the apparatus for this kind of work is bulky, expensive and requires great electrical energy. But it is possible to construct a simple and light portable electric welder that can cover a large range of jobs on light pieces of metal.

The apparatus described here is of the arc-welding type, as it utilizes an arc flame to produce the high temperature. For this reason, it might also be called an "electric torch," the arc having actually the effect of the hot flame of a torch. It may be used for a variety of work, not only welding, but also brazing, etc. This welder consists of two carbons of ⅝-in. diameter, such as are used for arc lamps but without cores (the cores produce too much smoke and are generally undesirable for welding service). The carbons are held in clamps, F, attached to the ends of holders, D and E; D is made of a brass strip, ³⁄₃₂ by ¼ in. and about 8 in. long. The holder D is placed between blocks, A and B, of hardwood or fiber and is clamped with 8-32 machine screws (8-32 screws are used throughout for this device). The screw heads should be sunk in counterbores, so that they cannot come in contact with the operator's hands. The other holder E is made of a lighter strip, ¹⁄₁₆ by ½ by 8 in., and is fastened to the block B with screws and nuts. These (and all the other) nuts should be sunk in the counterbores so as to prevent any pos-

sibility of a short circuit. A piece of wood, C, is fastened to the holder and forms a convenient handle. It should be wider than the strip (Fig. 2), to keep the operator's hand from touching the metal of the holder. The latter is bent outward, so that normally there is a large clearance between the ends of the holders D and E, also about ¾-in. clearance between the tips of the carbons. This strip E should be made of hard or spring brass; then it will stay in its bent-out position, and the carbons will come together only when the operator squeezes together the handles A and C. The rear ends of the strips are provided with contact screws, under which the ends of the cables 13 are clamped. These cables are made of rubber-insulated stranded copper wire of about 4,000 or 5,000 circular mils. The contact screws with the wire ends and the rear end of the welder are protected with a double layer of insulating tape.

This welder can be used with direct or alternating current. When using direct current, it is necessary to use a rheostat, R (see diagram Fig. 9). The current should be adjusted for about 10 amp. for lighter work, and for about 20 to 30 amp. for heavier work. For light work, 15-amp. fuses should be used, and a 50-amp. fuse for heavy work. Heavier wires should also be used for stronger current. Fig. 3 represents the strip D; Fig. 5, strip E; Fig. 4, clips F before bending; Fig. 6, central wooden block B; Fig. 7, block A, and Fig. 8, block C. Fig. 9 represents diagrammatically electrical connections from the line and fuse to the welder W, with rheostat R connected in series with one of the wires.

The rheostat (Fig. 10) can be easily built on a 24 by 24-in. wooden frame and a long spirally wound iron wire supported on porcelain insulators. Dimensions are given on the drawing. The wire should be from No. 14 to 16 gauge, thinner wire being used for lighter work, wound in a spiral about ¾ in. in diameter. It will take about 50 feet of this wire for a circuit of 110 volts. Current may be adjusted by placing jumpers 13, which represent pieces of copper wire tied between two adjacent spirals, so as to short-circuit them and to reduce the resistance. At first all of the wire should be included, then the carbons drawn quickly together and apart again. A good arc will be maintained with about 10 amp., with the carbons from ⅛ to ¼ in. apart. When the carbons are close together, the arc will draw more current, and will be hotter and shorter. In this condition it is more suitable for welding small pieces of iron or cast iron. Soft iron and steel weld the best; harder steel does not weld so readily. Nails are much harder to weld than a soft-iron rod or sheet iron. The arc concentrates at the tips of the carbons and flame from it plays outward, so that it can be used very conveniently for heating pieces to be welded. With increased distance between the electrodes, the current decreases, and the arc lengthens and becomes unstable. It is difficult to maintain the arc at currents below 5 or 4 amp. Smaller diameters of carbon are not satisfactory, even for very light work.

It is not necessary to use any flux when welding pieces of iron. But the same apparatus may be used for brazing, in which case powdered borax should be used on the surfaces. For instance, with this apparatus the ends of a bandsaw may be brazed together. For this purpose they should be tied together by means of an iron wire, and then the borax spread on. The heat of the arc should be applied carefully so as not to burn the saw. A good joint will be obtained by this method much quicker than by a regular torch.

It is absolutely necessary to protect the eyes with dark-blue or red glasses, the red glasses being better because they stop most of the very injurious ultraviolet chemical rays. When working for any length of time—say, a few hours at a stretch — it is necessary to employ a mask for the face, otherwise, the chemical rays from the arc will cause severe burns on the skin, like a bad case of sunburn. The same rheostat may be used for an alternating current of 110 volts. It has the disadvantage, however, of uselessly wasting a considerable amount of energy, dissipating it in heat. A much more efficient arrangement can be made with alternating current by using a choke coil instead of a rheostat. The choke coil lowers the voltage without wasting energy. Or a still better arrangement would be the use of an auto transformer, which not only saves the energy, but can actually give more amperes than the main fuse will stand (the auto transformer converts the electrical energy of high voltage and low current into a low voltage and high current with but little loss). For ordinary practice, a choke coil will be sufficient. It can be made

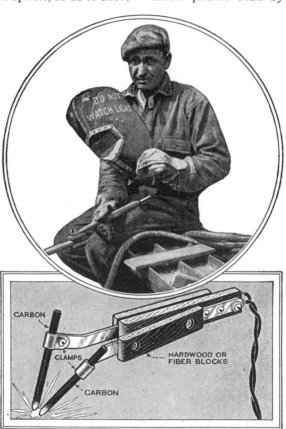

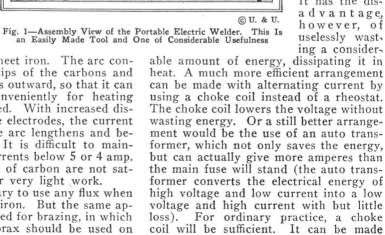

© U. & U.

Fig. 1—Assembly View of the Portable Electric Welder. This Is an Easily Made Tool and One of Considerable Usefulness

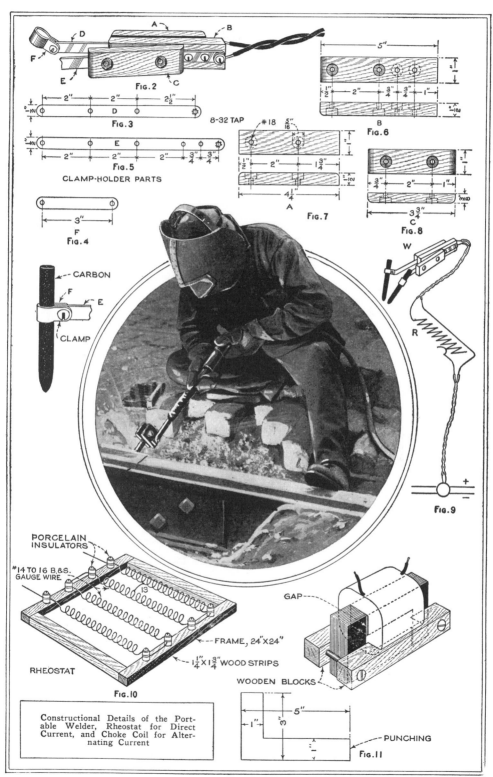

FIG. 2

D A B

F E C

FIG. 3

2" 2" 2½"
D

8-32 TAP

FIG. 5

2" E 2" 2" ¾" ¾"

CLAMP-HOLDER PARTS

3"
F
FIG. 4

5"
½" 2" ¾" ¾" 1"
B
FIG. 6

#18 5/16

½" 2" 1¾"
4¼"
A
FIG. 7

¾" 2" 1"
3¾"
C
FIG. 8

CARBON

F
E

CLAMP

W

R

FIG. 9
+ −

PORCELAIN
INSULATORS

#14 TO 16 B.&S.
GAUGE WIRE

13

GAP

FRAME, 24"X24"

1¼"X1⅞" WOOD STRIPS

RHEOSTAT

FIG. 10

WOODEN BLOCKS

5"
1"
3"

PUNCHING

FIG. 11

Constructional Details of the Portable Welder, Rheostat for Direct Current, and Choke Coil for Alternating Current

Photo Copyright, Underwood & Underwood

easily (Fig. 11) by making a coil of insulated d.c.c. copper wire, No. 10 gauge, about 80 turns. This coil should then be taped all over, and sheet-iron punchings assembled in it, forming a closed "ring." The L-shaped punchings used for two sides of the ring should have their long legs shorter than the ones on the other two sides, so that a 1/64-in. gap will be found on one side of the ring, as indicated. Without this gap the choke coil will have too much reluctance, so that there would not be enough current in the line for the arc. By changing the gap the coil may be regulated for any current desired. The punchings should then be clamped between two wooden blocks with screws, and the coil heavily coated with an insulating varnish.

This welder represents a very interesting device, and it can be used with a little practice for some very remarkable work on light pieces of metal, wires, bolts, sheets, etc. But it cannot be used successfully for heavier jobs, such as the welding of cracks in a cylinder.

Quick-Action Slot-Drilling Jig

The slot-drilling jig shown in the drawing is somewhat different in design, and much quicker in action than the usual type. Eccentric bushings, sliding pieces, and

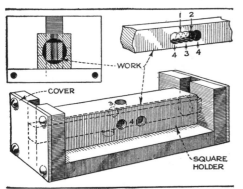

Quick-Action Slot-Drilling Jig for Cutting Slots in Square Shafts

other similar methods for drilling holes close together, or to break into each other to form slots, are generally slow in action; but as many different holes as are necessary to form a slot of any length can be drilled by using this jig, and only one movement is required between holes. The job for which it was used was the cutting of a slot in the middle of a square shaft.

The main part consists of a base with two endpieces screwed to it; these are slotted in the center to the size of the shaft, and afterward thin metal covers are screwed to the outside faces. Next a square holder is cut to fit nicely between the endpieces and drilled along its axis to suit the corner-to-corner dimension of the shaft. The sides of the holder are then drilled and reamed as indicated to take the drill and counterbore necessary to make the slot. This is done in the following way: Hole 1 is drilled first; the holder is lifted enough to clear the bottom of the jig so that it can be turned over to bring the next side uppermost, when hole 2 is drilled. The holder is turned again and a counterbore used to drill hole 3 between the two holes just drilled. The half holes, 4, at each end are then cut with the counterbore.

Cleaning Paint on Engines

A compound with which engines or other oily machinery can be cleaned thoroughly is made as follows: To 1 gal. of water add 1/4 pt. of lard oil. Mix them thoroughly, forming an emulsion. Rub the painted surfaces with the compound and remove it before it dries with a cloth.

Electric Drier for Kiln Samples

The U. S. forest products laboratory at Madison, Wis., has devised a portable electric drier for moisture-determination disks. It consists of a sheet-iron box, 4 by 13 by 6¾ in. in dimensions, lined with a layer of ½-in. asbestos, and divided into two compartments by a wire rack. The heat is supplied by two 40-watt carbon-filament lamps, placed in the bottom compartment, the sockets being screwed to the sides. Ventilation is obtained by eleven holes, ⅜ in. in diameter; six of these are drilled in the cover, three in the back near the bottom and two in the front. A cord and plug attachment makes it possible to connect it to any available lamp socket.

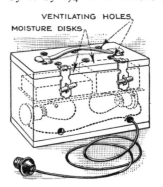

The 1-in. wooden disks used in moisture tests are easily dried in this box in about 24 hours. The maximum temperature attained is 230° F., which is reached only if the disks are allowed to remain in the drier for several hours after they are bone-dry. A slight scorching of the disks occurs under these conditions, but for all practical purposes this does not cause any appreciable error in the moisture calculations. The weight lost by the disk in drying is the weight of the moisture that was in it. This weight, divided by the weight of the dry disk multiplied by 100, gives the percentage of moisture in the stock in the kiln at the time the sample was removed. This drier is very well adapted to commercial practice. It can be carried around and used in any place where a lamp socket is available.

Effective Post Puller

Of all the post-pulling devices I have ever seen, the one shown in the illustration is the simplest and quickest-acting. It consists of a discarded sleigh runner, provided with a clevis, chain and a double-tree so that a team of horses can be hitched on, and a wooden lever with a sharp steel point, bolted to the runner as shown; in this particular instance the point is the tip of a discarded plow-share. To pull a post, the runner is placed close beside it with the point of the lever driven into the post as shown. When the

Simple Device Pulls Out Row of Posts in Rapid Succession

horses are then urged ahead and the runner slides forward, the lever pulls out the post. This operation is repeated for each post. The absence of loose parts and the elimination of tackle and chain make this device well worth the time and labor necessary to make it.—G. E. Hendrickson, Argyle, Wis.

Handy Cuspidor Carrier

Janitors of public buildings can make the task of collecting and carrying cuspidors much easier by using a holder of

Cuspidors Can Be Conveniently Carried Around with This Wire Holder

the kind shown in the drawing. It is made of stiff galvanized-iron wire, bent to the shape indicated, and a small piece of wood, with a pin driven in at both ends, to serve as a pivot for the jaws. In use, the jaws are hooked around the neck of the cuspidor and the opposite ends brought together; this causes the jaws to grip the cuspidor tightly and it can then be carried away.—A. C. Cole, Chicago, Ill.

Removing Compression Sleeves from Tubing

The cones or sleeves used on automobile tubing become firmly fixed after being used a few times. This results from their compressing the tubing directly under them, while leaving it the original diameter on both sides. Such sleeves are applied from $\frac{3}{16}$ to $\frac{1}{2}$ in. from the open end of the tubing and can easily be removed by slitting the tubing into quarters lengthwise and pressing the ends together. If the sleeves cannot be pulled off by hand after this treatment, pliers may be used with care.—E. T. Gunderson, Jr., Humboldt, Iowa.

Improvised Sheet-Iron Cutter

The writer discovered the homemade sheet-iron cutter shown in the drawing in a small country shop, where it had orig-

An Improvised Sheet-Metal Cutter That Has Proved of Value in a Small Shop

inally been hastily made to cut up a lot of old roofing into sheets of suitable size to use for the same purpose on another building. Since that time it has come in handy many times, and for iron of light weight, it is rapid, reliable and convenient to use, besides being very simply made.

Two harrow disks form the cutters. These are mounted on heavy shafts running in holes bored through the ends of heavy uprights made of maple. For a permanent construction, of course, it would be necessary to use bushings in the holes. The shafts are so mounted that the edges of the disks overlap about 1 in. The upper shaft carries a heavy coil spring that bears against a collar and keeps the upper disk against the one below. On the end of the lower shaft is fitted a large wooden pulley, which is belted to an overhead shaft to drive the disks at a speed of about 10 revolutions a minute. The upper disk revolves without the aid of a belt.—D. R. Van Horn, Walton, Nebr.

¶The addition of phosphorus and manganese to molten bronze purges the metal of metallic oxides, and produces an alloy of greater purity and strength.

Attaching Brass Valves

In screwing iron pipe into a brass-body valve, little or no pipe-joint compound need be used, as the brass is softer than iron and gives enough to form a tight joint. If white or red lead or pipe-joint compound is used, it should be placed on the pipe end rather than in the valve, so that it will not be carried by steam to the bearing parts of the valve where it may catch and hold scale and grit on the seats and disks.

Wrenches or tongs should be placed on the hexagon nearest the pipe end when screwing brass valves onto pipe; otherwise they are apt to spring the seats out of line. When screwing pipe into gate and other valves always close them tightly to make the bodies rigid.

Preserving Color of Copper Trimmings

For preserving the color of copper trimmings, such as cornices and leaders, there is probably no better application than boiled linseed oil, to which is added a small amount of Venetian red to give it color, but not enough to make it a paint. For coloring the copper to a dark brown, a solution of one ounce of sulphate of copper, one ounce of hypophosphate of soda and two drams of muriatic acid to one pint of water, or larger quantities in the same proportion, may be used on the copper surface once or twice, and the color can then be preserved by a coating of boiled linseed oil.

Repairing Glass Graduates

Although the small sizes of glass graduates which are used extensively by photographers and chemists, are not expensive, there are times when it is worth while to repair them if possible, especially if they are needed at once. One common occurrence is a broken base, so that the glass will not stand. A good repair is as follows: Two concentric circles are scribed on an old phonograph record, the inner one equal in size to the bottom of the graduate and the outer one to its top.  The circles are cut out with a fine saw and a radial slot is cut from one circle to the other. The piece of record thus cut is warmed up on a greased iron plate until it is sufficiently flexible to be bent with the fingers. It is then bent into place about the glass, a wedgelike section being whittled out along the slot so that when the adjacent edges are brought together a cone is formed. These edges are fused together by means of a hot stove-lid lifter or poker. After the cone has hardened, the graduate is put on the table, bottom side up, and melted sealing compound, such as is used in storage batteries, or ordinary sealing wax, is poured into the cone to make a solid base. This heats the whole mass so that it can be formed to the correct shape and the bottom pressed flat against a level surface. The compound left on the edges is trimmed off with a wet knife. It is obvious, however, that graduates repaired in this way should not be left in hot places, nor should hot liquids be poured into them.—Chas. M. Doten, Plymouth, Mass.

Taking Strain off Motor Leads

The leads to small electric motors are often subject to considerable strain where they are connected to the motor terminals,

and this causes the wires to break or become loose. A simple method of eliminating this trouble is to wrap the cord with tape and then clamp it securely to the motor or to the base on which the motor is mounted. Both methods are shown in the drawing. If the motor is portable, a metal strip and a small hose clamp are attached to one of the screws holding the end plate of the frame, and the hose clamp is tightened around the cord. If the motor is attached to a wooden base, as is often the case, a small wooden clamp, consisting of two pieces, notched in the center to hold the cord, is screwed to the base.—E. T. Gunderson, Jr., Humboldt, Iowa.

Mirrors Used in Repairing Sewers

Minor repairs in sewers or in other underground conduits, can often be made much more easily with the aid of re-

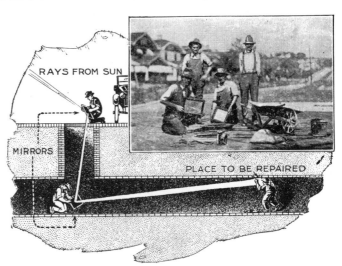

RAYS FROM SUN

MIRRORS

PLACE TO BE REPAIRED

Sun's Rays Reflected Inside of Sewer with Aid of Mirrors Give Workers Plenty of Light

flected sunlight. Two mirrors are used; one at the street surface and the other one in the sewer at the foot of the manhole, a beam of light being directed as shown. This method gives better illumination than flashlights.—Ivan E. Houk, Denver, Colo.

An Inexpensive Universal Joint

In light and medium-heavy machinery, a cheap, durable and efficient universal joint may be made from three straight chain links of round section. In connecting this form of a joint, the ends of the shafts must be slotted to receive the end links, and a bolt put through each to prevent the links from pulling out. A reinforcing collar is shrunk over the end of the shaft to strengthen the slotted part. Such a joint will drive at almost right angles and with very little friction.

Hardening Thin Steel

Thin strips of steel that must be hardened are difficult to handle without causing them to warp. A method used in a small shop for hardening saw blades, and which is applicable to other jobs of the same nature, is to clamp the blade between two heavy pieces of cold-rolled steel or iron and heat and quench the whole.

The Forms Are Stronger and More Rigidly Fastened and Braced than for Concrete Walls

The Rams Are Made of Beech and Oak Root

General View of the Earth House, Which Is Now Covered with a Coat of Cement

Setting the End Board into the Form; Note Solid Construction

The Trim Is Fastened to Planks Held by the Rammed Earth

Rammed Earth Lowers House Cost

By G. H. DACY

A WASHINGTON scientist has lately built a new style of house with walls of rammed earth, at a great saving over all other forms of permanent construction, thus reviving a building style of the ancient Greeks and Romans in order to curtail construction costs.

This home builder made a careful study of all the books he could find in our national libraries pertaining to "pise de terre" or rammed-earth houses. Then he communicated with builders in England, South Africa and New South Wales, where such houses are still in use. He learned all about the rudiments and advantages of such construction. Employing a trio of unskilled laborers who had never previously even heard of rammed-earth walls, he then embarked on his building adventure. Rammed-earth houses are cool in summer, warm in winter, vermin-sound and rat-proof, fireproof, weather-worthy and the cheapest durable structures that can now be built. The process is free to all, as it is unpatented.

The Walls of This House, Built by a Washington Scientist, Are Made of Rammed Earth at a Great Saving over Concrete, Brick or Wood

The building material is the earth excavated in digging the basement. Strong wooden forms are built similar to those used in concrete work, as the accompanying illustrations show. A mixture of loam and clay is best, with not more than one-fifth of the latter material, as too much clay makes the walls crack easily after they are dry. The top six inches of soil are discarded. The remainder of the soil is carefully screened to remove all large stones, vegetable matter and other organic material. A layer of the soil, 4 in. deep, is then shoveled into the form. The workmen, armed with 15-lb. rams, made of root wood of oak or beech and shod with metal plates, then tamp the soil firmly in place until it is reduced to one-half its original volume and rings when struck with the rammer. Then another layer of soil is added and compacted. Three men can build two cubic yards of

pise wall in eight hours, at a labor cost of $10. As soon as one course of wall is completed, the three-foot forms are raised and work on the next course is begun. The walls of the Washington house are 18 in. thick and 12½ ft. high. The house is 32 by 48 feet in floor dimensions. When rammed earth dries, it has the strength of reinforced concrete. A technical test of the pise from the soil used showed that a column of rammed earth, 18 in. square and 42 in. high, after drying for 16 days had a crushing strength of 18½ tons. A small block, 1¾ in. in diameter and 2 in. high, supported 280 lb. before it fractured. When the walls were finished, the owner desired to bore a small hole. He tried an auger, but it had no effect. Finally, he had to resort to a hammer and cold chisel and found that the task was as difficult as though he had attempted to cut through a stone wall. According to the home builder's experiences, pise gives an absolutely solid-walled house at about one-fourth the cost of a similar brick structure, one-half the cost of a concrete one, and seven-tenths that of a substantial frame building. Pise becomes stronger as years pass and finally turns as hard as stone. The oldest home on the American continent, built in 1556 in St. Augustine, Fla., is made of rammed earth. Hannibal built fortifications and watch towers of rammed earth in Africa and Spain, in 124 B. C., which are still standing and durable. Lyons, France, a city internationally famous for its venerable buildings, consists in large part of rammed-earth structures. In England are many homes which have been used for four to five centuries and are still habitable and weather-resistant. Thomas Jefferson, more than a century ago, investigated the possibilities of using pise construction in the United States. He found it practical and urged his friends and neighbors, and the colonists at large, to build rammed-earth walls. The forests were thick, however, and logs were abundant, so the settlers elected to build of wood instead of earth.

Pise houses are best built on concrete or masonry foundations, although the basement partition walls that carry the beams may be of rammed earth. The walls can be carried safely to a height of 50 feet. The first floor wall should be 18 in. thick, the second floor 14 in., and thus the walls can be tapered to a minimum thickness of 10 in. After drying, the exterior of the wall should be weatherproofed with a mixture of lime and tallow, cement wash or hot tar. Plaster can be applied directly to the inside walls and will adhere better than to wooden lath. Molding, mopboards and other woodwork may be held in place by the rammed earth, as there is no danger of the wood rotting. Wood taken from wrecked pise buildings in Europe has shown no damage from wear, worms or decay after two centuries of use.

Building contractors furnished bids on the brickwork on the house made of earth, the lowest of these estimates being $3,800. The actual cost of the rammed-earth walls of this building amounted to $1,800. By reviving a system of construction which is as old as the most ancient Roman ruins, this Washingtonian made a remarkable saving in construction costs and has paved the way for other house builders to do likewise.

Compensating Clutch for Driving Generators

When driving a small d.c. generator directly from a one or two-cylinder 4-cycle gasoline engine the lamps alternately

This trouble can be eliminated by means of the compensating clutch shown in the illustration. It is a separate unit driven by the engine and in turn drives the generator. The compensating action is accomplished by means of a spiral spring made from two phonograph springs in tandem, riveted together at their ends and screwed to the core and shell of the compensator pulley, as shown in the lower left-hand detail. These springs are strong enough for loads up to 1 hp. When the engine speeds up on the power stroke the excess energy is stored up in the compensating spring instead of being transmitted to the generator, and when the engine speed is retarded at the compression stroke, this energy is expended; the action of the spring thus keeps the generator running at a constant rate of speed. The whole assembly, including a pulley driven by the engine, the compensating pulley which drives the generator, and a heavy flywheel, are mounted on a countershaft which is placed between the engine and the generator and is belted to both. The rollers of the clutch are made from drill-rod stock. The entire assembly should be made of steel and the clutch members should be casehardened on the friction

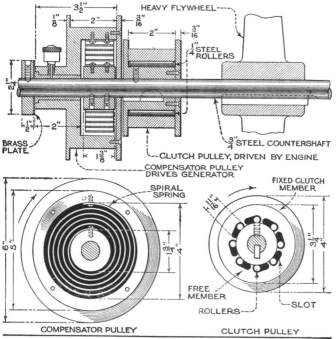

A Spring-Controlled Compensating Clutch on Countershaft with Separate Flywheel Prevents Fluctuation of Lights Connected Directly to Generator

brighten up and become dull, respectively, at the explosion and compression strokes, and unless these changes take place at a rapid rate the effect is very tiresome to the eyes.

surfaces, the parts being held together by setscrews or by steel keys. The particular design and dimensions given are suitable for a 500-watt generator, and only a slight alteration is necessary for larger sizes. The pulleys are faced with leather to prevent slipping, this facing being fastened by means of flat-head countersunk screws. The flywheel should weigh 40 lb. for a 1-hp. engine, and 100 lb. for a 2-hp. engine, and the size of countershaft should be ¾ in. for a 1-hp. and 1 in. for a 2-hp. engine.—A. N. Capron, Quebec, Canada.

Ventilating the Barn

Most barns are poorly ventilated, and this is both bad policy and a discredit to the owner. In cases where provision for ventilation has not been made when the barn was built, the arrangement shown in the drawing can be installed. The space between two studdings of the outer wall is boarded up, a vent being left at both top and bottom, which can be closed by means of a hinged board whenever necessary. A hole is cut in the roof above the boarded space, the plate over the studdings being avoided by the construction shown in the detail. A sheet-metal pipe, 4 to 6 in. in diameter and provided with a hood, is attached to the roof over the hole. The vents can be closed or opened according to

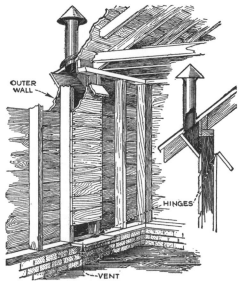

Proper Ventilation in Barns Provided by Means of a Simple Installation

weather conditions.—Robert Page Lincoln, Minneapolis, Minn.

Novel "Free-Water" Curb Hose

Neat appearance and protection against wear feature the "free-water" hose ar-

Novel and Convenient Curb Hose for Filling Automobile Radiators

rangement for a garage shown in the drawing, as contrasted with the common method. It is constructed and installed as follows:

The pipe from the underground water main is brought up to 1 in. above the surface of the curb, where a coupling is attached. A discarded harrow disk is placed over this, covering the handle of the winter shut-off valve, and a 2-ft. length of pipe is inserted through the center hole of the disk and screwed into the coupling. A locknut, with the threads filed out so that it will slide easily over the pipe, is put in place against the disk, and after a suitable length of hose with a faucet on the end is attached, a stout coil spring is slipped over both hose and pipe as shown. With this arrangement the hose is held upright or nearly so, and out of the way when not in use, while at the same time it is easily bent so that the faucet end will reach the filling cap of the radiator. During cold weather the harrow disk can be raised to close the shut-off valve.

⁋For general purposes in the home workshop it will be found that ordinary water glass (silicate of soda) is an excellent glue. It has also many uses as an adhesive and therefore should be kept on hand.

Baby Crib Serves as Machine Guard

When an inspector visited an eastern hospital, he objected to the open installation of the brine pump, with its motor and

Old Baby Crib Used as Guard around Refrigerating Machinery in Hospital

belt, in the refrigerating plant, and called attention to the law requiring a suitable covering for such machinery as a safeguard against accident. As the hospital is a charitable institution and depends on state aid, its expenditures must be economized, and for this reason it was desirable to avoid the cost of guard rails, etc. A simple solution to the problem was found by setting up a discarded baby crib around the apparatus, as shown. The same method of protection can be employed on farms, where the engine and generator of the electric-lighting plant are usually found in an unguarded condition in the basement.—Edmund A. Knoll, Erie, Pa.

Cutting Gauge Glasses on Lathe

Gauge glasses for showing the height of liquid in tanks and boilers are usually cut to length by hand, with one of the simple glass cutters that are to be had on the market. But, when glasses are to be cut in

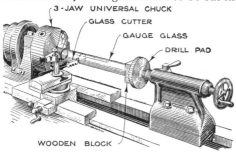

3-JAW UNIVERSAL CHUCK
GLASS CUTTER
GAUGE GLASS
DRILL PAD
WOODEN BLOCK

Lathe Set Up for Cutting Quantities of Gauge Glasses into Any Desired Length

quantities it is better to rig up a lathe for doing the work, as shown in the drawing. A drill pad is placed in the lathe tailstock spindle and the long piece of glass tubing is chucked lightly but firmly in the three-jaw universal chuck. Actual experience has proved that leather strips under the chuck jaws will prevent breakage better than felt, which is generally used. A heavy glass cutter is then placed in the toolpost and set in the right position when the carriage is clamped to the shears. A piece of wood is then put against the drill pad and the glass pushed against the wood firmly. Only one revolution of the spindle is necessary and this can be made by hand. After the glass has been nicked in this manner, a sharp, light tap on the end of the tube with the wooden block is all that is necessary to make it break off cleanly at the cut. If, for any reason, the glasses are cut too long they can be shortened by grinding them on a sandstone wheel, using plenty of water.

Extension for Machine Handle

It is often necessary to use an extension piece on the end of the feed screw on a hand milling machine so that the handle will clear a piece of work of unusual shape. An extension piece used for this purpose is shown in the illustration. It can be tightened up on the square of the feed screw, which eliminates the annoyance of the

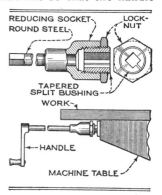

REDUCING SOCKET
ROUND STEEL
LOCK-NUT
TAPERED SPLIT BUSHING
WORK
HANDLE
MACHINE TABLE

device working off the square while in use, as is apt to occur with the usual extension. The piece consists of a reducing socket, a locknut, a taper-threaded bushing, and a length of round steel rod. The bushing is drilled and squared out to fit the feed screw of the machine, then sawed in two with a hacksaw. The rod is screwed tightly into the small end of the socket and the other end squared to fit the handle. When tightening the extension piece in place it is slipped on the square and the table locked. The handle is then turned, which tightens the socket on the split bushing, the latter gripping the square. The nut is then screwed back against the face of the socket.—Harry Moore, Montreal, Can.

Corking Painted Ironwork

Sweating or condensation of vapor on the surface of ironwork may be prevented on ships and other structures which are in or near the water, by applying a layer of powdered cork over the paint. Several coats of red lead are first applied, and while the last coat is still wet, as much finely ground cork as the paint will absorb is dusted on. When this is dry a final coat of paint mixed with turpentine is applied. This method may also be used for protecting iron or steel roofs from moisture on the underside.

Spring Bracket for Truck Tail Light

Drivers of trucks equipped with solid-rubber tires and oil-burning tail lights, frequently find the light out after driving for a short distance. This trouble is caused by the thumping of the solid tires and can be prevented by mounting the light on a shock-absorbing spring bracket as shown in the drawing. The bracket is made of flat iron; one piece has both ends bent over at right angles and is bolted or screwed to the truck. The other part is bent to a U-shape with one leg longer than the other so that it can be passed through the first piece, slots being cut for this purpose. Small holes for pins are drilled in the U-shaped piece to hold short coil springs as indicated. The bracket is then assembled and the lamp is securely bolted on.

Cement for Metals

A very good cement for uniting metal parts consists of 2½ parts zinc oxide, 1 part zinc chloride and 5 parts pulverized limestone and slag. The whole is mixed to a thick paste with water. If a slow-setting cement is desired, use 1 part of zinc sulphate instead of the zinc chloride. The adhesive power of this cement may be increased by adding 2 per cent of ferrous sulphate to the whole.—Frank N. Coakley, Buffalo, N. Y.

Non-Freezing Water Dish for the Poultry

A non-freezing water dish for the poultry is a necessity in late fall and winter, and it is a very simple matter to make one.

A Simple and Effective Non-Freezing Water Dish for the Poultry House

As shown in the drawing, a pit is dug, in the ground or poultry-house floor, to a depth sufficient to accommodate the lamp it is intended to use, and lined with concrete, the concrete extending upward to a height of about 10 in. above the ground. Through one wall, a pipe fitted with two elbows and a long nipple is placed, while the opposite wall carries a short pipe that merely extends outside, although it may be fitted with an elbow with the outlet turned down. The outside elbows prevent dirt from being scratched into the pit. Over the opening is placed a tight-fitting wooden cover, in which a hole is cut to fit the drinking pan snugly. The heating element is an old incubator lamp. A very small flame will keep the water warm even in zero weather. Fresh air follows the long pipe to the bottom of the pit and the hot air and gases pass out of the short pipe. There is room enough on the platform for a number of fowls, but, because of the height of the pan above the floor, no litter can be tossed into the water.

Remedy for Overheating Bearings

Persistent overheating of bearings that are in constant duty may be overcome by applying a paste of flour of sulphur mixed with lubricating oil. This permits the use of an oil cup. The mixture will also be found useful on heavy-duty bearings in cam rolls and similar machine parts.

A Ball-Bearing Disk Grinder

By J. V. ROMIG

ONE of the most useful machine tools for the small workshop is a good substantial disk grinder. On it the workman can do many jobs in a minimum of time and with little labor, and also have the benefit of an accurate and finished appearance on the work.

The disk grinder, as almost everyone knows, is a cast-iron disk or plate, mounted on an arbor or spindle, which has its working face covered with an abrasive sheet, using garnet or sandpaper for wood finishing and emery or carborundum

ment. While solid bearings will operate for a time at least, the ball bearing is the ideal type to use.

In order to secure the benefit of a good ball-bearing installation in this case, without going to great expense, use is made of the front-wheel hub assembly of a Ford car. This can be purchased complete with balls and races for a few dollars, and the ball races, being of the cup-and-cone type, carry thrust loads as well as radial ones. In place of the regulation front-wheel spindle, a new shaft is turned out

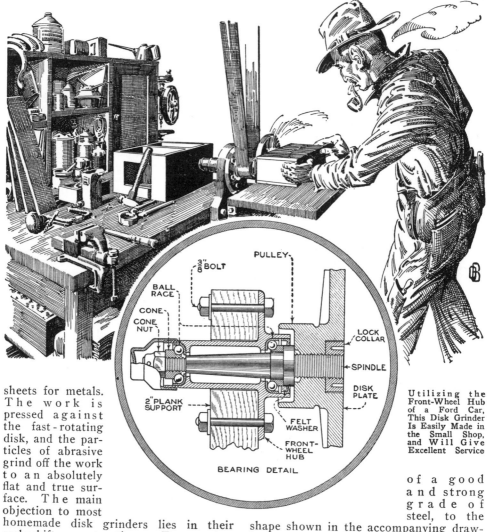

BEARING DETAIL

Utilizing the Front-Wheel Hub of a Ford Car, This Disk Grinder Is Easily Made in the Small Shop, and Will Give Excellent Service

sheets for metals. The work is pressed against the fast-rotating disk, and the particles of abrasive grind off the work to an absolutely flat and true surface. The main objection to most homemade disk grinders lies in their makeshift construction. For perfect work, a disk grinder must have good bearings, without any play or end move-

of a good and strong grade of steel, to the shape shown in the accompanying drawing, and hardened and ground. The bearing end is similar to the wheel spindle in all its threads, lengths and diameters, but is extended at the front end so as to carry the disk plate, as shown. This end is threaded up to the shoulder for the large front-cone collar, and the disk plate is bored and threaded to fit. The disk is made of good gray iron, and is accurately threaded and turned, so that when screwed home on the spindle and rotated, it will run

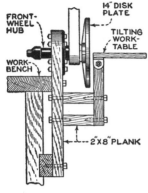

perfectly true and in balance. If out of balance, the plate will vibrate at high speed, and the builder is advised to find the heavy side, and chip the back of the plate until the plate balances in any position. The pulley is cast integral with the plate, as shown. In order to hold the plate tight on its threads, a recess is turned in it to take a collar. This collar locks the plate tightly, and should come just flush when screwed up tight with a pin spanner.

The mounting is simple in the extreme. A plank is screwed to the edge of the workbench, and a hole is bored through with an expansion bit large enough to allow the hub extension to pass through. Six ⅜-in. bolts hold the flange of the wheel hub firmly against this support. A worktable is made out of wood, as shown in the small drawing, and mounted on pivot brackets to allow it to be tilted at an angle for tapered or bevel work.

Even a ball bearing will wear in time, and this installation is the handiest possible for the purpose of adjustment. The hub cap is removed and the front cone is drawn up tight, so that the disk and spindle can be rotated freely without binding, after which the locknut is screwed home and the adjustment made permanent. The hub cap is also an automatic oiler in a way, as when it is filled with grease or vaseline and screwed into place, it drives the grease through the whole bearing and keeps the races perfectly lubricated. (Still better lubrication is assured by fitting an alemite coupling in a hole drilled and tapped into the hub shell behind the plank support, and using the gun to fill the shell, and to keep it filled.)

Disk grinders of this size should run at 2,000 r.p.m., which will give uniform results on both metals and wood. Abrasive sheets are listed in all catalogs of machinery-supply houses, and if the builder so desires, he can get quotations direct from any big abrasive house, who then will refer him to a local dealer. The sheets are easily applied, and give efficient service if used according to directions of the maker and distributor.

Measuring Irregular Objects

Accurate measurements of irregular objects can be made quickly and easily with the aid of photography. The illustration shows the method of doing this, and the inserts show some of the work. The sensitized paper is put in a printing frame and this is laid face up on a table. The object is then placed on the paper and a cardboard tube of suitable diameter to fit within the frame is set up as indicated. The printing is done by holding an electric lamp at the other end of the tube for about 30 seconds. Care must be taken to hold the lamp over the center of the tube so that the rays striking the paper will be nearly vertical. The inside of the tube should be painted dull black to prevent reflection. After exposure, the paper is developed in the usual way and an accurate outline of the object will show up on the prints. By this method gearwheel teeth, keys, etc., can be measured much more quickly than by using a scale and calipers. When very accurate measurements are required, as is the case with small clock gears, etc., film should be used instead of paper and the resulting negative should then be enlarged.

Printing Outline of Irregular Objects on Sensitized Paper to Aid in Measuring Them

Rack for Blueprints

In shops and drafting rooms, blueprints can be handled conveniently by binding them together and keeping them on a rack of the kind shown in the drawing. Each

Convenient Rack Made of Pipe and Fittings Keeps Blueprints in Orderly Arrangement

set of blueprints is bound together at one side by means of two slats, through which three stove bolts are inserted. A galvanized-iron hook is provided in the center to enable the holder to be hung up on the rack. The rack is made of lengths of 1-in. pipe and fittings; the legs are provided with floor flanges, which are screwed to the floor. The construction is clearly shown in the drawing. — G. A. Luers, Washington, D. C.

Reducing Open-Fireplace Hazards

No single fire hazard affects the home and family more closely than defective chimneys, flues and fireplaces. People do not intentionally live in dwellings harboring a constant hazard of this kind, yet hundreds of thousands of these are in existence now, and new ones are being built every day. They are common in all types of construction. No so-called "fireproof" or "permanent" exterior walls will prevent interior fires where it is impossible to dispense with inflammable objects. Defective chimneys and fireplaces hold second place in the list of known causes of fire in order of importance.

To insure satisfactory results from an open fireplace, it is essential that the flue have the proper area; that the throat be correctly proportioned and located; that a properly constructed smoke shelf and chamber be provided; that the chimney be carried high enough to avoid interference, and that the shape of the fireplace be such as to direct a maximum amount of radiated heat into the room.

A fireplace properly constructed will carry all the smoke up the chimney and radiate the maximum amount of heat into the room. Woodwork for mantels, shelves or lumber framing should be carefully placed to avoid fire hazards. Several details which will minimize danger may be inexpensively included in the design for any house. To secure best results the following proportions are recommended: For fireplaces up to 48 in. wide, a height of 32 in. and a depth of 22 in. are ample. The sides should be splayed in about 3 in. on each side. Starting about 8 in. from the hearth, the back should slope forward under the rear flange of the damper. The higher the opening, the greater the chance of a smoky fireplace.

Tightening Guy Wires in Fan

Guy wires on a suspended overhead fan were tightened in a novel way as shown in the illustration. Two screws were used for each wire, one a flat-head screw and the other a screwhook. The former is driven into the wall nearly home, and the latter driven in to the right of it at a distance slightly greater than

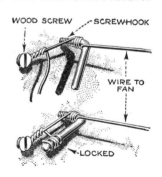

the length of the hook. The wire to the fan is twisted around the flat-head screw, leaving a short end, then passed over and around the screwhook, as shown. It is not necessary to pull the wire tight when doing this as it is evident that, when the screwhook is turned to the right it will coil the wire once at each revolution and so tighten it to any desired degree. For the final tightening, the handle of the screwhook is brought in alinement with the wire running to the flat-head screw, and the loose end of the wire is twisted around the screwhook to lock it.

Shop Notes

How to Make a Fireless Brooder

By J. V. ROMIG

ONE of the first and most necessary things to have after chicks have been hatched or purchased is a brooder. The poultry farmer starting in can save considerable expense by making his own; the construction is not by any means difficult, and anyone at all handy with tools can make a very efficient and creditable piece of equipment by proceeding according to the directions given in this article.

The brooder is of the fireless type, in which use is made of the principle of conservation of body heat rather than of supplying heat from an outside source. This is effected by the use of a hover board which is hung with canton-flannel strips, under the folds of which the baby chickens can nestle. It can be used both inside and outside, but it is preferable to keep it for the first ten days of the chicks' lives in

A Simple and Easily Constructed Brooder of the Fireless Type

a warm building, after which it may be set out in the open.

Old packing-case boards of 1-in. thickness can be used for the sides, bottom and roof, and if they are of the tongued and grooved variety so much the better. The outer housing, or frame, is nailed together as shown in the detail drawings, and then short pieces of board are drilled with a number of ¼-in. holes and nailed across the corners of the inside of the housing.

pivoted covers fitted over them. The air will enter through these holes and percolate through the holes in the corner boards and in the hover board, ventilating the inside of the brooder thoroughly. The canton-flannel strips should be wide enough to rest on the bottom of the brooder, so that a direct draft cannot blow through it. In warm weather, the top can be lifted and blocked up, to allow more air to reach the inside of the brooder.

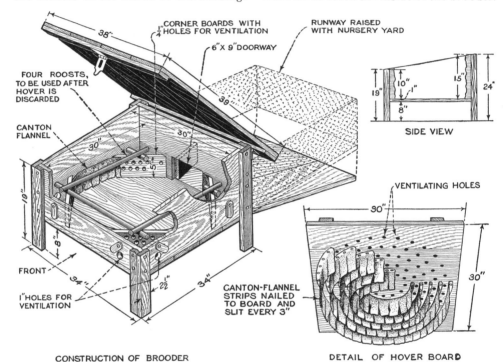

CONSTRUCTION OF BROODER   DETAIL OF HOVER BOARD

Details of the Homemade Fireless Brooder; Note the Hinged Runway, Which Serves as a Nursery Yard, and the Roosts for Use When the Chicks Outgrow the Brooder

Around the octagonal inclosure thus formed, a strip of heavy canton flannel is tacked, the tacks being driven around the upper edge. This strip is then slit every 3 in. nearly to the top edge; it should not be tacked completely around the inclosure, an opening being left at the back, where the door is cut in the housing.

The hover board is made slightly smaller than the inside of the brooder, so that it will rest on the corner boards and can be easily removed for cleaning. It is 30 in. square, and ¼-in. holes are drilled in circles through it, as shown. Strips of canton flannel are then tacked to the underside, so that a circle of holes will come between each pair of strips, and the strips are slit every 3 in. in the manner previously described. Two 1-in. holes are drilled in each corner of the housing, and little

As the chickens grow taller, blocks can be placed under the hover board to accommodate them. After they have outgrown the necessity for the brooder, the hover board is removed, and a four-pole roost substituted.

A 6 by 9-in. opening, fitted with a door, is cut in the back of the brooder housing, and a runway, the full width of the brooder, hinged just below the door. This can then be raised when the chicks are too small to be allowed to run in the yard and surrounded with chicken netting to form a perfectly safe nursery yard.

¶A convenient bench knife can be made from the broken blade of a jackknife by flattening one end of a piece of brass tube of suitable diameter and soldering the blade into the flattened end.

Stop for Radial Drill

For many kinds of work the stop shown in the drawing is a real timesaver on a radial drill. With the aid of this device it is possible to duplicate double holes in any number of pieces with the same accuracy as by using a jig. The parts required are a piece of round stock, tapped at one end to screw onto a bolt in the T-slot of the drill table, and fitted with a sleeve at the other end. The sleeve is tapped on opposite sides for setscrews and a hole is drilled through it to take an auxiliary arm, also made of round stock and bent to a hook shape as shown, to engage the handle by which the drill arm is swung. The parts are assembled as shown to the right in the illustration.

This stop was used successfully in the production of a number of pieces requiring two holes, the centers of which had to be located exactly alike in all the pieces. The adjustment of the stop was made as follows: A sample piece with holes already drilled was bolted in place. By swinging the drill arm backward and forward and lengthening or shortening the auxiliary arm, the drill was made to stop over the holes as the drill arm reached the end of its swing on either side as determined by the stop. The sliding auxiliary arm and the saddle carrying the spindle were then locked, and the work was

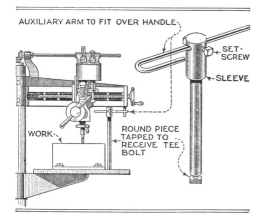

Device on a Radial-Drill Press Allows Duplication of Holes as Accurately as with a Jig

drilled and reamed with very accurate results.—Harry Moore, Montreal, Can.

Water Heater for Contractors

The drawing shows a novel and serviceable heater for running water, that will prove useful to contractors who have to heat large quantities of water for concrete

Novel Contractors' Water Heater That Is Inexpensive to Make and Convenient to Move

or plaster work. The heating unit consists of a number of lengths of pipe connected with elbows as shown, the bottom end being connected to the water supply and the upper end having an extension with a faucet attached. A fire is built inside of the coil and this heats the water in a short time. This heater is inexpensive to build and is light in weight, so that it can be easily moved about from one job to another.

Filling In Broken Enamel

Fine sealing wax is good for filling in cracks or broken spots on enameled surfaces, as it hardens at once, takes color without absorbing the oil and does not shrink. Use a wax of the proper color to match the surface to be repaired, fit it in, and smooth the surface down with a hot palette or putty knife. Give it one or two coats of color to make it match the remainder of the enamel exactly, and then varnish.

Tray for Beeswaxing Screws

Woodworkers and others who are accustomed to dip wood screws in beeswax to make it easier to drive them into the wood, will appreciate the usefulness of the dip-

Handy Dipping Tray and Dipper for Beeswaxing Wood Screws

ping tray and dipper shown in the drawing. The tray is made of sheet metal, bent over and riveted so that it is 1 in. deep, and stands on legs about 6 in. high. The wax is placed in the tray and melted by means of a Bunsen burner or small alcohol lamp. A dipper is used to hold the screws; this is made from a piece of sheet metal, having a number of slots cut to form tines, which hold the screws as indicated in the detail. The screws are picked up simply by running the dipper through a box of the screws.—Vernon F. Clayton, Detroit, Mich.

Worn Paving Brick Make Manholes

Bricks from worn-out street pavements need not be hauled to the city dump as worthless. They can be used in building manholes. For this purpose discarded bricks are just as good as new ones, because, in manhole construction, the spaces between the bricks, no matter how ragged, are filled with cement mortar. Such manholes will obviously cost much less than those built with new brick or concrete, and are practically as durable.—Ivan E. Houk, Denver, Colo.

Testing Crankshaft for Cracks

When overhauling the engine it is desirable to examine the crankshaft for cracks. Some cracks may be visible to the eye, but in most cases a crack is too fine to be seen, yet, if ignored, it will gradually increase in size until the shaft breaks—hence the importance of finding hair cracks. A simple method of making such cracks visible is to suspend the shaft from one end by means of a rope and then strike the crank cheeks in turn a sharp blow with a hammer. The vibration forces oil out of the crack and the shadow of the fine oil line is distinct on the clean surface of the shaft. Any crankshaft found to have a crack in it should be discarded.

Cutting Circular Holes in Sheet Metal

It is often necessary to cut circular holes in instrument boards for speedometers, clocks, etc. This cutting cannot be done very well with an ordinary saw, and therefore the circular saw shown in the photograph was made. It consists of a hacksaw blade screwed to the edge of a circular piece of wood, and the shank of an old drill bit. The piece of wood is turned down to a suitable diameter and $\frac{1}{2}$ in. wide, with a boss about 1$\frac{1}{2}$ in. in diameter in which the drill shank is pinned. The material should be hardwood, such as oak, as it must withstand considerable strain. A thin, flexible hacksaw blade is bent around the edge and both ends of the blade are cut

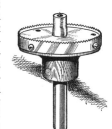

off so that the ends fit together exactly. The temper is taken out of the blade at several points, about 2 in. apart, so that screw holes can be drilled through it. Small round-head screws are used to fasten the blade to the disk. A hole is drilled through the center to receive the drill shank, or a similar piece of round steel, about $\frac{3}{8}$ or $\frac{1}{2}$ in. thick and 4 or 5 in. long. The shank should project beyond the saw teeth so that it will serve as a center guide, which is inserted into a small hole drilled first. A $\frac{1}{8}$-in. hole is drilled through both boss and shank, and a nail is driven through to serve as a pin, the ends being flattened to keep it in place. By grinding out a number of the teeth at intervals along the edge it will be easier to turn the tool, if it must be used in a hand brace or drill.

Brake for Shop Trucks

When loading hand trucks with heavy boxes it is usually necessary to slide them onto the truck, and the latter must either be held by another person or the wheels "scotched" with blocks to keep the truck from moving. Recently a small plant fitted the shop truck with a brake as shown in the drawing, and the truckman is now able to load it alone without blocking.

The attachment is easily made; two strong hinges are fastened to the underside of the truck in front of the rear wheels, one end of each hinge being allowed to hang loose. The loose ends are connected by a strip of heavy sheet metal, which is fastened to them with screws. In the center of this strip is riveted a V-shaped piece of metal to act as a catch for a piece of round rod which is bent around the axle of the rear wheels. The part of the rod between the axle and the V-piece should be so long that it will tilt the loose leaves of the hinges a trifle forward, holding their lower ends above the floor. At the other end a cylindrical weight is driven on the rod. When the truck is to be loaded, the weight is lifted with the foot, which allows the hinges to drop into contact with the floor. The truck is then given a forward push, causing the hinges to bring up against the rear wheels and raise them a little, so that the truck is securely blocked.—Harry Moore, Montreal, Can.

Brake on Factory Truck Enables Worker to Load It without Blocking Up the Wheels

Cattle Guard Made of Cactus

A section foreman on an Arizona railroad conceived the idea of using cactus plants for a cattle guard at railroad crossings. The first one he built proved so

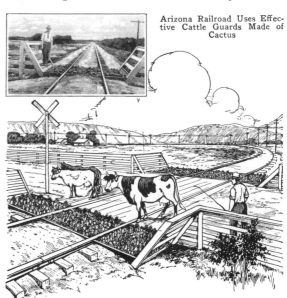

Arizona Railroad Uses Effective Cattle Guards Made of Cactus

successful that the railroad company decided to use his method exclusively. The guard consisted of a wooden frame of 2 by 6-in. material under the tracks, as shown in the drawing. In this boxlike structure, sand and gravel were placed to a depth of a few inches and the cactus planted in it. As the cactus used for this purpose grows in abundance along the railroad these guards cost nothing outside of the wood and labor to construct the frames. That it is also efficient is shown by the fact that during the first six months not a single animal attempted to cross it. Both horses and cattle in this region are familiar with the sharp thorns of cactus and avoid it as they would a rattlesnake.—Robert H. Moulton, Chicago, Ill.

Keeping Record Map Up to Date

A wall map in the office of an electric-light company was used to indicate the changes and extensions in the overhead lines. It was at first found difficult to make the alterations on the map satisfactorily, but all trouble was overcome by placing it in a picture frame having a glass front and indicating the changes on the glass with various colors of waterproof ink.

Movable Workbench

In an automobile repair shop in western Maryland the writer observed a small repair table, made from an old steel oil drum and mounted on casters so that it could be

Sturdy Workbench Made from Oil Drum and Mounted on Casters

moved about. A wooden top was bolted on the drum, and on this top a small vise and hand grinder were mounted. A semicircular opening was cut in the side of the drum so that oilcans, greasing equipment, waste and various tools for tire and other repair work could be stored when not in use. Casters were riveted to the side near the bottom, as indicated in the detail. Obviously, the use of this table saved many steps to and from the workbench and thus eliminated waste of time. It was possible even to put an engine on this sturdy table and move it to another section of the shop.—G. A. Luers, Washington, D. C.

Efficient Drawing-Pen Cleaner

Drawing pens and pens on compasses can be cleaned easily with an ordinary pipe cleaner. The cleaner is bent to form a loop, the ends being twisted together and inserted in an improvised handle. The loop is brought close together and passed between the jaws of the pen. Such a cleaner is inexpensive and will not injure the most delicate pen.

Making Small Laps

Where tubing is available, it makes very good laps, but few shops carry a supply of tubing in all sizes, and some may not have it at all. Good laps for drill-jig bushings and similar work, however, can be made of cold-rolled steel or drill rod, which comes in all sizes, and can usually be found in any shop. The rod is sawed lengthwise down the center, and adjusted by spreading the ends apart.

Safe Ladder for the Silo

Most silos have an inside ladder but not many have one on the outside, although the necessity for one here is sometimes just as great. In case the silo is made of hollow concrete blocks, a neat and durable ladder can be built integral with it on the inside, outside or both. The rungs are made from a number of lengths of $\frac{5}{8}$-in. iron rod, bent to the shape shown. These are inserted between the blocks, which are grooved to receive the rungs snugly. The ends of the rungs are bent over into the hollows of adjacent blocks to prevent them from being pulled out, and the rungs themselves should extend out far enough to offer a sure foothold even when overshoes are worn. A sufficient number of courses of blocks at the bottom might be

Steel Rungs in Silo Wall Make Strong and Durable Ladder

laid without rungs, to prevent youthful investigators from climbing the ladder.

EMERGENCY EJECTORS

By
FREDERICK W. SALMON
AM. SOC. NAVAL ENGRS.

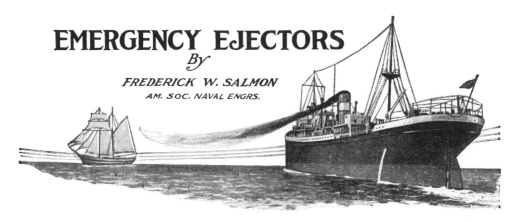

THE ejector is often a very useful device on and about ships, as it is about the only one that the ship's crew can make in a short space of time that will move a large quantity of water. Every seagoing engineer should therefore know as much about it as possible, particularly how best to construct one out of pipe and fittings and use it to get the best results. The writer has found such ejectors of great value on many occasions, and gives here the results of his experience in condensed form.

It is perhaps best to commence with a short description of the theory of the ideal ejector, and so in Fig. 1 is shown a simple elementary type. The water enters the ejector at A, and passes to the steam jet in a spiral so that the streamlines will be easy and the angular deflection small, thus keeping the hydraulic loss low. The incoming water is accelerated in the narrowing passage until it attains its maximum velocity in the throat B. The particles of the condensed steam enter the water at this point and impart to it a large portion of their energy, after which the water moves at a decreasing velocity until it reaches the normal pipe section at C; at the same time the pressure is increased. The things to strive for in the design are: To have the water enter with the least shock or eddy loss and with the least surface or skin loss; to provide just sufficient condensing surface on the steam nozzle; to avoid all sudden changes of form in the throat; to get the water column back to normal velocity at C in the least practical distance, and to prevent radiation losses

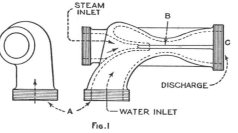

STEAM INLET

B

C

DISCHARGE

A

WATER INLET

Fig. 1

Drawing Illustrating the Principle of the Ejector

as far as possible. Fig. 2 shows a home-made ejector of a type often seen; sometimes it will operate and sometimes not, depending on the conditions under which it is tried. Its principal faults are: The steam jet is not of nozzle shape; the water is not properly guided and meets a sudden obstruction at B; there is no throat at A nor recovery cone at C, and no relief for starting at D. In the ejector shown in Fig. 3 some effort has been made to provide a throat at A by using a nipple of smaller size than the ejector body, fitting the nipple by means of the bushings B and C, but this usually results in the steam nozzle being much too long, causing both steam and water losses. This type is open to about all the criticisms directed against that shown in Fig. 2, but it will generally drive out a little water against a higher head than Fig. 2, and so it is often used as a makeshift. Fig. 4 shows an ejector that can be made of practically the same material as that in Fig. 2, but which, experience has shown, is about as efficient a device as can be made with pipe and fittings. The steam nozzle is hammered or swaged a little toward the proper nozzle shape, smoothed out on the inside with an improvised reamer, and turned, ground or filed on the outside (to lessen the draft or wake in the passing water) to a thin edge, say 1/32 in. for the smaller to 1/16 in. for the larger nozzles.

The water passages can easily be made to the shapes indicated at A and B with zinc, white metal, solder, babbitt, or even lead. To make A, screw the steam nozzle tightly into the galvanized-iron plug C, and mold A to the shape desired with plaster of Paris, sand or even clay. As soon as this is hard, use it as a pattern and make a mold in sand, or whatever is available, with a regular cope and a runner or gate. Open the mold, take out A, C and D and remove all the plaster or whatever was used to form A; then clean the surfaces of C and D well. Fill the inside of the nozzle with sand, rammed hard, to prevent any of the metal from running into it, see that the mold and cope are in good order, put in C and D; then put on the cope and pour. Twenty minutes' work will make a good cast. To make the throat piece, drill a few holes in a galvanized nipple E to hold the fitting securely, and turn or carve a piece of soft wood to form a core for the throat. The cylindrical ends should fit the nipple easily, and the core should be cut in two and the two halves doweled together with a nail, as shown, to permit withdrawal. Place the core in position in the nipple, first coating it with paraffin or grease, and, through the holes in the nipple, fill the space between core and nipple with plaster of Paris. When this has set, withdraw the core, and the nipple can now be used to make a sand core for the actual casting. This is done by cutting some small disks of paper to fit the smallest part of the throat, slipping a wire nail through the center of the disks before they are placed in position, to act as a dowel for the sand core. The sand is now rammed in from both ends until the nipple is well filled, then withdrawn and dried thoroughly. Remove the plaster from the nipple, clean the inside surface well, replace the dried core and bed the whole nipple in sand, with one of the holes up. Pour through this hole the babbitt, or whatever else is used, and, when cold, remove from the sand and clean out

the core. All this can also be done in from twenty minutes to half an hour. These times only include working time, of course; in addition to this it may require several hours to dry the sand properly in order to prevent it from "blowing" when the hot metal is poured into the molds. Zinc is much more likely to blow than white metal or lead. Four tablespoonfuls of molasses or sirup, mixed in a cup of water, and added to 2 qt. of fine, dry beach sand will generally make a good core, or a good molding sand, for this work. If either of these ingredients is not at hand, one teaspoonful of wheat flour mixed in ½ pt. of water and gradually heated until boiling will answer the same purpose; a short piece of broomstick or the butt end of a marlinspike makes a good rammer. This ejector will deliver from 40 to 80 times the square of the water-pipe diameter in cubic feet per hour, or from 300 to 600 times the square of the pipe diameter in U. S. gallons per hour. Commonly the suction and discharge pipes are of the same size. In the smaller sizes, the diameter of the steam pipe is half that of the water pipe; a 2-in. steam pipe, however, is large enough for a 5-in. ejector. The ejector should not be expected to deliver against a great head—probably not over 25 ft.—but, by piping the discharge like a siphon, a 15-ft. static head can be cared for over a ship's rail of from 40 to 50 ft. above the water level.

There is not much reliable data as to the steam consumption of such ejectors, but from experiment, it appears reasonable to expect that they will use about 1/10 to 1/12 of the weight of water they lift, when not immersed in water themselves. The discharge water will generally account for about 98 per cent of the heat in

Figs. 2 and 3, Types of Ejectors Frequently Met, but Inefficient in Use; Fig. 4, Construction of Ejector Made of Pipe and Fittings

the steam, but the useful work done, in pounds of water lifted a given number of feet in height, is rather low per pound of steam used. To get the best service, the ejector must not be submerged, but should be set as near the surface of the water as possible. It is often of advantage in starting the action of the ejector to have a relief cock provided, as shown in Fig. 5. This is operated by a rod so arranged that the weight of the rod tends to shut the cock, which should be of the same size as the steam pipe.

In Fig. 5 a good piping arrangement is shown for use when the whole unit has to be lowered into a compartment or hold. Unions are used at B and C to facilitate assembling and repairing. Four suction branches are best to use; two are shown at D and E, and the other two are screwed into the cross below these, and are placed at right angles to them. It is desirable to use a standpipe G, to prevent the end of

the suction pipe from being lowered into mud and stopped up quickly. There should be a total of about two hundred ⅜-in. holes in the five pipes; this will give a ratio of hole to pipe area of about 3 to 1; more than this would be better, and each hole should be countersunk with the point of a ⅝ or ¾-in. drill.

The steam and discharge pipes should be clamped together about every 6 ft. A simple and good way of doing this is shown in the upper detail. For temporary service, a wood block has been found satisfactory as a separator, if made amply large, cut to fit the pipes roughly, and provided with a piece of asbestos under the steam pipe. As an example of the practical application of the principles described, let us assume that we wish to remove water

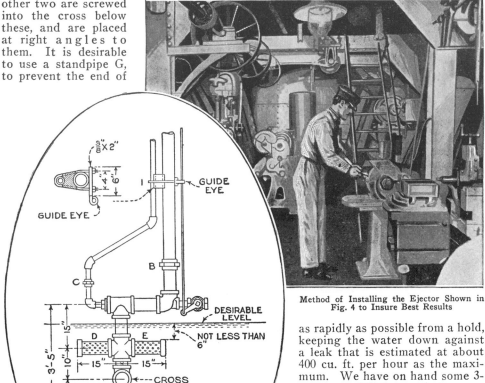

Method of Installing the Ejector Shown in Fig. 4 to Insure Best Results

as rapidly as possible from a hold, keeping the water down against a leak that is estimated at about 400 cu. ft. per hour as the maximum. We have on hand some 3-in. pipe and fittings; what can we do? Under favorable circumstances we may expect an ejector made of this pipe to deliver from 360 to 720 cu. ft. per hour, according to the rule previously given, so we proceed to make up the ejector, using a 1½-in. steam pipe and the same size of relief cock. This ejector will then gain rapidly on the water.

Tilting Shaker for Sand Screen

Screening of sand for use in concrete on small jobs is usually accomplished with a small screen held and shaken by hand.

A Fixed Sieve That Hastens the Riddling of Sand on Concrete Work

This process is slow and laborious, and a more expeditious and less tiresome method is to use a fixture of the kind shown in the illustration.

Either a round or square screen is adapted for the fixture, which is made simply by attaching two long handles to one end, and two "legs," which are pivoted to two pieces of 2 by 4-in. stock driven into the ground. Two bolts form the pivots, and make the sieve readily detachable when necessary. The sieve is operated by tilting, which slides the sand from one end to the other while dropping it into a barrow placed underneath.

Prolonging Life of Wooden Well Curbs

Wooden well curbs are used quite extensively in rural districts. If they are air-tight or nearly so, moisture arises during cold weather and causes the curb to mold and rot. One should, therefore, allow the moisture to escape. This can be done by cutting away part of the curb and placing a screen over the opening, or if the curb has a lid, by closing this only loosely. It has been found that with either of these precautions a curb will last longer.—Bunyan Kennedy, McCool, Miss.

Keeping Grease from Auto Brake Bands

Having grease flow out of the differential on the brake bands is objectionable in that it is difficult to clean off, catches all the dirt and dust and may prevent the brakes from functioning properly. This trouble can be remedied by means of spring washers that fit snugly on the axle shaft.

These are caught in the vise, one at a time, and the ends spread so as to form a steep spiral. They are then forced on the axle so that one end of each washer will interlock with the end of the next and form a complete screw extending from the wheel bearing on each side to the differential. It is necessary, of course, to place the washers on the axle in such a manner that the excess grease will be screwed back to the differential housing, and not away from it.—G. G. McVicker, North Bend, Nebr.

Radius-Turning Tool

Most of the tools or attachments for the forming of radii on the lathe are either too cumbersome or too large to handle small diameters, but the tool illustrated is about as small and neat as it is possible to make. The main body is made from soft steel, of the same size as the usual lathe-tool shank, the front end being forged flat to form the base of the swivel head. The latter combines the pivot, tool-holder, exten-

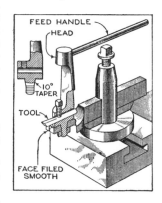

sion-handle holder, setscrews for tightening the tool and pivot stud; the whole thing being worked out of cold-rolled stock. The pivot stud is turned concentric with the tool head while the extension-handle holder is turned eccentric to the whole. A piece of ½-in. rod about 14 in. long is screwed into the upper end of the head and serves as a handle for turning the device in an arc. The face of the body is filed off flat and true and the distance this face projects beyond the true center should be marked with stamps. This distance is then subtracted from the radius to be cut and the result will be the distance the tool must extend beyond the face of the holder. The pivot should be taper-turned and rest in a taper seat as well as on the flat; a nut will hold the two together at the right tension for easy turning and without chattering.

As will be seen by a reference to the drawing, the top of the tool should pass through the same line as the regulation lathe tool. A tool of this type is a great labor and timesaver as, when removed from the toolpost, the accuracy of the setup remains undisturbed.

Reinforcing Corroded Steel Tower

A 75-ft. steel tower supporting a 20,000-gal. tank at the oil mill of the Lookout Oil and Refining Co. at Corinth, Miss., became so weak from corrosion that a collapse was imminent. The general manager, Mr. M. Reynolds, suggested a plan of repairing the tower that proved perfectly successful, and saved the cost of a new tower.

The four main columns consisted of 7-in. wrought-iron pipe, with cross members of 3½-in. pipe, spaced 12 ft. apart. Wood forms, 15 in. square inside, were built around each column, with projecting forms 12 in. square extending out on the cross members for 18 inches. The forms were finished and the concrete poured in 12-ft. sections, care being taken that the reinforcing iron lapped the points where pouring ceased on each section.

After the concrete had been poured, 10 days were allowed for it to cure, and, when the forms were removed, the columns were found to be perfect, with no evidence of honeycombing. The completed job was found perfectly satisfactory.—H. C. Harrington, Gen. Supt., Chattanooga, Tenn.

Left, the Forms in Position; Center, a Portion of the Corroded Tower; Right, the Completed Job

Seam Folder for Tin Work

One of the occasional tasks of the sheet-metal worker is to seam together sheets of tin for roofing. Of course, shop equipment can be purchased with which to do

Simple Device Aids Sheet-Metal Workers in Making Seams in Tin Roofing

this work, but the small tinsmith, whose infrequent use for such a device does not justify the expense of purchasing one, will find the rig shown in the drawing just as good for his needs, and its cost is negligible. Two pieces of 1-in. wood of equal size, say, about 10 in. wide and 3 ft. long, are fitted with strips of flat iron on one edge and hinged together with several hinges, fastened to the top. In use, the boards are placed so that the iron edges are over the open seam, as indicated in the detail. Then the boards are pressed down by standing on them, and the seam is ready for soldering. A leather handle is attached to one of the boards, so that the "press" can be moved from seam to seam easily. —G. A. Luers, Washington, D. C.

¶When a barrel of gasoline is allowed to remain in one position for a long time, it frequently happens that the last few quarts of gasoline contain sufficient water to cause trouble in the engine or stove. The water can be removed by dropping a large cotton cloth into the gas and wringing it out. The cloth absorbs the water.

Huge Water Sprinkler Used by California Rancher to Irrigate Land

water to carry over a radius of 100 ft. The sprinkler is moved by hand or horse four or five times a day, and has proved a real money saver.—Geo. E. Bowers, Escondido, Calif.

Brush Finish for Brass

Brass and similar metals may be given a brush finish by rubbing them with steel wool. Care should be taken that the rubbing is done in one direction, otherwise a scratched surface will result. A lacquer should be applied to prevent tarnishing. A thin solution of white shellac in alcohol, applied with a brush, is satisfactory for large work. Small pieces can be dipped in the solution.

Huge Homemade Field Sprinkler

A California rancher has improvised a large field sprinkler similar in design to those commonly used on city lawns. It is built upon an old buggy chassis and is made of pipe and fittings picked up on the ranch. The sprinkler arms are 20-ft. lengths of 1-in. iron pipe, giving a spread of 40 ft. and, ordinarily, a reach of 60 ft. The ends of the arms are bent in opposite directions and five small slits are cut with a hacksaw, at regular intervals, into the side of each arm. These slits are, of course, cut on that side of the arm toward which its end is bent, so that the force of the outflowing water causes the pipe to turn. The central support for the arms is made of 2-in. pipe and fittings, and the arms are braced by guy wires from the top of a smaller pipe, as shown. A length of old fire hose is used to connect the sprinkler to the supply pipe from a power-driven pump. Sometimes the wind causes the

Keeping Paint Brushes Soft

Everyone who has to do an occasional job of painting knows how easily brushes are spoiled by letting them stand in paint pots. To keep my brushes in good condition without the necessity of cleaning and drying them thoroughly every time I had finished using them, I obtained an empty 5-lb. tin can, originally used for carbonate of soda; this can was about 5½ in. in diameter and 10 in. deep. One

inch below the top I punched eight holes in the side and inserted L-shaped lengths of wire, about 2 in. long. These I soldered to the outside, with one end projecting inside of the can to form a hook. Through the handle of each brush I drilled a small hole exactly 5 in. above the bottom end of the bristles so that these would not touch the bottom of the can. After the brushes were hung up in the can enough turpentine was poured in to submerge the bristles and the cover was then put on to prevent evaporation. In this way the brushes were kept in good condition and ready for use at any time.—C. E. Weibezahl, Syracuse, N. Y.

Making Durable Valve Washers

During a number of years as a railroader and general repairman I have seen much trouble that was due to faulty washers in valves, and in seeking a remedy, I have found that washers made of lead and new babbitt are both durable and leak-proof. In valves for hot or cold water I use lead alone; for steam valves, a mixture of half lead and half new babbitt. Although lead alone will hold steam, I prefer the half-and-half mixture, as it is more durable. New babbitt is used because old bearings and the like are apt to contain bits of iron and steel.

From a small ladle I pour the molten metal into the washer cup of the valve; then, when the metal is cool, I level up the surface with a file. If the valve leaks when tested, I take it out and file the washer on the side where the marks show that it bears heaviest. In this way one can form a valve washer that will last for months, or even years. If there is no screw to hold the washer, the rim of the cup can be dented slightly at the sides to hold it in place.—Clarence Uplinger, Cincinnati, Ohio.

Hinged Track Section in Barn

In a large western dairy barn, with several grain bins at one end and a double conveyor track running from these bins along two rows of mangers, the track crossed over a driveway without leaving sufficient headroom for a loaded rack to pass under it. The trouble was readily overcome by cutting off the sections of track over the driveway and mounting them on lengths of 4 by 4-in. timbers. These were hinged at one end so that they could be swung entirely out of the way to allow the load to pass. When swung back

Sections of Conveyor Track Cut and Hinged on End to Permit Passage of Loaded Rack

again, the timbers are held in line by heavy cleats.—Dale R. Van Horn, Walton, Nebr.

Getting Rid of Chinch Bugs

Chinch bugs proved to be one of the most costly pests of the corn belt last season. Damage amounting to millions

Dripping Creosote in Furrow to Protect Field from Chinch Bugs; Cyanide Hole in Foreground

of dollars was caused in the migration from wheat fields into corn, sorghum and other "row" crops. The bugs "march afoot" and methods of controlling them have been based on the establishment of barriers to stop them from reaching their objective. At the Kansas state agricultural college various systems were tested last summer, and a combination of creosote and calcium cyanide was found most effective. The creosote was dripped into a furrow along the side of the field to be protected, and every few feet along the furrow holes were dug in which flakes of calcium cyanide were deposited. Unable to cross the creosote line, the bugs crawled along it until they reached a cyanide deposit and were killed by the deadly and low-lying gas given off by that substance. Barriers of calcium cyanide, without creosote, were found ineffective.

"Working Model" Aids Drawing Students

Drawing instructors often find it difficult to explain to their students how three different views of a model or other subject

A Simple Model to Illustrate the Principles of Projection That Will Prove Valuable to Drawing Students

are projected on paper. The model shown in the illustration makes the task easy and the students are enabled to grasp the principles of projection very quickly.

The model consists of a substantial wooden base, about 13 in. long and 10 in. wide, to one side of which is fastened a frame holding a sheet of glass. The frame is about 12 in. high, and to one side and the top two similar frames are hinged, the top one folding down against the side one when the latter is brought against a step cut in the base, thus inclosing the object on three sides. The object is a block 2 in. square and 4 in. long, supported on a wooden pillar at an oblique angle to each of the three frames or planes of projection. The projection lines are represented by small brass rods, three of which are fastened to each corner of the block at right angles to each other, and running to the three glass planes. On each plane is drawn an accurate projection of the block by simply joining the points represented by the ends of the rods behind the glass, and dotted lines running from these points to the edges of each plane show clearly how one view is projected from the other.

The swinging of the frames into one plane puts the drawings in the final position required on a flat sheet. This makes it perfectly simple to explain how the object is "swung" in the mind's eye to obtain three different views on the drawing paper.
—Sherwin M. Turrill, Maywood, Ill.

A Simple Recessing Tool

An easy way to make a tool suitable for recessing caps, shouldered nuts, and the like, in the hand screw machine is shown in the drawing. The tool is made in two pieces, the shank and toolholder proper, the former being turned to fit the turret and the front end slotted across. The toolholder is milled across both sides, leaving a flat portion which fits the slot in the shank. The front is bored out to take the recessing tool

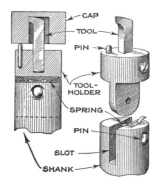

and drilled at one side for a pin. The toolholder can be held to the shank by a screw or taper pin, as desired, provided that it is allowed freedom to move in the slot. A flat spring, bent upward at each end, and fastened to the shank with two small screws, serves to keep the tool from flopping about. It can be seen that when the pin driven into the face of the toolholder reaches the face of the work it causes the tool to feed inward and thus cut the recess. It is important when setting a tool of this character to note that the tool travels a little in a direction parallel to the bore of the work after the pin touches the face of the piece. Consequently the tool should be set so that it is a trifle away from the back face of the work when the pin touches the front face. When the tool has reached the desired depth of cut it will have traveled in a slight arc and should finish the cut touching the back face.

⁋Small articles, such as nuts and screws, that have fallen into some inaccessible place can often be picked up by means of chewing gum stuck on the end of a stick.

Getting the Most Out of the Grinder

By G. A. LUERS

MANY owners of bench hand-driven emery grinders get little out of them beyond the grinding of chisels, scrapers and an occasional screwdriver or other tool. A few men, on the other hand, with a little ingenuity, accomplish real work with them, and get the utmost in service out of the high-speed little tools. In the small shop or garage, where space is at a premium, and where the purchase of even one additional tool means a hardship at times, the hand grinder may be made into a machine of numerous uses and undoubted value.

The first thing to be done to increase its usefulness is to fit it with some kind of a foot treadle, so as to leave both hands free to handle the work. This may be done in a variety of ways, none of which are shown, as the job is a simple one for any mechanic, and depends, to some extent, on the location of the grinder. With the treadle in place, much work can be done that would be impossible without it.

A common round wire scratch brush, fitted in place of the grinding wheel, permits the tool to be used for such work as roughening tire casings and tubes for patching. Anyone who has attempted to hold a heavy casing open while scratch brushing the inside for a patch will appreciate the saving made in time and temper by the use of the little machine. The scratch brush will also serve for free-

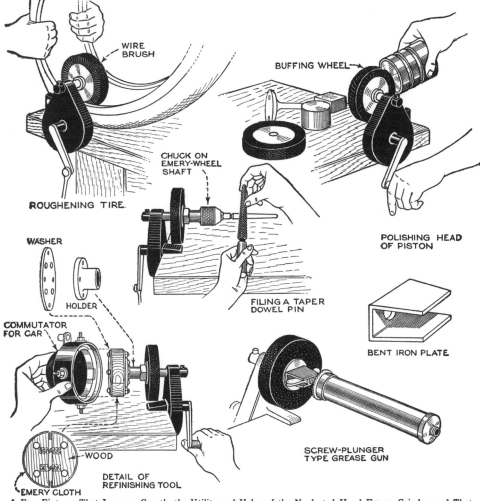

A Few Fixtures That Increase Greatly the Utility and Value of the Neglected Hand Emery Grinder, and That Save Time and Dollars in the Small Shop

ing engine parts of carbon, cleaning pieces to be soldered and removing rust.

To polish the brass and nickel parts of a car, a buffing wheel is substituted. This wheel also makes it possible to give the tops of pistons and valves that fine polish that is so effective in preventing the rapid accumulation of carbon. In fact, the uses of the buffing wheel are legion around the shop and garage.

If a small drill chuck is used on the spindle of the grinder, a surprising number of jobs can be done with it. Holes that are not required to be accurately located can be drilled, small round parts can be filed to size, needle valves trued, dowels fitted, engine-valve stems polished—in fact, almost any work for which a small polishing lathe is commonly used. On one occasion I saw a car owner true up the commutator segments of his generator by means of the chuck on his grinder and a small improvised end support. If a small split wooden pulley is

made and mounted on the spindle of the grinder, as shown at the lower left of the drawing, it becomes an easy matter to true up the inside of Ford commutators. Small springs are placed between the sections of the pulley and the surface is faced with emery cloth. This has been found very useful in a Ford service station. In the same shop is found the device shown at the right. This consists merely of a piece of sheet steel or iron, bent to a U-shape, and drilled at the bottom of the "U" to fit over the spindle of the grinder. It is a tiresome job to unscrew the plunger of a large grease gun by hand for refilling, but by placing the end of the plunger in the U-shaped chuck and running the grinder, the plunger is turned out in a few seconds.

The examples shown are merely a few of the many uses to which the hand grinder can be put in the small shop; any mechanic can think of many more and increase the utility of a little-used tool.

Simple Brake for Hand Hoist

The illustration shows an unusual hand-hoist construction, which has a self-locking brake. The drum on which the hoisting ropes are wound is turned down to two diameters to obtain greater leverage, the rope to the load being wound on the smaller section and the pull rope on the larger. The load rope is attached so that

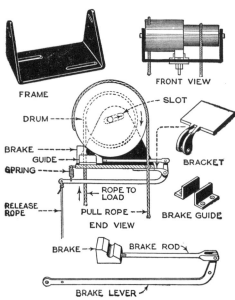

FRONT VIEW

FRAME

DRUM

BRAKE

GUIDE

SPRING

RELEASE ROPE

ROPE TO LOAD

PULL ROPE

END VIEW

SLOT

BRACKET

BRAKE GUIDE

BRAKE

BRAKE ROD

BRAKE LEVER

Unusual Type of Hand-Hoist Mechanism Which Is Equipped with Self-Locking Cable

it will be wound up when the drum is rotated toward the right, as indicated by the arrow in the center figure, and the pull rope is attached so that it will unwind while the former is winding, and vice versa. The drum is held in a steel frame of the type shown at the upper left, slots being used for bearings to permit a slight lateral movement of the drum, which engages it with or releases it from the brake arranged below. The bearing slots are inclined so that when the pull rope is unwound the shaft climbs up the slots, releasing the drum from the brake. On the other hand, the shaft runs down the incline of the slots the moment the pull rope is let go and the drum is held securely when it rubs against the brake. The brake, brake-rod and brake-lever assembly is shown in the lower detail. It is attached to the frame under the center of the drum so that the brake works against the larger section. Two pieces of angle iron are fastened to the frame to serve as guides for the brake, and a short coil spring is attached to the frame and brake lever to hold the brake tightly against the drum. A small bracket to hold the brake lever is cut, and bent to the shape shown in the right-hand detail; it is attached to the underside of the frame, and the brake lever is pivoted on it. A rope attached to the end of the brake lever enables one to release the brake.

❡ Burnt umber with white and orange-chrome yellow will give a variety of clear, warm drab colors.

Finding Loose Wristpins

A wristpin may be loose enough to knock and yet, when examined, no perceptible play may be found in it. In such a case the connecting rod should be held in a vise and the piston rocked up and down in the plane of the wristpin. If an oil film comes and goes between the pin and its bushing the pin is too loose, and new pins and bushings must be fitted. The old bushings may be reamed out and oversize pins fitted, if desired.— H. F. Blanchard, Tuckahoe, N. Y.

Auxiliary Wheels for Barrow

For certain purposes, such as sweeping cuttings from the floors of shops, and similar work, a pair of small auxiliary wheels added to the shop wheelbarrow will prove very practical.

This arrangement enables the worker to slide the barrow from machine to machine as desired, with the ease of moving a three or four-wheel truck, yet when the barrow is full, it may be lifted and rolled away in the usual manner to the yard, or through passageways where it would be impossible to handle the ordinary truck. A push moves the barrow several feet,

Small Auxiliary Wheels Added to the Barrow Lighten the Labor of Sweeping the Shop

while without the small wheels the handles must be lifted to move it.

⟨A non-magnetic cast iron is being produced by a concern in England.

Tying Bundles of Wall Paper

In order to tie up bundles of wall paper quickly and conveniently, a dealer provided the novel holder shown in the photo and drawing. It is made of wood and has four arms extending from the top. Rolls of

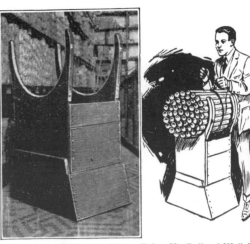

Convenient Holder Facilitates Tying Up Rolls of Wall Paper

wall paper are placed in the space between these arms, and it is then an easy matter to tie a cord around the rolls and make a bundle. This method was found much better than the usual one of holding the rolls while attempting to tie them up.— Charles A. Goddard, Los Angeles, Calif.

Testing Fit of Rod Bearings

When adjusting a connecting-rod bearing (with the engine in the car), the simplest way to determine when the bearing is just tight enough is as follows: Remove shims or file the cap until the rod is just too tight to be moved lengthwise by hand, but not too tight to be shifted slightly by tapping with the hammer.

Repairing Leaky Spark Plugs

Spark plugs having a removable center wire sometimes leak compression at this point. Often the reason is that the insulator has chipped away where the flange on the wire seats against it. This trouble can usually be remedied by slipping a thin brass washer, of the same kind as that used on top of the plug, over the center wire and drawing it up against the porcelain. As such washers are too large for this use, they must first be trimmed down with tinners' snips.—E. T. Gunderson, Jr., Humboldt, Iowa.

An Efficient Film-Drying Cabinet

The film-drying cabinet shown in the illustration was cheaply constructed, and a similar one can easily be made by anyone handy with tools. It will hold over 100

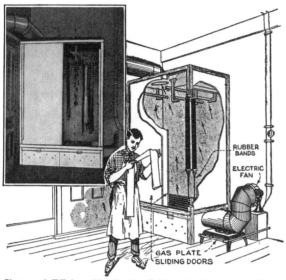

Cheap and Efficient Film-Drying Cabinet for Professional Photo Finishers That Hastens the Work

rolls of film, and will dry them in from 30 minutes to one hour.

The cabinet is made of wallboard, which can be obtained from any builders' supply house, nailed to a stout wood frame. Racks, made of 1 by 1-in. wood, are fastened to the top to hold the upper end of the films, and about 1 ft. from the floor a number of wood strips are nailed across

the cabinet to hold the bottom ends. Holes are cut in the top and bottom of the cabinet, as shown in the drawing, to receive the ends of lengths of stovepipe. The upper pipe is led outdoors, and the bottom one is connected by means of a couple of elbows to an electric fan. A gas plate is set below the bottom pipe, a little away from the cabinet, to heat the air as it passes through. The upper ends of the films may be attached to the cross strips by means of thumbtacks, or the strips may be provided with nails on which to hang regular film clips. A number of film clips, each pair of which is joined with a stout rubber band, are provided to hold the bottom ends of the films. One clip is fastened to the bottom of the roll and the other to one of the lower cross strips. As an alternative, the bottom strips may have nails part way driven into them also, and the ends of the rubber bands be hooked over the heads of the nails. It will be found desirable to provide bands of varying lengths, to take care of different films.

It will be noted in the drawing that the front of the cabinet bottom is hinged to form a door. This is convenient for removing the dust that accumulates in the bottom. The wallboard front of the cabinet is made in two sections arranged to slide in the frame. This construction has been found better than doors opening outward, as it saves considerable space and eliminates the necessity for catches on the doors.—H. C. Graves, Watertown, N. Y.

Riveting Disks to Hubs

When attaching a disk to a hub on small work the common practice is to make the hub long enough to project through the disk, which has been beveled, and then hammer the hub so that the metal spreads and holds the disk more or less tightly as shown in Fig. 1. This method has the disadvantage that the disk has a tendency to run out of true due to uneven riveting.

A better method is shown in Fig. 2. The hub is made with a cup edge and the disk is given a wide bevel. A tubular tool is turned up to the shape shown, hardened, polished, and revolved in a drill press so that when it is brought down on the hub it curls the metal out and forces it down into the bevel, and finally burnishes it neatly.

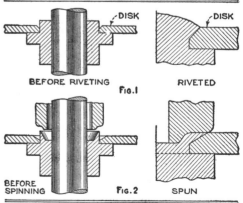

Common and Improved Method of Attaching a Disk to a Hub

Celluloid Keeps Report Sheets Clean

Anyone working in a shop where it is impossible to keep the hands clean, knows how difficult it is to keep report and record books clean if the workmen have to make entries in them. However, the difficulty is easily overcome by keeping a few sheets of thin celluloid handy on the shop desk (old photo negatives about post-card size, with the emulsion cleaned off, will do nicely). When a workman has to do some writing he lays one of these on the paper where his hand rests, and as he writes, the piece of celluloid will slide over the paper with the hand.

Spring Clip for Tank-Wagon Gasoline Hose

When required to make some kind of holder to keep the gasoline hose from

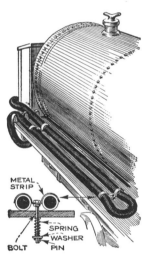

coming off a tank wagon or damaging the paint, the writer devised the clip shown in the drawing, which has been in operation for some time and has proved very satisfactory. It is simple to make, instantaneous in action, and is much better than straps.

The clip itself is made of the heavy galvanized strap which comes around bundles of sheet metal; this material is good mild steel. A ½-in. bolt 7 or 8 in. long, with two nuts, and a light coil spring with a washer and cotter pin are the materials required for each clip, in addition to the steel. The method of mounting the clip is clearly shown in the drawing.—B. E. Dobree, Victoria, B. C., Can.

Motorcycle Wheel Improves Wheelbarrow

An ordinary wheelbarrow is difficult to handle in soft dirt or sand because the wheel sinks down into the soil, sometimes so deeply that it is almost impossible to

Pushing Heavily Loaded Wheelbarrow over Loose Sand Is Facilitated by Use of Motorcycle Wheel

push it, especially under a heavy load. An Oregon farmer, who experienced this trouble in transporting grapes from his vineyard, fitted a wheelbarrow with a motorcycle wheel. The tire is partly inflated and will not sink deeply into the sand, even when the barrow is loaded to its full capacity.—Ed. Fraser, Ashland, Oregon.

Cutting Slots in Small Rods

Cutting slots in small rods is usually quite a difficult task. However, a simple method of doing it is shown in the illustration. The rod is first bent sharply at the point where the slot is to be cut and is then inserted in a vise, as indicated, so that a hacksaw can be used to cut the slot. After the slot has been cut the rod is straightened.

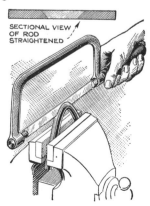

Homemade Swing Cut-Off Saw

By D. R. VAN HORN

THE swing cut-off saw is a very handy addition to the woodworking shop, and the making of one is no very hard or expensive undertaking, as the saw in the illustration shows. This saw was made from scrap, with the exception of the saw and its bearings, and the motor, which was

spring, the other end of which is fastened to one of the top braces. Between the irons the motor support, of 2½ by 8-in. stock, is fastened by means of angle irons bolted to the support and side irons. At the end of the 26-in. piece a 2 by 2-in. brace is bolted, the bolt running through the end of a 19-in. piece of flat iron, which completes the lower end of the frame.

This end carries the saw, which runs in bronze bushings salvaged from an old automobile. A 2 by 2-in. brace is bolted across the lower frame irons above the saw, and the saw spindle is fitted with a 2-in. pulley. The motor is fitted with a 4½-in. built-up wooden pulley, and the saw

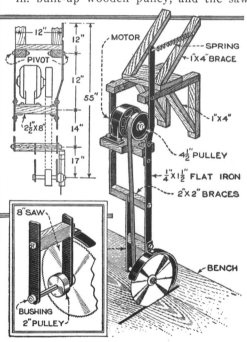

A Swing Cut-Off Saw That Is Very Simple to Build and That Will Give Just as Good Service as the Most Elaborate Commercial Saw

purchased from a secondhand dealer. The whole saw is self-contained and is so nicely balanced that a touch is sufficient to move it against the work. The saw guard makes it safe to operate, and a convenient switch permits it to be started and stopped instantly. The construction of the wall hanger is simple. Two triangular brackets, of 1 by 4-in. stock, are firmly fastened to the wall at the proper height and braced as shown in the drawing. If desired, the hanger may consist of a piece of 2 by 8-in stock, with the braces and back members of 1 by 4-in. stuff, thus making the top of the brackets solid instead of open. To the sides of the hanger two flat side irons, one 26 in. and the other 55 in. long, are bolted, the holes for the bolts being drilled so that the irons will swing freely but without sideplay. Part of the longer iron extends above the hanger and is drilled at the top to take a strong

with a heavy sheet-steel guard, riveted to a small angle, which is held by the bolt that fastens the lower 2 by 2-in. brace. The 8-in. saw will handle up to 2-in. stuff and is run at 3,000 r.p.m

It may be seen from this that the construction is exceedingly simple and inexpensive. The costliest part of the outfit is the ½-hp. motor, and even this may be picked up secondhand for very little money.

❡A good rule to follow when grinding milling cutters is to allow 7° clearance for roughing and 5° for finishing cutters.

Breaking Up Old Concrete Pavement

When breaking up an old concrete pavement on the main street in Scottville, M i c h., dynamite could not, of course, be used, owing to the proximity of the store windows on both sides of the street, so the method shown in the photo was tried and found successful. A strong chain with a hook was hitched to a powerful caterpillar tractor, the hook being placed under the edge of the pavement and a block of wood put under the chain to make the hook pull upward when the tractor moved forward.

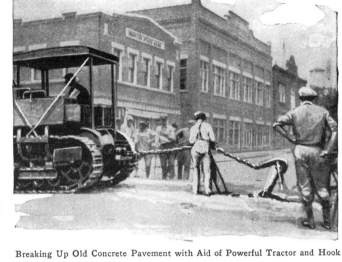

Breaking Up Old Concrete Pavement with Aid of Powerful Tractor and Hook

Each "bite" of concrete was several square yards in area.—M. M. VanValkenburgh, Cadillac, Mich.

Drawer Foils Petty Thieves

Garage men and other mechanics, who are employed in shops where the public is free to enter, are often inconvenienced by the loss of small tools and personal articles. To keep these in a locked drawer is too inconvenient and therefore the arrangement shown in the illustration was devised by one mechanic. An ordinary

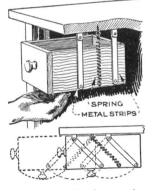

drawer is provided with a knob on the front in the usual way and another knob on the underside, the former being merely a "dummy," while the latter is actually used to open the drawer. Two lengths of 1 by 1/8-in. flat iron are hinged to the underside of the bench top on either side of the drawer, the lower ends being fastened to the drawer with flat-head screws. A stout coil spring is also attached to the drawer and the underside of the bench top as shown; it should have enough tension to keep the drawer and its contents in the position indicated in the lower detail so that a straight pull on the front knob will not open the drawer. It can, however, easily be opened by pulling downward and forward on the hidden knob underneath. A keyhole in the front of the drawer will add to the deception and lead the petty thief to believe that the drawer is locked.

Attaching Carpet to Concrete Floor

Attaching a carpet to a concrete floor is rather difficult because nails or tacks cannot be driven into the concrete. It can easily be done in the following way, which, however, requires the use of padding under the carpet: Drill holes in the concrete along the edge of the wall about 1 ft. apart, and plug these with hardwood. A tapered wooden strip of approximately the same thickness as the padding is run

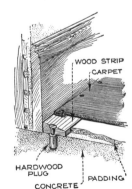

along the edge of the room, being screwed to the wooden plugs. The padding is then laid on the floor, and the carpet stretched over it and tacked to the strip.

¶When no resin is at hand, a glazed and slipping belt can be made to grip by throwing a handful of ashes on it.

A Novel Ratchet Screwdriver

In tightening screws set in the ends of square-section pieces not furnished with a through hole, use was made of the novel ratchet screwdriver shown in the illustration. It was made by bending a length of ¼-in. rod to clear the end of the work and flattening one end.

Novel Ratchet Screwdriver Used to Drive Screws Hard to Reach with the Ordinary Type

The flattened part was drilled to take a ratchet piece, slotted in the usual manner and held in place by means of a pin. A groove is cut in the top of the rod and a piece of ⅛-in. wire, attached to the top of the rod, slides in this. The ratchet action is simple; the operator presses on the handle to cause the wire to engage with one of the grooves of the ratchet. The screw is driven in by moving the rod with the other hand. To turn the rod back, the pressure on the handle is released and the wire slides out of the ratchet slot.

Making and Using Small Cone Bearings

Cone bearings are ideal for small model work for the reason that they are adjustable for wear, and for smooth-running models, a nice snug bearing, without shake, is desired. Cone bearings are also used in preference to straight bearings, as it is almost impossible to make a small bearing accurate in alinement and so that it will not wear large in a short time. The split bearing is also less desirable in model work as it makes for difficult construction.

The first type of cone bearing shown in the drawing, and the simplest, is one with a cone turned on the end having the hardest wear, such as the crank end of a small crankshaft. This bearing has a take-up collar setscrewed to the shaft, which is used to hold the latter in a proper adjustment. A solid rear bearing is used for this type. The space between the two bearings forms an ideal oil chamber which adds to their life.

The second style is of the double-cone type and has a cone turned on the shaft at one end and carries a loose or sliding cone on the opposite end. The sliding cone is setscrewed to the shaft, the screw resting on the slanting flat which prevents the cone from shifting backward when adjusted in place. This is a very good design of bearing, as wear can always be taken up on both bearings alike. Such a bearing is suitable for high-speed and precision work on such machines as small internal grinders and the like.

The third type is known as the cone-type lathe spindle. A cone having two tapers is turned on the chuck end of the spindle. The shallow taper is 15° and the steep taper or thrust angle is turned at an angle of 45°. As most thrusts are endwise on a lathe spindle, a light fiber washer and adjusting collar are provided to keep the bearing tight. The bushing of the other bearing is a taper fit in the frame of the machine and, being split, is adjustable for tightness by advancing it forward into the taper hole. This type of bearing is only found in the most accurate and ex-

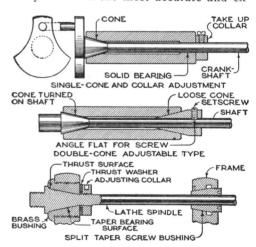

Three Types of Cone Bearings for Model Machinery of Different Types

pensive lathes and is used to best advantage on small precision machinery.

Index to Volume 21
Shop Notes for 1925

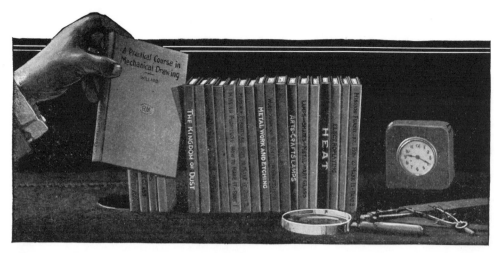

Make Your Own Furniture and Decorative Articles

"What an attractive magazine stand. Where did you get it?" ¶ "I made it myself." ¶ "You did?" ¶ "Yes, and I also made this book case, those four chairs, the davenport, the center table—but wait till you see my shaving stand. That is a novelty and a good piece of work, too, if I do say it myself." ¶ Wouldn't you like to be able to tell your friends that you made the furniture in your home? Almost anyone would. ¶ It is entirely possible if you have the complete and simple directions contained in Popular Mechanics Amateur Furniture-maker's Library.

Amateur Furniture-maker's Library

This library tells exactly how to make practically all of the furniture you might need about a home. It also includes instructions for making outdoor rustic furniture and decorative lamps and shades. The library is made up of seven cloth-bound, pocket-size books as follows:

1. Wood-working for Amateur Craftsmen.
2. Mission Furniture, How to Make It, Part 1.
3. Mission Furniture, How to Make It, Part 2.
4. Mission Furniture, How to Make It, Part 3.
5. Rustic Carpentry.
6. Arts-Crafts Lamps.
7. Lamps and Shades in Metal and Art Glass.

These books include instructions on selecting material and tools as well as plans for making 235 articles. Anyone at all handy with tools should be able to make any of these articles and have a lot of fun doing it. If the books were bought separately, they would come to $3.50. The price of this complete **Amateur Furniture-maker's Library** is **$3.15**

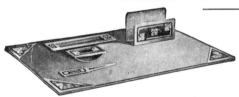

A Practical Course in Mechanical Drawing

Mechanical Drawing is one of the most popular and most profitable subjects for the boy or young man of today. It is an essential accomplishment in practically all lines of engineering, and almost indispensable in many other occupations. It is often the secret on which advancement is based.

Popular Mechanics cloth-bound book, "A Practical Course in Mechanical Drawing," provides an easy and convenient way to learn Mechanical Drawing. It includes instruction for the beginner in both technical drawing and lettering, as well as exercises for the more advanced. It was written by William F. Willard who has personally taught hundreds of students, most of whom have become famous in industry.

The price of this valuable book is only 50 cents. It really should be accompanied by at least three of our Shop Notes Annuals, which contain dozens of kinks on mechanical drawing, as well as ideas on many other mechanical subjects. **The four volumes for draftsmen..** **$2.00**

How to Make Decorative Articles from Metal

Book ends, desk sets, blotting pad corners, paper knives, stationery racks, desk calendars, match boxes, jewelry, and dozens of other articles are easily made by amateurs. Popular Mechanics Decorative Metal-worker's Library tells you exactly how to make 76 useful and decorative articles and how to plate them with copper, nickel, silver or gold.

Many have used these books as the basis for a pleasant and profitable home business, making the articles described for local stores and to sell among neighbors and friends. The library consists of two cloth-bound, pocket-size books as follows:

Decorative Metal-worker's Library

1. Metal Work and Etching
2. Electroplating

These books are written with the amateur in mind and are "Written so you can understand it." The price of the library is **$1.00**

POPULAR MECHANICS PRESS
Room 107 Popular Mechanics Bldg., CHICAGO, ILL.

HOW TO MAKE THINGS

Fascinating to any boy, yet practical enough for men with technical skill, the four books of the NEW BOY MECHANIC LIBRARY have been recognized as the most useful books in any home. Their interest to the whole family lies in the fact that devices are described that are of use about the home, in the garden, shop, and in outdoor sports and games of all kinds.

What You Will Find to Interest You in

THE NEW BOY MECHANIC LIBRARY

3,849 Ideas　　　　**Four Beautiful Volumes**　　　　**3,917 Illustrations**

A faint idea of the world of useful articles in these books may be had from the following list of the main subjects treated. Look over this list. Any one or two articles that interest you may make the books worth much more than their small cost.

Electrical devices
Photography
Carpentry
Automobile
Household helps
Toys
Painting
Boats
House decoration
Camping
Drafting
China painting
Decorative metal work
Fishing
Furniture
Farming
Gardening
Poultry
Fruit growing
Laboratory helps
Models
Magic
Entertainments
Music
Outdoor games
Outdoor winter sports
Stoves
Radio
Wireless
Furnaces
Tricks
Puzzles
Bicycle
Flowers
Hunting
Trapping
Library helps
Metal working tools
Secret locks
Indoor games
Kites
Parachutes
Plumbing
Sheet metal work
Pets
Swings

Hammocks
Sleds
Wood working
Motor sleds

Toboggans
Wind wagons
Dog cart
Water sports

Tents
Skiis and skiing
Indian snowshoes
Power devices

Decorative leather work
Gymnasium
Iceboats
Skating

SEND NO MONEY
Simply send your name on the attached coupon and indicate whether you want the complete library at the special price of $7 or a selection of individual books at $2 each. There are four books in the library and you will be pleased with your purchase if you take them all. However, you may already have one or more of the volumes, and will want to complete the set by ordering the rest. Book 4 is brand new. It contains the latest articles on radio as well as over 3,000 other articles. Send No Money. Simply sign and mail the coupon. The books will be sent to you at once. When the postman delivers them, hand him the price of the books plus the few cents postage. That is all. If you want the books sent direct to a friend, it will be necessary for you to send the cash with the order.

The Four Books

$7

MAIL THE COUPON TODAY

POPULAR MECHANICS PRESS
Popular Mechanics Building, Room 107　　　　CHICAGO, ILLINOIS

POPULAR MECHANICS PRESS
Popular Mechanics Building, Room 107, Chicago, Ill.

Please send me at once C. O. D. the Boy Mechanic Library at $7. ☐ (Put a cross in the square); (or—the individual books you want). ☐ Book 1, $2; ☐ Book 2, $2; ☐ Book 3, $2; ☐ Book 4, $2.

Name ....

City ....

Street.................................... State........................

A Plan for Profiting from Other People's Ideas

If we used only our own ideas, we wouldn't get ahead very fast. Popular Mechanics has made it a business for over 20 years to assemble the ideas of people from all parts of the world and publish them for the benefit of others. Now, you may have these ideas in convenient books called **"Popular Mechanics Handbooks."** The ideas are all classified and arranged for your convenience. The books are made up into libraries as follows:

Popular Mechanics Libraries of Experience

Automobile Mechanic's Library

Automobile Repairman's Handbook No. 1..........$ .50
Popular Mechanics Lathe Handbook No. 1......... .50
Drilling and Thread Cutting Handbook............ .50
Popular Mechanics Shop Notes (14 volumes)...... 7.00
Auto Owner's Handbook No. 1.................... .50
Auto Tourist's Handbook No. 1.................. .50

Total for the 19 volumes.....................$9.50

Special price if all are ordered at once......$8.50

Automobile Mechanic's Reduced Library

Automobile Repairman's Handbook No. 1..........$ .50
Popular Mechanics Lathe Handbook No. 1......... .50
Drilling and Thread Cutting Handbook............ .50
Popular Mechanics Shop Notes for 1924.......... .50

Price for the four books....................$2.00

Automobile Owner's Library

Automobile Owner's Handbook No. 1...............$ .50
Auto Tourist's Handbook No. 1.................... .50
Home Mechanics Handbook No. 1.................. .50
Popular Mechanics Shop Notes for 1924........... .50

Price for the four books....................$2.00

Boy's Library of Useful Handbooks

Outdoor Sports The Year 'Round....................$1.00
Concrete Handbook No. 1........................... .50
Popular Mechanics Boat Book...................... .50
Popular Mechanics Book of Playthings .... .50

Price for the complete library...............$2.50

Women's Library

Popular Mechanics Handbook for Women ....$ .50
Home Mechanics Handbook No. 1.................. .50
Popular Mechanics Book of Playthings.............. .50
Outdoor Sports The Year 'Round 1.00

Price for the complete library................$2.50

An Amateur Mechanic's Library

Home Mechanics Handbook No. 1...................$ .50
Popular Mechanics Carpenter's Handbook.......... .50
Popular Mechanics Lathe Handbook No. 1......... .50
Drilling and Thread Cutting Handbook............ .50
Popular Mechanics Concrete Handbook No. 1...... .50
Popular Mechanics Shop Notes for 1924........... .50

Price of the complete library...............$3.00

Shop Notes

For 22 years Popular Mechanics Shop Notes books have been the standard source of information for professional shop men and amateur mechanics alike. Each of the 14 volumes now available contains dozens of practical ideas that may be of great money value to you. The complete library of 14 volumes may be had for $6.50. Single volumes are 50 cents each.

Order libraries direct from the publishers,

Popular Mechanics Press
Room 107, Popular Mechanics Bldg., Chicago